NEW DIRECTIONS IN

HOSPITAL AND HEALTHCARE FACILITY DESIGN

■ Richard L. Miller, AIA
Earl S. Swensson, FAIA

McGraw-Hill, Inc.

New York   San Francisco   Washington, D.C.   Auckland   Bogatá
Caracas   Lisbon   London   Madrid   Mexico City   Milan
Montreal   New Delhi   San Juan   Singapore
Sydney   Tokyo   Toronto

Library of Congress Cataloging-in-Publication Data

Miller, Richard L. (Richard Lyle)
    New directions in hospital and healthcare facility design /
Richard L. Miller. Earl S. Swensson.
        p.   cm.
        Includes bibliographical references and index.
        ISBN 0-07-063014-3
        1. Hospitals—Design and constuction.   I. Swensson, Earl S.
II. Title.
        [DNLM: 1. Hospital Design and Construction. WX 140 M649n
1995]
RA967.M49   1995
725'.51—dc20
DNLM/DLC
for Library of Congress   94-25320
                                                                 CIP

1 2 3 4 5 6 7 8 9 0 1IMP/1IMP 9 0 0 9 8 7 6 5

ISBN 0-07-063014-3

The sponsoring editor for this book was Joel E. Stein. It was set in ITC Stone Serif and Futura by Zenda, Inc.

Printed in Hong Kong through Print Vision, Portland, OR.

McGraw-Hill books are available at special quantity discounts to use as premiums and sales promotions, or for use in corporate training programs. For more information, please write to the Director of Special Sales, McGraw-Hill, Inc., 11 West 19th Street, New York, NY 10011. Or contact your local bookstore.

CONTENTS

ACKNOWLEDGMENTS

No book—especially no book about a subject so complex as healthcare facility design, no book that touches on a topic so ephemeral as our collective future—can be written without help from others. One of the elements of the Synergenial Design practiced by our firm, one that we consider central and one of which we are most proud, is the involvement of all those affected by the work—users as well as creators—in its planning and execution. In that spirit, this book is a synergenial project, and we wish to recognize all those who participated in the endeavor.

First there are the writers and wordsmiths of Zenda, Inc.: Alan Axelrod, Patricia Hogan, and Charles Phillips. Not merely talented in stringing words together, Zenda's team also edited the manuscript for clarity and precision and designed and produced the elegant setting that houses the text. It was, however, their gift for listening to those for whom they were doing so that was essential to bringing our ideas into the public space of the printed page.

First and foremost, those they listened to were not the authors of the book, but the employees of Earl Swennson Associates. Crystal Ullestad, our liaison with the writers at Zenda, coordinated the project from start to finish. It was she who worked with Patricia Hogan to make sure that the book stayed on schedule, she who provided guidance and direction for us when the road ahead looked thorny and twisting indeed. She was aided in her efforts by Don Zirkle, who spent hours researching the facts for the text, badgered repositories and libraries for materials, gathered case studies and artwork from other architects, assisted in the final photo selection, ran interference between Zenda and ESa staff, reviewed the completed text, and—as if that weren't enough—executed a number of the drawings we used. In carrying out their work on the project, the folks at Zenda and Crystal and Don on our staff were guided by the outline of topics to be covered and case studies to be included that Harold Petty, Todd Robinson,

Sam Burnette and Don Zirkle himself put together. Part of their work in creating the outline consisted of a number of brainstorming sessions, one of which at least lasted all day: it was here that they did the essential thinking about the text and the entire subject in general, pointing out areas of key concern, providing general information about the healthcare environment, offering their criticisms and providing their insights. These three assisted Don in selecting the artwork, and they read and critiqued the manuscript of the text. Kathy Carr, too, reviewed the text for accuracy, especially from the viewpoint of interior design.

Other ESa employees provided support and technical assistance as well: Lisa Chumbler and Shali Nelson produced the prints and graphics for ESa projects included in the book; Kerry Foth generated the computer graphics of the Centennial Medical Center ICU and an exterior perspective of the center itself; Shirley Condra typed the correspondence to those architects, professional organizations, and healthcare facilities we contacted, plus handled the incoming information and release forms on photographs and images; Ginger Schaffer, Rhonda Conner, and Laurie Stanley provided general clerical support for the project.

To these, and to all the ESa employees who helped make this book a reality, we offer our sincerest thanks.

Not only ESa staff participated in the initial day-long retreat and brainstorming session that kicked off the project. There, gathered around the room to share their knowledge and their insight were William W. Arnold, III, Kenneth N. Barker, Ph.D., Michael Boroch, Gene Burton, Donna Finney, Jeff Hardy, Teri Louden, and Charles Phillips. The discussions they participated in, the criticisms they offered, the general information they provided, and the concerns and issues they raised were key to the success of the project, and it is hard to express the value we place on their initial contributions.

If the day-long retreat was the first stage of the synergenial process, the reading and review of the completed manuscript by those who know the field and some who might be expected to use the published book was the necessary final stage. Kenneth N. Barker, Michael Boroch, Gene Burton, Dan Buxbaum, Donna Finney, Elbert Garner, Teri Louden, Clayton McWhorter, Roscoe R. Robinson, M.D., Dick Rosenvold, and Bob Vraciu—some there at the beginning, others essential in looking at the book from the different point of view of the potential consumer, others who provided us with useful comments on the general topic—made invaluable contributions by pointing out errors and omissions and by providing suggestions about how to improve the work. We would especially like to thank Dr. Thomas F. Frist, Sr., for his comments on the cover design of the book, which saved much work down the road. We have a better book for their help, and we appreciate the time and effort they gave to the project.

In addition to those already named, we wish also to thank George Dawson, Doug Deck, Dr. Thomas F. Frist, Jr., Richard M. Bracken, James H. Henry, and Darrell Powers for their support and the American Hospital Association for letting us use its library. Last, but not least, we wish to extend our appreciation to the Honorable Jim Cooper for gracing our book with his elegant and succinct foreword.

To these, and others too numerous to mention, belong not only our thanks but our praise for helping to make a work of which we are proud. What is good and true here is in no small part their doing—the errors and mistakes we, the authors, must assume as our own.

—Richard L. Miller and Earl S. Swensson

FOREWORD

When I first met Earl Swensson and Dick Miller, I was pretty naive. I though architects simply did what their clients told them to do. But these guys really listen. They listen so well that they may know more about your business needs than you do.

I have talked to health policy experts from all over the United States. I did not realize that I would find some of the deepest thinkers, not in a university or a think tank, but in a Tennessee architecture firm.

The more I though about it, the more sense it made. Who wants a "yes" man? Who wants and obsolete building? What we all want are truthful answers, even if they are not what we want to hear. We want enduring buildings and design. We want the next generation to ask who did such a good job of planning back in 1994?

Then they will become clients.

Most business people are so pressured by day-to-day events and by quarterly reports that it is hard to take time to look over the horizon. It is important to talk to those who do, and to be challenged by what they see.

Swensson buildings have already stood the test of time. No one has a perfect crystal ball, certainly not in a field that is embroiled in multiple revolutions like healthcare. The uncertainty of national reform legislation itself is daunting, much less the scientific, organizational, behavioral, and cultural changes we are witnessing.

We can learn enough from history to at least make new mistakes. And we can minimize the risks of future pitfalls.

Americans demand a health system that puts their needs first. We should not even use the word "patient," because if you are a patient, the health system may already have failed you. We are customers, and like any customer, we should be able to shop for healthcare like we shop for anything else.

This means picking our own doctors and health plans based on price and quality and consumer satisfaction. Employers will no longer be able to herd us into a plan of their choice. The employee will be empowered to choose, with the same group rate and tax break that only the largest company now has.

While you are healthy, healthcare should be fun. In the jargon, there will be a much greater emphasis on prevention, public health, primary care, and pre-hospital care. When you are sick or injured, you should have a continuum of care. Every possible type of institutional, short-stay, subacute, post-hospital, hospice, and home care will compete for your business.

Today's patients will not even recognize the health facilities of the future. They will not scare, confuse, or patronize you anymore. Doctors will have to report their outcomes so that you can judge them. They may have the white coat, but you've got the checkbook. And bureaucrats, whether in government or insurance companies, will finally learn their place. They should not ration care or second-guess healthcare professionals.

State lines and county lines, capitals and county seats, will be much less important in determining the location of care. People are mobile and their care should be also. When you are sick or injured, the last thing you want to think about is political jurisdictions. All that matters is convenient access to quality, affordable care, wherever it is located. Bricks and mortar are much less important than service.

This is likely to be the golden age of the private sector in healthcare in America. A disciplined private sector, not callous or laissez-faire, will be given its chance to prove that government takeover of healthcare is not inevitable or even desirable. The regulatory paradigm will be "please-the-customer," not "please-the-bureaucrat."

Earl Swensson Associates has been pleasing clients and their customers for many years. What does the integrated health and delivery system of the future look like? This book will not only show its facade, but its interior.

U.S. Representative Jim Cooper (D-Tennessee)
Shelbyville, Tennessee
June 21, 1994

PREFACE

Writing about the future can be a tricky business, especially in a field such as healthcare, where the politics are volatile, the issues complex, and the economics daunting.   Clearly, anyone looking for a purchase on the future of healthcare would do well to listen to what R. Clayton McWhorter, chairman and chief executive officer of HealthTrust, Inc., told us when we asked him to review a manuscript of this book: "In today's healthcare arena, changes are occurring so rapidly and dramatically that yesterday's trends will not be tomorrow's trends, causing one to stay fluid and flexible as strategies for the future are developed."

For that reason we want to make clear in the beginning that we are not writing about the vicissitudes of reform nor are we attempting to provide here a comprehensive discussion about the future of healthcare. Instead, we are writing about new directions in hospital and healthcare facility designs—new directions that we, as designers of healthcare facilities, recognize and can document. They are directions currently underway, and they are directions away from the past and toward the future, but they are after all only directions. Our modest hope is that by observing these trends and discussing them, we can offer some practical aid to architects and healthcare administrators who must plan and design and build today for a future that none of us in the end can know in all its specific and detailed splendor. Our methods are not those of crystal-ball gazers or biblical prophets; they are more traditional—research and analysis; observation and reasonable inference. We provide a historical perspective about hospitals and their design in the past and discuss what types of considerations ought to go into design in the future; we discuss specific trends in the design of healthcare facilities recently built or in the planning stages; and we proffer our observations about the fundamental changes—what we call paradigm shifts—that we see occurring in the whole notion of "health" and the impact those shifts will have on design. We view these shifts as matters much broader than something one might address in the individual provisions of this or that healthcare reform package designed to redress the ills of the past and please those of any particular political persuasion. The paradigm shifts are a way of looking at the future in the long term rather than through some short-term vision of a quick fix to current ills.

Consider the issue of cost containment and capitation, for example. It takes no Jeremiah to see that cost containment will play a growing role in the immediate future of healthcare, whatever shape reform takes. Indeed, because of the current emphasis on costs, no doubt Michael Boroch, a partner in the healthcare consulting firm of Loudon & Company, is correct to assert: "The payor has emerged as the most important consumer. Previously the provider had the upper hand, but now the payor drives many decisions affecting healthcare. The payor will ask for proof of procedures and will demand that things be done in the least costly setting. Incentives will be provided for the best outcome at the lowest cost." And with the payor driving healthcare decisions, Richard M. Bracken, president of the Nashville Healthcare Network, may be right to conclude that "the management of hospitals will be such that they will operate more as cost centers than revenue centers." But does this mean, as some in the healthcare field predict, that the hospital of the future will be a stark, bare-bones facility, stripped of all amenities and limited to a stringent design that concerns itself only with what is cheapest?

Such a disutopian view of healthcare facility design often comes from the fears about capitation, a form of payment for medical services that many see as the inevitable outgrowth of current reforms. This is not the place to fight the battle for or against capitation. Far more to the point, we recognize—as do most of those concerned with contemporary healthcare policy—that capitation will almost certainly become the dominant means of payment in American healthcare delivery within the next five years. Under capitated payment contracts, the payor—whether an HMO, an insurer, or a government agency—pays physicians and hospitals a fixed amount per month for each member in the payor's health plan regardless of whether a member makes twenty visits, has open heart surgery, or never darkens the door of a doctor's office or hospital entrance. Provider fees are negotiated in advance; the doctors and healthcare facilities participating in the plan are required to provide all medical, hospital, and healthcare services covered by the contract regardless of actual costs; consumers get all their care from the network of providers signing the contract, and from no one else; and providers are paid per capita every month, even if no patients use their services: they are paid to be on call, as needed.

Capitation is nothing new; insurance companies have been writing capitation contracts using monthly or annual insurance premiums with American employers for almost sixty years. What is new is that payors are shifting the risks of such capitation to providers by setting provider fees in advance of service rather than paying out after treatment on a fee-for-services-rendered basis. If those belonging to the healthcare plan require services that cost less than the contract's pre-arranged budget, the doctors and hospitals make money; if the costs of treating patients exceeds the capitated payments, they lose money. For this reason, capitation is a form of reimbursement that drives providers to be more efficient, both to hold down costs and eliminate unnecessary treatments. Critics claim that because physicians would benefit economically by systematically undertreating patients, capitation may subvert quality care. Moreover, since reimbursements go down under capitated plans and cash flows are often squeezed by them, "delivery systems"—i.e. the network of physicians and hospitals contracted—will be forced to ration. However, since no reform we know of currently eliminates competition between either payor groups or networks of providers, any network that skimped on treatment or introduced rationing—and any HMO or insurer that allowed a network to do so—would find its customers moving to a competing plan. On the other hand, though capitation puts providers at some economic risk, it allows physicians and hospitals once again to take control of their patients (by eliminating outside third-party review in the patient-doctor relationship) and of both their economics and their allocation of patient-care resources. Under capitation, providers will decide which patients need treatment and how much will be spent on them. In doing so, they must satisfy consumers and provide quality care or they will lose money, and its is precisely here, more than in the form of payment per se, that the new direction in healthcare truly lies. For provider capitation is being born from the need for cost containment, and cost containment is a result of general "consumer" dissatisfaction with a national healthcare industry that is the most expensive and least comprehensive among any of the industrialized nations of the world.

In other words, cost containment and capitation are part of the shift from a provider-driven system to a consumer-driven one, and it is the broader shift that we should be keeping our eyes on when we talk about facility design for the future. As Roscoe R. Robinson, the vice-chancellor for Health Affairs at Vanderbilt University, says: "Anticipated changes in healthcare delivery will require that our facilities be designed primarily for the convenience of the patient rather than the provider. There will be an increasing emphasis on decentralized facilities for specific types of care, e.g., primary care. Many such structures are described in this book, each of which accents the importance of patient-friendliness." The debate over payment is merely one sign of consumers taking a harder look at their healthcare system. Those facilities that attract paying customers, even if the payments are capitated, will be more likely to succeed. Providers who try to manage patient care by skimping on service will lose out to self-disciplined providers who offer cost-effective, high-quality services. It is for that reason that we concentrate here more on the shift in paradigm toward patient-focused care than on one of its results, method of payment, when we discuss effective designs. On the other hand, patient-focused care itself could be the subject of an entire book, and we have neither the space nor the inclination to go into that kind of detail; instead, we posit the shift toward such care as a premise for a discussion of the designs meant to facilitate such care.

And that throughout has been our strategy in the book that follows: to treat not the specific, and often hotly debated issue, but the underlying changes in society that call up the issue; to discuss not the underlying changes in all their detail merely for the sake of proving our deep understanding of American society, but to use those changes as a jumping off point to track the new directions in practical design these changes are creating.

One final example should suffice: take the issue of long-term care. Long-term care is the bug-bear of current healthcare reform; everybody admits it is a problem, no one really knows what to do about it. Insurance companies, despite much effort, have not yet succeeded even in coming up with satisfactory actuarial tables for extended care, whether in hospitals, nursing homes, or family-based settings. Reform packages typically duck the issue by keeping Medicare operating as is and slowing integrating long-term care into the overall "universal" healthcare system. The issue is how to pay for long-term care and still reduce the overall percentage of the annual national economy consumed by healthcare costs, but the underlying change that created the problem is the aging of the American population. We approach the issue by addressing the underlying change: given the paradigm shift toward aging, we must stop designing for a healthy thirty-year-old male and begin designing for a less-than-healthy seventy-year-old woman. For those planning facilities now that will be viable well into the future, this paradigm shift must be taken into account. It may be impossible to say precisely how long-term care will be funded; it is certainly undeniable that people are living longer and that the aging population is the fastest growing segment of the healthcare "market"; but the relevant fact for us here, and for those using this book, is that architects and administrators must plan now for the older, more infirm patients who will be occupying more and more of the space in the facilities they build.

This book then is for practitioners more than for theorists, for those looking to build more than for those looking to predict, but it is a book for practitioners and builders who know that what they practice and what they build must be thoroughly informed by clear-headed theories about and sober-eyed looks at the road to the future.

NEW DIRECTIONS IN

HOSPITAL AND HEALTHCARE FACILITY DESIGN

1

Principles: New Paradigms for a New Century

■ The Perception of Crisis

We have been raised to believe in medical miracles. And with good reason. Within the span of the century that is about to end, medicine has evolved from the relatively ineffectual—and often downright harmful— study and palliation of illness and injury to a system of positive, effective, life-prolonging intervention. In the second half of the century, that intervention has increasingly emphasized the component of diagnosis, so that the trend has been toward earlier intervention and, most recently, prevention or, as it is more accurately termed, "wellness." All students of medical technology are agreed that genetic science and drug therapies will play an increasingly important role in medicine during the coming century, a trend that will pose profound moral questions, of course, but a trend that also promises not merely the effective alleviation of much suffering, but its absolute avoidance.

We have been raised to believe in such miracles. But if you ask the proverbial man on the street to list the medical issues that most concern him, one item may or may not be AIDS—a terrible disease that has thus far stubbornly resisted cure—another might be cancer. However, there is one item that is almost certain to figure on the list: *How will I pay for medical care?*

Many, maybe most, people fear the cost of illness almost as much as illness itself. Healthcare costs have persistently exceeded general inflation, and, as many employers find it difficult or impossible to continue providing the level of healthcare insurance American workers have long taken for granted, millions are finding themselves with inadequate insurance or none at all.

Certainly, the 1992 election of President Bill Clinton was in no small part driven by healthcare reform issues. Yet, while everyone wants access to high-quality healthcare, there is precious little consensus on how to fund it. A poll conducted by the Gallup organization at the beginning of the decade details the range of confusion. As reported by *Health Care Strategic Management* in August 1990, Gallup identified six types of healthcare consumers:

1. The Young and Skeptical (15 percent of the adult population). These well-educated men and women, in their thirties and forties, are unhappy with the healthcare they receive and generally distrust the medical profession. While they support increased government involvement in funding healthcare, they are skeptical about government's ability to manage major programs.
2. The Self Reliants (15 percent of the adult population). A well-educated, upper-income man in his fifties, the "Self Reliant" believes that government should stay out of most healthcare funding and that the individual is responsible for his own welfare.
3. The Secure and Satisfieds (24 percent of the adult population). Highly educated, financially secure men and women in their mid forties, this group is generally happy with the way they receive healthcare, but nevertheless supports a federally funded health insurance program.
4. The Passives (13 percent of the adult population). Young men and women with lower levels of education and income, the "Passives" are generally unhappy with the healthcare they receive, support federal health spending, but are unwilling to pay higher taxes for healthcare programs.
5. The Coping but Concerned (18 percent of the adult population). Middle-aged and older working Americans in their fifties and sixties, these people have low incomes and feel they have little control over their lives. Like the "Passives," they are largely dissatisfied with the healthcare they receive, they believe the federal government has a responsibility to take care of its citizens, yet they are doubtful about large-scale, federally funded programs.
6. The Struggling Singles (15 percent of the adult population). The typical "Struggling Single" is a single mother in her late thirties who, having difficulty making ends meet, is very concerned about paying for healthcare and depends heavily on government assistance in this area.

Looking at such data, politicians and policymakers struggle to discern an unambiguous mandate. Two points, however, emerge clearly and certainly. The first is that, in the face of spiraling costs and the unprofitability, impracticality, even impossibility of insurance fully funding these costs, managed care and related cost-containment programs, which were the "wave of the future" in the 1980s and which dominate the health insurance field today, are here to stay and are likely to become increasingly stringent in the controls they apply. The second point is even more basic: A population that was traditionally regarded as a pool of patients and potential patients is now seen as a pool of "healthcare consumers" participating in a "healthcare marketplace."

Healthcare providers, including those responsible for planning and administrating hospitals and healthcare facilities, are understandably anxious about the growing impact of managed care and cost containment, but it is the startlingly rapid transition from provider-dominated payment systems to a consumer-centered marketplace that is the more profound paradigm shift.

Since Thomas S. Kuhn's groundbreaking book, *The Structure of Scientific Revolutions,* many of us have learned to think not in terms of an era's "Zeitgeist," but in terms of changing paradigms: models, patterns, sets of assumptions about a field, profession, or society that explain that field, profession, or society to us and thereby guide our thinking and behavior in relation to the field, profession, or society.

In *The Social Transformation of American Medicine,* Paul Starr traces the accumulation of economic, social, and political power by American physicians and chronicles the evolution of the hospital, which is intimately bound up with the elevation of the physician. Starr outlines three phases in the evolution of the American hospital.

The first, spanning approximately 1750 to 1850, witnessed the development of two kinds of institutions: "voluntary hospitals," which were operated by charitable lay boards, though usually affiliated with some Protestant religious body, and "public hospitals," operated by municipal or county governments and developed from the almshouses maintained by many colonial communities. The second phase, which began during the mid nineteenth century and ran to its end, saw the formation of "particularistic" hospitals funded by religious or ethnic institutions. The period also witnessed the growth of specialized hospitals for women and to treat certain diseases. In addition, homeopaths and other members of "medical sects" opened their own specialized hospitals. Finally, from 1890 and into the first three decades of the twentieth century, profit-making hospitals came into operation, funded and run by corporations or by physicians themselves.

This development reflects the emergence of a paradigm shift from a healthcare system controlled by religious, charitable, and governmental

Kaiser Foundation Hospitals/Baldwin Park Medical Center MOB, Baldwin Park, California. This state-of-the-art complex, situated in a parklike setting, contains a medical office building (MOB), parking garage, medical center, and patient tower. The clerestory windows and skylights define the hospital's circulation patterns, and the architect's use of color aids wayfinding. *Photo by Lonnie Duka. Courtesy HMC Group.*

West Houston MOB, Houston, Texas. Glazing makes the West Houston facility energy efficient. Patients enter the MOB through a doorway separate from the physicians' entrance. *Photo by Bill LaFevor. Courtesy Earl Swensson Associates.*

Health Central, Ocoee, Florida. A facility of striking colors, Health Central provides "one-stop shopping" for health services, combining an acute care hospital with outpatient services. *Photo by Michael Lowry. Courtesy HKS, Inc.*

authority to a system centered on and controlled by the healthcare providers themselves, chiefly physicians. By the first quarter of the twentieth century, physicians had focused the practice of medicine on the hospital institution, much as the clergy had for centuries focused the practice of religion on the church. Moreover, physicians structured payment systems in such a way that the "doctor-patient" relationship was free from "lay" interference, the healthcare provider setting fees and enjoying unrestricted and sovereign discretion in using the hospital's resources to resolve his patient's problem. To be sure, the wealthy could afford to buy more—and often better—medical care than the less fortunate. However, as Starr points out, even the elite voluntary and municipal hospitals as well as the most prestigious private hospitals, which were teaching hospitals associated with universities and medical schools, actually brought together the top and bottom strata of society. Physicians needed patients who could afford to pay, but they also needed poorer patients for research and teaching purposes.

For some five decades, this provider-centered paradigm not only worked, but was accepted uncritically. Like the hospital itself, it had become an "institution" in the social sense. Then, by the middle of the 1980s, *apparently* in direct response to a faltering economy, reduction in insurance benefits, and sharply rising healthcare costs, this paradigm shifted rapidly from those who provide the care to those—individual and public—who pay for the care.

Johns Hopkins Hospital Outpatient Center, Baltimore, Maryland. The center, with its light, airy appearance, features clear signage to assist patients in way-finding and in identifying departments. *Photo by Dan Forer. Courtesy Payette Associates.*

Mary Imogene Bassett Hospital/Bassett Clinic, Cooperstown, New York. The retail optical facility in the hospital offers an extra convenience for patients. The attractive lighting and finishes make the hospital inviting for patients and visitors. *Photo by David Lamb/David Lamb Photography. Courtesy Cannon, Inc.*

The shift came with such apparent suddenness that it was perceived as a crisis, not only by financially beleaguered patients ("consumers"), but by healthcare providers and by those who plan and administer hospitals. By the close of the 1980s, within the hospital industry, profit margins sharply declined, beds were empty, "product portfolio" had matured, administration had become an entrenched and coagulated bureaucracy, CEOs were being hired and fired at a rate outpaced only by the entertainment industry, and, in desperation, management embarked on an epidemic of poorly-thought-out attempts at diversification into other industries, some related to healthcare, many totally unrelated.

In 1985, for example, inpatient hospital use declined by almost 20 percent, while profit margins remained high. Two years later, even in the

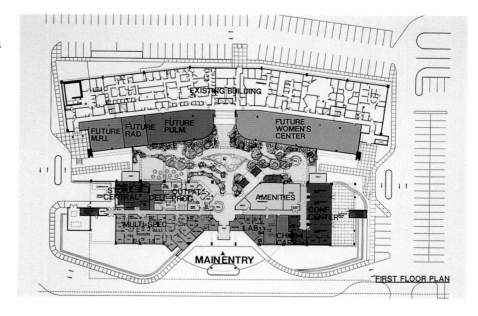

Mt. Sinai Integrated Medical Campus MOB, Beechwood, Ohio. Plan. Access to the addition of an existing facility is through a pleasant atrium which provides inviting areas for sitting and eating. *Courtesy Earl Swensson Associates.*

St. Luke's Hospital Medical Tower, Houston, Texas. St. Luke's futuristic design signals to its patients that at this state-of-the-art medical facility and teaching hospital they will receive the best care possible. The medical tower features thirteen floors of medical offices, and reflecting the trend away from inpatient care, devotes one entire floor to ambulatory surgery. *Photo by Paul Hester/Lisa Hardaway & Paul Hester, Photographers. Courtesy Cesar Pelli and Associates.*

face of declining inpatient population, hospitals enjoyed revenues 100 percent above 1980 levels. Yet, after another two years, by the end of 1989, the record-setting margins had evaporated, and it was administrator turnover, at 25 to 30 percent annually, that broke all records.

Administrators perceived all of this as a crisis and feared for the survival not only of their particular hospital, but of all hospitals. Indeed, in the short run, while major regional institutions are doubtless safe and will endure, many other traditional acute-care hospitals will probably close. In the longer term, hospitals of all kinds—those flexible enough to adapt to the paradigm shift by focusing on such services as early diagnosis, wellness, outpatient treatment, and the management of chronic illnesses—are likely to survive, even prosper, albeit as significantly different institutions from what has been the norm for a half-century or more.

■ The Reality of Paradigm Shift

The perception of crisis is the product of an exclusive focus on the short term. Unfortunately, the term "paradigm" itself has become such a buzz word among management consultants that the concept it connotes—the very assumptions by which we structure our reality—may also be confused with the paraphernalia of crisis and quick fix. Analyzing, understanding, adapting to, and, finally, anticipating paradigm shifts are essential to seeing beyond—and getting beyond—immediate crises in order to seize the larger, longer-term opportunities for which a crisis often serves as a messenger.

The transition from a provider-centered to a consumer-centered healthcare system is only one among a number of profound and interrelated paradigm shifts currently active and shaping the emerging social

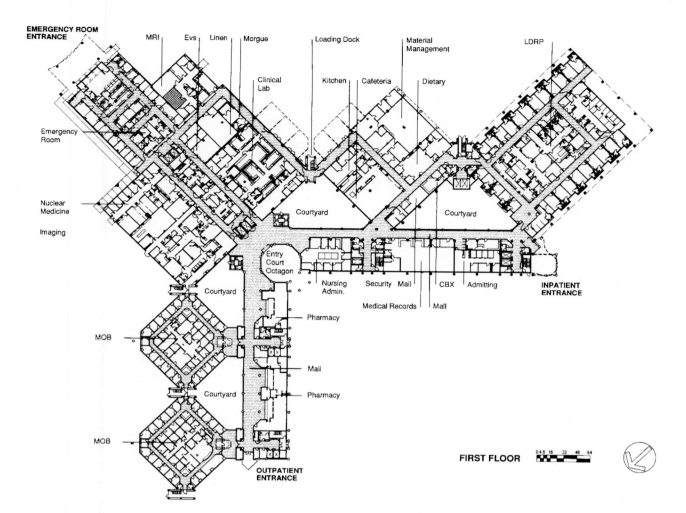

EMERGENCY ROOM ENTRANCE · MRI · Evs · Linen · Morgue · Loading Dock · Material Management · LDRP

Clinical Lab · Kitchen · Cafeteria · Dietary

Emergency Room

Nuclear Medicine

Imaging

Courtyard · Courtyard

Entry Court Octagon

Courtyard

MOB

Pharmacy

Nursing Admin. · Security · Mail · CBX · Admitting · INPATIENT ENTRANCE

Medical Records · Mall

Mall

Courtyard

Pharmacy

MOB

OUTPATIENT ENTRANCE

FIRST FLOOR   0 4 8 16   32   48   64

New Medical Center/Kaiser Foundation Health Plan, Inc., Fresno, California. Floor plan, first floor. The plans for this facility feature the flexibility for future expansions. The building is arranged along a mall that separates inpatient and outpatient services. *Courtesy Ratcliff Architects.*

and technological climate in which architects, healthcare and hospital administrators and planners, healthcare providers, and public policy makers must collaborate to create hospital and healthcare facilities with quality, cost effectiveness, and flexibility sufficient to carry them well into the twenty-first century.

As architects who work extensively in designing for the healthcare industry, we have been struck by the profound and governing presence of four major paradigm shifts and a welter of less sweeping, but still significant minor shifts. The major transitions are:

▲ From YOUTH to MATURITY: Since the beginning of the industrial age, youth or newness has been the focus of our desires. We have preferred to abandon what is old, whether things or people. Now that paradigm is changing and giving way to maturity, which means neither young nor aged, neither new nor old. Maturity entails the acquisition of an evolving wisdom that transcends either-or stereotypes.

▲ From REMEDIATION to HEALTH: In medicine today, the key terms are *wellness, prevention, outpatient service, diagnostic services.* Ten years ago, *hospital stays, high tech, specialist services,* and *acute care* were buzz words. Contemporary American medicine is undergoing a dramatic shift from remediation—the pure art of healing—to

Centennial Medical Center Campus, Nashville, Tennessee. Site plan. A major urban facility, which offers many services, occupies a substantial piece of real estate. *Courtesy Earl Swensson Associates.*

1   Physicians Park MOB
2   Patient tower (New hospital)
3   Parkview building
4   The Atrium
5   Physicians Building A
6   310 Building
7   Physicians Building B
8   345 Building
9   356 Building
10 Parking garage
11 Daycare center
12 Parking garage
13 West Side Building
14 2201 Medical Plaza

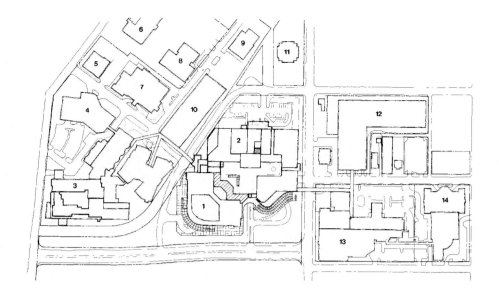

health—an art of well-being and health maintenance. The new paradigm has greatly affected hospital architecture and is also figuring in the needs of those who use virtually every other type of building as well.

▲ From SPECIALIZATION to WHOLENESS: More and more, architects are asked to create "womb to tomb" environmental solutions— structures and facilities that serve a multiplicity of users and that are capable of evolving with maturing needs. Twenty years ago, we built hospitals; ten years ago, the cutting edge was the healthcare campus; now the emerging state-of-the-art thinking centers around such concepts as the "health park," which is wholly integrated within a community, the "medical mall," or the "medical hotel."

▲ From REACTION to ANTICIPATION: It is no longer sufficient for a facilities planner, hospital administrator, healthcare policymaker, or architect to recognize a need and respond to it. Human needs are by their nature dynamic; contemporary technology has accelerated that dynamism. Structures—whether social or physical—designed for human beings must, therefore, emulate that dynamism by embodying the anticipation of evolving needs.

In addition to getting in sync with these major paradigm shifts, hospital planners and designers also need to recognize the following transitions:

▲ From EXCLUSIVITY to SYSTEM. The traditional definition of the so-called "healthcare system" does not define a *health* care system at all, but, rather, a *disease* care system. And "system," by this defini-tion, encompasses only that portion of the population actually and currently receiving professional treatment. The rest of the popula-tion is outside the "system." Therefore, taking the larger view, this traditional definition emphasizes fragmentation rather than genu-ine system. The current paradigm shift places the entire population within a *health*care system. At any particular time, any particular individual may be located along a continuum within a whole-system of healthcare. The hospital or healthcare facility must learn to serve those in the community who currently require treatment as well as those healthy individuals who may benefit from wellness programs. Architects will be called upon to plan facilities that provide for extensive community outreach and that overcome the image of the hospital as an isolated fortress surrounded by a *cordon sanitaire.*

Kaiser Permanente Regional Data Center, Corona, California. With healthcare reform, sophisticated information networks will become more important. Facilities similar to the Corona data center will become more common. *Photo by Jordan Lagman. Courtesy Widom Wein Cohen.*

▲ Related to the above is a shift from a focus on SICKNESS to WELLNESS: Intervention exclusively during illness or injury is fragmented, episodic care. Emerging healthcare delivery systems will focus on wellness and health maintenance. In accommodating this shift, hospitals will undoubtedly become more closely integrated into the community.

▲ From FRAGMENTATION to INTEGRATION. In the past, integration of medical care meant gathering a panoply of doctors and a warehouse full of equipment under one enormous roof and calling the result a hospital. In fact, in the early Industrial Age, such an arrangement was less fragmented and more efficient than if physicians had labored in total isolation from one another. In the Information Age, however, it is no longer sufficient—and no longer always necessary—to gather personnel and equipment into a single building or complex. The technology now exists for deep integration of treatment among any number of healthcare professionals. Care delivery functions, finance, and administration can be thoroughly integrated, and data can be disseminated community-wide, state-wide, nation-wide, and internationally. On the simplest level, planning and designing a hospital will involve accommodating information technology. More significantly, this technology provides further incentive for decentralizing healthcare facilities. For example, a physician will be able to transmit data from her office to the hospital rather than compel her patient to visit the hospital in person.

Thornton Hospital, University of California at San Diego, San Diego, California. In a facility of timeless design, Thornton Hospital specializes in patient-focused services, evident in patient rooms that provide extra seating in the window sill and clerestory windows that allow plenty of natural light. The bedside computer facilitates charting so that the nursing staff has more time to care for the patients. *Photo by David Hewitt/Anne Garrison. Courtesy Stone Marraccini Patterson.*

▲ HIERARCHICAL to FUNCTIONAL. Traditional hospitals are organized according to management hierarchies. Like many large corporations, hospitals tend to suffer from bloated layers of management, which mask the fact that, at its most basic and essential, a hospital is a "neighborhood" business centered on a relationship between the doctor and the patient. The shift toward the functional reduces management hierarchies and calls for building designs that are less corporate and more humanly scaled, that are flexible enough to treat a patient's condition rather than fit a patient into a particular department, and that are generally less monolithic in concept as well as appearance.

▲ PASSIVE PARTICIPATION to ACTIVE PARTICIPATION. Along with a healthcare marketplace that was wholly provider centered came a doctor-patient relationship in which the patient was expected to (in a phrase so common we take it for granted) "put himself in the hands of" the physician, as if he were in a state of perpetual anes-

Reston Medical Center MOB, Reston, Virginia. The furnishings selected for this MOB, while perhaps not usual for a medical facility, reflect traditional designs of its Virginia locale. Floor surfaces have been designed to eliminate the bumps that may inhibit wheelchair-bound patients. *Photo by Bill LaFevor. Courtesy Earl Swensson Associates.*

Left: Covington Medical Park, Tacoma, Washington. Attractive wood trim, upscale furniture, and warm colors give the dining area an appealing atmosphere. It looks more like a good restaurant than a hospital. *Photo by Gary Knight. Courtesy Earl Swensson Associates.*

Middle: Centennial Medical Center, Nashville, Tennessee. The Physicians Park atrium uses the hospitality model of design, featuring non-institutional furnishings and materials. The atrium provides the visual connection between the center's hospital and the MOB. Signage at the elevator aids patients and visitors in way-finding. *Photo by Gary Knight. Courtesy Earl Swensson Associates.*

Right: Gulf Coast Medical Center, Baytown, Texas. A warm environment, attractive sitting areas, and abundant plantings invite patients and visitors into the facility. *Photo by K. D. Lawson. Courtesy Earl Swensson Associates.*

thesia. As the market has shifted from the provider to the patient, so the patient expects—and is expected to—take a more active role in his treatment, making more informed choices and collaborating with, rather than submitting to, health professionals. Hospital and health facility architecture will accommodate this shift by drawing more extensively on retail and hospitality models of design and by including in their designs information-access facilities open to patients.

▲ INSTITUTIONAL to NON-INSTITUTIONAL. This may be the single *most visible* shift, so far as design is concerned. The architecture of traditional hospitals invokes the overwhelming and oppressive majesty of the institution and is aimed at impressing the individual with his or her comparative insignificance. The new, non-institu-

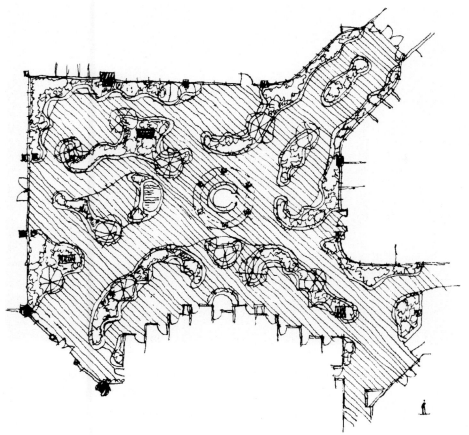

Centennial Medical Center/Garden Court, Nashville, Tennessee. Floor plan. The eight-story atrium, which connects the facility's MOB with its hospital, offers soothing running waters, a pleasing array of plantings, and private seating areas for families and visitors. Some of the patient rooms overlook the atrium. *Sketch by Earl S. Swensson. Courtesy Earl Swensson Associates.*

tional paradigm seeks, through design, to empower the individual, not to debilitate him or her. Architects are turning from the traditional institutional models to retail, hospitality, and residential models of design in order to create friendly, non-threatening, and reassuring hospital environments.

These are the broadest of the paradigm shifts that drive hospital and healthcare facilities design at the cutting edge. Following from these are several more specific trends:

▲ From INPATIENT to AMBULATORY care
▲ From FREE-STANDING COMMUNITY hospitals to MEGACORP-OWNED facilities
▲ From URGENCY care to PRIMARY care. Traditionally, patients with urgent (but non-emergency) medical needs entered the hospital emergency department if they had not established a relationship with a "family physician." Increasingly, ambulatory care centers, conceived very much along the lines of the retail model, have replaced the hospital emergency room (and even the personal physician) for urgent care. To remain competitive, hospitals are sponsoring primary care centers very much distinct from the traditional emergency room.
▲ From NURSING HOME to SUBACUTE CENTER. Long-term care facilities may be integrated with hospitals and will emphasize

UCLA Medical Center Outpatient Care Center, Los Angeles, California. The MOB features simple geometric patterns yet presents a decidedly non-institutional appearance. Parking below the building offers to patients convenient access to the building. *Photo by Tom Bonner. Courtesy Mitchell/ Giurgola Architects.*

Right: Johnson City Specialty Hospital, Johnson City, Tennessee. A hospital's main entrance can disappear at night unless lighting is part of the design. Johnson City's entrance is easy to find. *Photo by K. D. Lawson. Courtesy Earl Swensson Associates.*

Above: Vanderbilt University Medical Center, Nashville, Tennessee. The waiting area of the center's Dialysis Clinic provides a pleasing variety of shapes, colors, and textures. *Photo by Randy Janoski, Janoski Fotographix. Courtesy Earl Swensson Associates.*

The Atrium at Centennial Medical Center, Nashville, Tennessee. A two-story lobby offers a pleasing vertical public space in a multi-purpose facility. The seating needs of the lobby for an MOB are minimal, as most offices have adequate seating for patients. *Photo by Gary Knight. Courtesy Earl Swensson Associates.*

rehabilitation over "warehousing" or maintenance. Instead of being consigned to a nursing home, the hospital-based nursing home will care for a patient for shorter periods of time, fostering more extended periods of home care, self care, or semi-sheltered care.

In general, medicine will see a shift from

▲ INSTITUTIONAL DEPENDENCY to SELF CARE. Architects will work with administrators and facilities planners to create design strategies that will enable the hospital to participate in and foster this movement toward self care.

■ Speaking the Language of Business

In the pages that follow, we will consider in practical detail strategies for accommodating and anticipating the paradigm shifts we have just outlined. All of the traditional concerns of the architect still apply, and the architect or facilities planner also needs to be sensitive to the social, economic, and technological issues that impact healthcare today. In the new market-driven healthcare climate, however, all of those involved in planning, designing, and allocating resources for hospitals and healthcare facilities must become fluent in the language of business if they are to be heard.

What is the language of business?

Following the old paradigm, it was simply stating matters in terms of dollars and cents. Following the new paradigm, it is the art of expressing oneself in terms of cost effectiveness—which is a very different thing.

How does one become fluent in the language of business?

By making the shift to the new paradigms of business. In the past, hospitals could operate on the assumption that monies were available to cover costs, whereas now the trend is toward cost containment and managed care. Formerly, medical services were provider-driven; they are now market-driven. The purchasers of healthcare were traditionally obliged to assume all economic risks; now providers are taking on more of the risk. In the past, high cost was almost casually equated with high quality; consumers have learned to differentiate between the two and, formally or informally, evaluate the services they choose by applying the equation: *Value = Cost + Quality.* Along with this comes a questioning of the appropriateness of the cost and quality offered by the healthcare provider; consumers shop for value.

As healthcare consumers shop for value, so do healthcare providers. Investment in technology was formerly based on clinical benefits; technology purchases are now evaluated in terms of cost versus benefit.

Lynchburg General Hospital, Lynchburg, Virginia. In the hospital's outpatient waiting area, the barrel vault serves as the organizing element, focusing attention on the information desk. Patterns of light as well as the patterns in the floor provide visual appeal. Floor surface in the main traffic area is of easy-to-maintain material, while the floor of the sitting areas—which bears less traffic—has more comfortable carpeting. *Photo by Jonathan Hillyer. Courtesy Earl Swensson Associates.*

St. Louis Children's Hospital/West County Satellite Health Center, St. Louis, Missouri. A design that is light, airy, playful, and healthy, appeals to children. *Photo by Alise O'Brien. Courtesy Hellmuth, Obata, & Kassabaum, Inc.*

Concomitant with this, whereas healthcare providers once set no limit on access to technology, they now evaluate its appropriate usage. Providers can no longer assume unlimited pass-through of costs and profits; prices are now subject to the discipline of the marketplace and must be perceived as equivalent to "product value." However, one item of technology formerly perceived as optional, infotechnology, is now seen as an absolute requirement.

This is what it means to design *cost-effective* structures, and the new paradigm entails some very difficult choices. In the recent past, healthcare providers worked in a culture of healthcare entitlement. The predominant culture still endorses healthcare for everyone, but necessitates rationing of technology. In the recent past, healthcare providers were "mission-oriented." Today, that mission is to varying degrees defined as delivering value to market. In the past, purchasers of healthcare services focused on episode costs. Today, the trend is toward a focus on the cost of caring for a defined population, and, whereas healthcare providers have been accustomed to emphasizing services and procedures—the hospital was where you went when you were sick—the trend now is to promoting, managing, and maintaining the health of the community. Finally, healthcare providers have resisted any policy that questioned the cost of sustaining life. "Life at any cost" was, after all, as old as the Hippocratic Oath. Today, healthcare providers at every level are questioning those costs.

■ Architecture and Medicine

Learning the language of business is invaluable for planning and communicating design strategies in the field of healthcare. But, in speaking this language, we must never forget that hospitals are more than business. They reach to the very core of society and civilization as expressions and instruments of our deepest humanity and compassion.

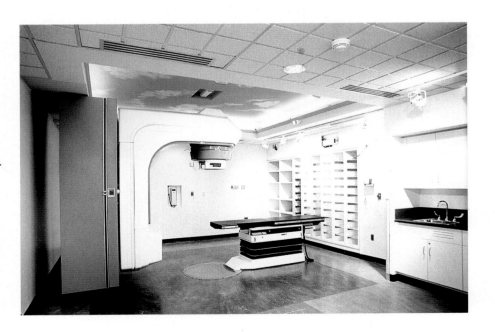

Mt. Sinai Medical Center, New York, New York. Designing spaces for linear accelerators—used in radiation oncology—requires special considerations. The color and pattern in the floors helps alleviate the cold, clinical feel of the facility. So does the pattern in the ceiling, which also relieves the tedium of patients who must spend time on their backs. *Photo by Jeff Kelner. Courtesy Larsen Associates.*

The architect's role in shaping these expressions and instruments is a socially crucial one. Indeed, the practice of medicine and the practice of architecture are more intimately related than may be superficially apparent. When the social reform-minded dramatist Henrik Ibsen wrote *The Master Builder* in 1892, it was natural for him to choose as his hero—and the ideal of the socially responsible man—an architect. Since ancient times, the vocation of architecture had been seen as nothing less than the vocation of building, shaping, and rebuilding the human world. Beset with the burgeoning urban squalor of the Industrial Revolution at full tilt, no era turned more earnestly to the architect than the age of Ibsen. From the late nineteenth century to the mid twentieth, social thinkers looked to the architect for society's salvation. In a different play, *The Enemy of the People,* Ibsen found another metaphorical figure to represent the socially responsible man: the physician.

That the playwright should have chosen an architect and a physician to represent essentially the same thing makes perfect sense. At its best, architecture is a profession of wellness—a sister, in fact, to the medical profession. Our firm, Earl Swensson Associates, which for more than thirty years has designed hospitals, wellness centers, elderly care facilities, hotels, industrial and office buildings, educational facilities, apartment buildings, retail stores, and correctional facilities, has coined a new term to describe this approach to architecture. "Synergenial Design" was created from *synergism* and *geniality* to describe a design approach that acknowledges both the synergistic nature of the problem-solving process and the congenial, user-sensitive attributes of a successfully designed solution. Synergenial buildings are functional environments that evoke positive responses from their users on physical, intellectual, and emotional levels.

The synergism comes from combining state-of-the-art technology and sound economics with the information—scientific and functional—at the contemporary architect's disposal to produce an effective design inspired by the people who are going to use it. The hope is that a design so inspired will appeal to all the human senses all the time, making its attraction subtle, sophisticated, even subconscious—genial rather than critical. However, "Synergeniality" can be evaluated in terms of "the Five Ps":

▲ *People*
THE TEST OF SYNERGISM
Time management: The management technique for accomplishing a proposed design.
THE TEST OF GENIALITY
Senses: Eliciting desired human responses from all aspects of a proposed design.

▲ *Purpose*
THE TEST OF SYNERGISM
Client/User: Determining the desires of the client and the needs of the users of a design in order to satisfy them.

THE TEST OF GENIALITY
Task performance: Establishing the ergonomic and psychological conditions that optimize a proposed design's effectiveness.

▲ *Price*
THE TEST OF SYNERGISM
Financing: Identifying all factors affecting the financing of a proposed design, as well as any financial limits, conditions, and time restrictions.
THE TEST OF GENIALITY
Lifetime cost: Anticipating total financial ramifications over the life of a design, from initial investment to future returns.

▲ *Place*
THE TEST OF SYNERGISM
Locale: The accurate report of existing physical and legal conditions that affect a proposed design and the acknowledgment of anticipated changes.
THE TEST OF GENIALITY
Climatic setting: Acknowledging the atmospheric conditions of a design that affect the senses and emotions.

▲ *Perspective*
THE TEST OF SYNERGISM
Technology: Utilizing technical advances to execute a proposed design.
THE TEST OF GENIALITY
Historical/cultural setting: Cultivating the proper appreciation for the cultural context of a design.

If there is any single yardstick that we will apply in evaluating the buildings discussed in this book, always in the context of the emerging paradigms governing society in general and the healthcare industry in particular, it is the concept of Synergenial Design. There is no disguising the fact that the Synergenial approach grew primarily from thirty-plus years of practice rather than from a predisposition to develop a comprehensive, all-encompassing theory. And it is no accident that its most intensive development came in connection with our extensive work in the healthcare field. We have witnessed firsthand the shift away from acute-care hospitals. Beginning in the early 1980s, our hospital clients were asking us to develop a panoply of new types of facilities: outpatient clinics, wellness centers, medical office buildings with ambulatory surgery capabilities.

As we—and others—studied the changing nature of medical care and the effect it was having on architecture, we began to discover just how much an effect architecture had on medicine. Patients exposed to noise or stuck in windowless rooms required stronger painkillers, became anxious or even delirious more readily, and more often fell into depression. When a patient could gaze out a window for even a few minutes at trees, water, or gardens, his or her blood pressure dropped dramatically. Clearly, there were healthy rooms and unhealthy rooms, and we began to extrapolate from there, cautiously working toward the somewhat dangerous notion of a healthy architecture—one that, like contemporary medicine, seeks to be preventive, to promote health, rather than to be remedial, to "cure" ills already present.

Now, as an aesthetic category, "health" has a long pedigree. The notion of health was basic to Aristotle's poetics, a fact recognized and exploited by the University of Chicago's "New School" of literary criticism back in the 1950s. Opponents of the so-called "Chicago school" found the pronouncing of this or that work of literature or art healthy or unhealthy not merely irresponsible exegesis, but intellectually quite dangerous, no doubt hearing in the word the echoes of Nazi aesthetics. The idea of health as a normative value has been so abused that one could easily be leery of applying it—even when appropriate. Yet, undeniably, there are healthy buildings and unhealthy ones, and a responsible and judicious approach to the concept should not be dismissed simply because the term was politically misused in the past.

Nothing would seem more natural than to look to hospitals themselves for examples of healthy architecture, since they by definition should be structures intended primarily to promote the good health of their users. Yet, as everyone knows, hospitals have traditionally been distinctly *un*healthy environments, places to avoid unless you are so ill that you cannot do so. Not only are many hospitals unhealthy in the strictest sense of the word, they are far too often dismally *inhospitable*.

So far as existing hospitals are concerned, this is the rule rather than the exception: Sick men and women, accompanied by anxious and worried families, arrive at most hospitals only to be greeted by harsh lights, stark corridors, weird-sounding equipment, acrid and unpleasant smells, and a cold, soulless expanse of marblelike hardness and stainless steel. Not only are patients denied access to medical information, they are stripped of their privacy upon arrival and given no opportunity or space for intimate talks or private grief. Under the acceleration of medical technology, many hospitals became huge machines, built—or, more often, awkwardly retrofitted—to accommodate rapidly changing equipment and ever more bureaucratic staffs. In the name of technology a host of dehumanizing structures were built, and, in the name of sanitation, sterile environments were created.

Far from promoting health, hospitals can actually make sick people worse. As Wayne Ruga, an organizer of the annual Symposium on Healthcare Design, recently said: "When a patient's anxiety increases, the immune system is suppressed, and the body is weakened in its ability to fight disease." There is actually a phenomenon known as "ICU syndrome," which occurs when a critically ill patient is subjected twenty-four hours a day to the harsh and unvarying light, the incessant beep of monitors and thump of respirators, and the disorienting sameness of the stark white or sickly green walls still typical of many intensive care units. The syndrome consists of sleep disturbances, hallucinations, and, on occasion, mild psychosis.

As the paradigms shift, these sick buildings will not only harm those who use them, but will also injure, perhaps fatally, the institutions of

Some hospital environments do little to promote wellness. The institutional feel of this facility is exacerbated by the poor lighting and the unappealing colors and finish materials. *Photo by Laura Rosen. Courtesy Larsen Associates.*

which they are the physical expression. They cannot compete in the emerging healthcare marketplace. The new consumer will not tolerate, let alone choose them.

Undeniably, the role of the traditional, acute-care hospital is diminishing. In the language of business, its market share is decreasing. Is this, then, a singularly inopportune time to promote new construction?

Hardly.

For it is not that the hospital is *dying*. Rather, it is being *redefined* in the name of survival as well as service—by physicians, researchers, technologists, politicians, insurance providers, government bureaucrats, and by patients. Working with and among all of these, the architect gives form to the emerging redefinitions. In the hospital project, the architect faces the opportunity and challenge of creating new, exciting, useful, and humane structures, what we call "healthy buildings."

2

The Traditional Hospital:
A Warehouse for the Sick

■ Harm and Discomfort

We architects pride ourselves on the conviction that the spaces we design profoundly affect the people who use our buildings. But, as Craig M. Zimring observes in "Stress and the Designed Environment" (*Journal of Social Issues* 37, no. 1 [1981]), "For many of us, the built environment is no more conspicuous than the surrounding air." Zimring continues: "Like air, the built environment only intrudes on our consciousness when it causes particular harm, discomfort, pleasure or awe."

Now, with this in mind, ask somebody—anybody—how he or she feels about hospitals. Our prediction is that the vocabulary of the answer will resemble "harm" and "discomfort" rather than "pleasure." Perhaps the response of a few individuals will veer toward "awe," but this is scarcely more useful or salutary a feeling to have in a hospital than a sense of harm or discomfort. Awe is not a comfortable or reassuring emotion, a fact attested to by the linguistic root it shares with *awful,* a word that once meant "filled with awe," but that came to be synonymous with such terms as *terrible, dreadful, horrible,* and so on.

The hospital—whose linguistic roots, not coincidentally, are the same as those of *hotel, hostel, hospitable,* and *hospitality*—should connote the qualities and emotions embodied in the names the U.S. Navy has traditionally assigned to its hospital ships: hope, solace, repose. Instead, the hospital evokes emotions that range from discomfort, to anxiety, to outright phobia in many persons who simply "cannot stand hospitals."

There was a time, of course, when such a response would have been perfectly reasonable. In the days before antisepsis and anesthesia, let alone antibiotic drugs and X-ray machines, hospitals were indeed places to be avoided. You generally went to a hospital only if you could afford nothing better—that is, physician-attended home treatment—and, if you did go to a hospital, it was very likely that you would not leave it alive.

But those days are long past. Most people enter the hospital in every expectation of emerging with their condition either cured, improved, or at least palliated. Today, dread of hospitals, though a common response, is "irrational" or "unreasonable."

Yet, of course, it is perfectly understandable, and it is a set of emotions with which we all sympathize. Rodney M. Coe summed up the "meaning of hospitalization" in his *Sociology of Medicine* (New York: McGraw-Hill, 1970):

> Many . . . attributes of illness may be carried over to the hospital situation and, perhaps, even exaggerated by some features of the hospital. In the first place, the hospital is a strange environment for most people. It has different sounds and smells than the environments to which most of us are accustomed. There is a sort of "air of emergency" about the place as doctors, nurses, and other uniformed personnel move rapidly from one place to another. . . . [There is also] the threatened disruption of normal roles—particularly separation from the family and from the work role.
>
> The onset of illness is . . . an intensely personal matter calling for personalized or supportive responses from the personal community in the form of expressed concern and succorant behavior. Under ordinary circumstances, this would likely be the type of response elicited from family members and friends. When the sick person is removed from the home setting and admitted to the hospital, he is not only deprived of these primary-oriented responses, but also exposed to a series of interactions with others which are characterized as objective and impersonal. They may range from the somewhat bureaucratic, officious behavior of admitting clerks and other administrative personnel to the professional scientific aplomb of nurses and examining physicians.

The architect may well protest that none of this is his fault. Illness is anxiety provoking, and if medical personnel are officious, bureaucratic, and impersonal, well, it is hardly the doing of hospital architecture.

True enough. But the architecture of the hospital is an expression of the cultural and emotional dynamics of the institution. It is as much an expression of these dynamics as the words and demeanor of the medical professionals and others who attend patients. In a speech published in the *Journal of Health Care Interior Design* (vol. 1, 1989), physician-architect Neil Kellman recalled that

> after one of his bicycle accidents, my son emerged from a CAT Scan and called out, "Dad, there's a rabbit in this big machine!" Since he kids around a lot, I asked him what he meant; so he suggested we take a look. Somebody had thoughtfully taken stickers of rabbits and put them up inside the CAT Scanner.

Although he admitted that this was a "trite little example," Kellman was delighted by this instance of thoughtful expression in the hospital environment.

Common sense would tell us that if such a "trite" little thing as some rabbit stickers in a CT scanner made a young patient feel better, what wonders would a *generally* humanized hospital environment bring about? Why not simply take a pledge, this very moment, to design human-scaled hospital and healthcare facilities that evoke feelings of familiar domesticity rather than cold institutionalism? After all, folk wisdom, mother wit, common sense, and a burgeoning volume of scientific studies (for a survey of some of these, see Richard S. Lazarus, Ph.D., "Psychological Stress and Coping in Adaptation and Illness," *International Journal of Psychiatry in Medicine* 5, no. 4. [1974] and Margaret A. Williams, "The Physical Environment and Patient Care," *Annual Review of Nursing Research* 6 [1988]) argue that emotional stress tends to exacerbate physical illness, whereas environmental factors that contribute to a sense of emotional well-being tend to ameliorate physical conditions.

Unfortunately, there are two major reasons why architects, planners, and hospital administrators cannot simply—as it were, unilaterally—decide to humanize hospital design.

The first reason involves areas in which techno-medical needs conflict with the patients' "human" needs. No matter how well designed, any hospital is, by definition, a compromise between these two sets of needs. The most "human" environment for a sick person is the home, and, indeed, many medical futurists see an increasing trend away from hospital care to home care. But, for the immediate future and certainly for individuals requiring advanced diagnostic, surgical, or life-support treatment, it is necessary for the patient to leave the home environment and come to a central location in which the necessary personnel and equipment are assembled and available. The very fact that the patient must be brought to the physicians and the technology rather than these being brought to the patient at home is a compromise.

Beyond this come many other compromises. One of the most basic is the conflict between the efficiency needs of care providers and the social psychological needs of patients. In the 1970s, for example, there was great interest in hospital plans that provided for nursing units designed in a circular fashion, with the nursing station located centrally within the unit. Nurses who worked in circular units reported that patient supervision was much easier and that they could even spend more time with individual patients than was possible in layouts of the more conventional double-loaded corridor design. One researcher, however, went beyond surveying the nurses to asking patients what they thought of the design. Overwhelmingly, patients complained that the design cost them their privacy (E. Jaco, "Ecological Aspects of Hospital Patient Care: An Experimental Study," in Jaco, ed., *Patients, Physicians, and Illness: A Sourcebook in Behavioral Science and Health* [3d ed.], New York: Free Press, 1979).

How important is a sense of privacy to the emotional state of a hospitalized person? This depends in large measure on the length of the hospitalization and the nature of the illness. However, among patients hospitalized with psychiatric disabilities, loss of privacy can be frankly traumatic (Erving Goffman, *Asylums: Essays on the Social Situation of Mental Patients and Other Inmates,* Garden City, New York: Doubleday, 1961), and many studies exist demonstrating the importance of territory and personal space in the hospital environment (for a survey of some, see Robert Sommer and Robert Dewar, "The Physical Environment of the Ward," in Eliot Friedman, ed., *The Hospital in Modern Society,* Glencoe,

Illinois: The Free Press, 1963). Yet no one would deny the desirability of making the nurse's demanding job less arduous and more efficient.

As this single example of conflicting needs demonstrates, designing "human" hospitals is a desirable goal, but it is not the only goal, and, like all design tasks, that of designing a hospital requires a thoughtful balancing of various needs. The trouble is that what we are calling the traditional hospital—and, as we shall see, that tradition actually takes many forms and is enacted in a range of degrees—tends to resist compromise and ignore the difficult question of balance. Hospitals of the old paradigms are, in varying attenuated degrees, what Goffman calls "total institutions."

■ Total Institutions

Total institutions are organized to provide for *all* the basic needs of the batches of people who live in them. As Goffman explains,

> First, all aspects of life are conducted in the same place and under the same single authority. Second, each phase of the member's daily activity is carried on in the immediate company of a large batch of others, all of whom are treated alike and required to do the same thing together. Third, all phases of the day's activities are tightly scheduled, with one activity leading at a prearranged time to the next, the whole sequence of activities being imposed from above by a system of explicit formal rulings and a body of officials. Finally, various enforced activities are brought together into a single rational plan, purportedly designed to fulfill the official aims of the institution.

There is also a "castelike" split between those who administer the institution and those to whom they minister. Patients entering the old-paradigm hospital are subjected to what Coe calls "stripping"—which he likens to the process a Marine inductee undergoes, exchanging distinctive civilian clothes for a nondescript uniform—and must submit to a system that more or less strictly controls resources as well as authority. One resource that old-paradigm hospitals tend to dispense in parsimonious fashion is information. Richard M. Titmuss ("The Hospital and Its Patients," in Alfred H. Katz and Jean Spencer Felton, eds., *Health and the Community,* New York: Free Press, 1965) pointed out that lack of information is a major source of patients' complaints about a hospital.

> What is it that patients complain of more than anything else in relation to the hospital—"No one told me anything"—"I don't know." How often one comes across people who have been disillusioned because the medical magic has not apparently or not yet yielded results, ignorant of what the investigations have shown, what the doctors think, what the treatment has been or is to be, and what the outlook is in terms of life and health.

Finally, the total institution exerts control on the patient by restricting his mobility, a factor that not only makes it easier for medical staff to attend to the patients, but also intensifies (for better or, more certainly, for worse) the status of being ill.

All of these measures of control at once depersonalize the patient and segregate him from the general population, intensifying the anxiety, shame, guilt, and fear that often accompany illness and injury.

Again, the architect may ask: What has this to do with me and my job?

The architecture of the old-paradigm hospital grows from the idea of a total institution. The older hospitals, those of the first third of the twentieth century and earlier, may inspire awe, but it is the awe evoked by a hybrid between a cathedral and a prison. These hospital buildings are characteristically monumental, often employing neo-gothic decorative elements and relying on hard, unyielding materials, including cold marble that, most unfortunately, bespeaks a mausoleum rather than a place of comfort and healing.

Many hospitals built during the 1950s and 1960s partake more of a functional modernism, deliberately stripping away such ecclesiastical reminders as gothic ornamentation in order to present a front that is efficient, professional, and sterile—figuratively as well as literally. Where marble and granite predominate in the public areas of the earlier buildings, stainless steel and glass are much in evidence in the later structures. The style of both types of building, however, communicates an allegiance to the totality of the institution. That is, though the hospital building of the 1920s is likely to look very different from that of the 1950s, a casual observer—or user—is apt to describe their architecture with the same word: *institutional*.

■ The History of an Institution

Grim as it may be at its all-too-common worst, the design of the traditional or old-paradigm hospital is neither an accident nor a mistake. It is the product of ever-evolving ideas of society, science, and the status of the medical community.

Temple of Asclepios, 400 B.C., Greece. By the time of Hippocrates, the temples of Asclepios offered a place of worship and shelter for the sick. Healing temples of the times resembled spas, emphasizing exposure to fresh air, sunlight, rest, baths, exercise, and reasonable diet. *Sketch by Earl S. Swensson.*

THE HEALING TEMPLE OF ASCLEPIOS AT EPIDAURUS, GREECE - 5TH CENTURY BC

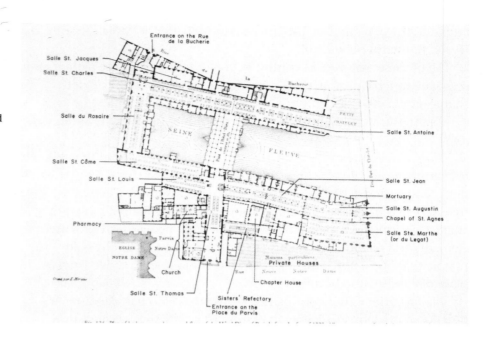

Western Europe's oldest hospital, the Hôtel Dieu in Paris—first constructed in 550 A.D., and rebuilt in the thirteenth century—functioned much like a modern hospital. Patients were separated according to type and severity of illness, the facility was organized by various departments, and patients who could afford to pay were charged for the services they received.

The first evidence of something resembling a hospital—that is, institutionalized care for the sick—may be found as early as 1200 B.C., when patients were cared for in Greek temples. By 400 B.C., the time of Hippocrates, the temples of Aesculapius appeared, structures devoted not only to worship but specifically to sheltering the sick. Most historians consider these the first hospitals in the Western world. They were not primarily inpatient institutions, but more closely resembled spas, emphasizing exposure to fresh air, sunlight, rest, baths, exercise, and a reasonable diet. Medication apparently was prescribed, but in moderation.

In Egypt, priest-physicians administered medical care, including the prescription of drugs and the performance of some surgery, in temples by 600 B.C. By far the most advanced hospitals of the ancient world seem to have been the *cikistas* of India, built between 273 and 232 B.C. Here Hindu physicians brought surgery to a high degree of development and administered efficacious medicines. Moreover, a hallmark of the *cikistas* was their cleanliness, and, as in the modern hospital, patients stayed overnight and were ministered to by attendants.

During the European Dark Ages, medical knowledge was largely "forgotten," along with much other wisdom of the classical world. However, ecclesiastic "hotels" were erected beside many churches to shelter the sick, who were cared for by priests. Treatment was very limited; instead, caring, compassion, and spiritual comfort were emphasized. The religious aspect of the ecclesiastical hotel increasingly displaced the succorant functions of these institutions throughout the course of the medieval period in Europe. The ecclesiastical hotel developed into buildings with large open wards featuring an altar and sometimes a chapel at the end or in the middle. The layout of the ward was meant to ensure that patients could hear and see religious services.

During this same time in the Middle East, efficacious physical medicine evolved into a sophisticated art. There is evidence that Mohammedan physicians used inhalant anesthetics and had at their disposal a wide range of drugs. Thirteenth-century Cairo's Al-Mansur Hospital included separate wards for serious illnesses, had outpatient clinics, and included homes for long-term convalescence.

It was during the early Renaissance that the word *hospital* came into being, derived from the Latin *hospes,* "host" or "guest," and that hospitals began to exist separately from churches. The oldest hospital in Western Europe is the Hôtel Dieu in Paris, which was built in 550 and rebuilt during the thirteenth century. By the early Renaissance, it was functioning in a manner strikingly similar to that of a modern hospital. Patients were classified and separated according to type and severity of illness, and there was a separate unit for women convalescing from childbirth. The hospital was divided into various departments, each governed by a head, the entire institution was directed by a "board of provisors," and patients who could afford to pay were charged for services rendered.

The Protestant Reformation closed many of the Catholic hospitals in Protestant countries, and these were taken over or replaced by privately financed and conducted institutions. In Catholic France, prior to the Revolution, hospitals remained essentially religious places, with wards laid out to provide patients with an opportunity to hear and see religious services. Secularization proceeded rapidly following the French Revolution, however.

Despite secularization, many hospitals retained the look of essentially religious structures, indicating the institution's former affiliation with the Church. In England, however, the characteristic eighteenth-century hospital came to resemble a Palladian mansion, except that the heights of the various stories were equal, whereas the domestic Palladian model varied story height as a reflection of the differing social functions of each floor. The eighteenth century was a boom time for English hospitals, in part due to the military, which built facilities to promote the maintenance of adequate manpower in the army and navy. One military hospital, at Stonehouse, Plymouth, built in 1762, actually embodied in its design the most advanced medical thinking of the period. In the mid eighteenth century, the prevailing theory of the causality of disease was the mias-

ILLINOIS SOUTHERN HOSPITAL, FOR THE INSANE. ANNA. UNION CO.

Illinois Southern Hospital for the Insane. Hospitals of the eighteenth and nineteenth centuries were modeled after the Palladian model. *Courtesy Bettmann Archive.*

Pennsylvania Hospital. The Palladian model dominated hospital design in the eighteenth and nineteenth centuries. These charitable institutions almost exclusively dealt with the sick who were too poor to have personal physicians tend to them in their homes.

matic or zymotic theory, which held that illness was the result of miasma or "bad air" (witness the term *malaria,* literally "bad air") and that an effective deterrent to miasma was the circulation of plenty of fresh air. With this in mind, the Admiralty hospital at Stonehouse was built as a series of detached pavilions connected by an open arcade, thereby exposing patients to the maximum natural ventilation possible.

Stonehouse was precocious, however, since the pavilion plan, endorsed by the medical profession, would not come into its own until well into the nineteenth century. Most eighteenth-century hospitals adhered to the Palladian model, which befit their dignified status as charitable institutions and pleased the subscribers and boards of governors, who were gentlemen accustomed to the elite gentility implied by the Palladian form.

Significantly, the imposing, mansionlike edifice functioned almost exclusively as a means of dealing with the sick poor. Well-to-do and middle-class persons preferred home treatment. The baronial architecture conveyed authority and control, and, indeed, the hospital institution was aimed at *regulating* the sick poor as much as *caring* for them. Concentrating the needy in a central location made treating them a more economical proposition, it allowed staff to supervise moral conduct, and it discouraged malingering. It also firmly controlled resources, changing the basis of poor relief from cash to food, medicine, and medical attention.

Many early twentieth-century hospitals feature architectural elements that betray distant ecclesiastical ancestry, but the architectural and bureaucratic roots of the modern hospital as a "total institution" are to be found in eighteenth-century England. Like most old-paradigm hospitals still in use today, the eighteenth-century buildings featured corridor plans that reflected and reinforced rigid social organization, a hierarchy extending down from the board of governors and their customary resident member, called the house visitor, progressively downward to the medical staff, the pharmacist (apothecary), the nursing staff, servants, and, lastly, the patients. Significantly, at London Hospital, it was the administrative committee room that occupied the most prominent space, the middle of the first floor. This prominence foreshadows late-twentieth century practice, where administrative and bureaucratic bloat became the norm; a

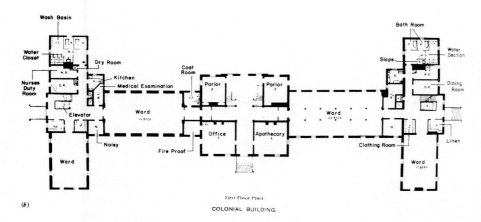

Pennsylvania Hospital. Floor plan. The Palladian design conveyed control and authority over the patients within. The early American hospital, supervised by men of means, sought to regulate the moral behavior of the sick poor as much as to care for their ailments.

study published in The *New England Journal of Medicine* (August 5, 1993) linked 25 percent of hospital costs to paperwork.

Arranged along two corridors leading out from the committee room were the staff rooms, whose occupants were ranged in diminishing social order, beginning with the physicians, who were closest to the committee room, and terminating with the nurses, who were farthest from it. The patient wards were located on the building's south side. Access to each was by single doors on either end of a corridor. The doors opened onto a ward lobby, from which three 15-bed wards radiated, allowing nursing staff to supervise three wards simultaneously and control entry to and exit from them. Rules of the London Hospital did not permit a patient to come and go of his own volition.

By the late eighteenth and early nineteenth centuries, hospitals had shed their Palladian pretensions, along with most other ornament, and become increasingly austere and—there is no other word for it—institutional. Some buildings combined gracious detail with lines and proportions more suited to a penal institution, which, as Adrian Forty points out in "The Modern Hospital in England and France: The Social and Medical Uses of Architecture" (in Anthony King, ed., *Buildings and Society: Essays on the Social Development of the Built Environment* [London, 1980]), "was the result of the governors' own conflicting motives. On the one hand, they desired a fine building, a noble institution that would beautify the town, advertise their philanthropy and attract more funds. On the other, they wished to deter undeserving cases, reduce the costs of sick relief, and moralize the poor out of their habit of reliance on the charity of others."

During the transition from eighteenth to nineteenth century, hospitals played a key role in, even as they were transformed by, the development of medicine as a sovereign profession. Eighteenth-century physicians were classed with tradesmen and, indeed, servants. Generally speaking, they put themselves at the beck and call of their wealthier patients, whom they visited and treated at home. In contrast, hospitals, which were mainly patronized by the poor, concentrated patients for the convenience of the physician.

The distinction went even deeper. The eighteenth-century physician's paying clients, treated at home, exercised a great deal of authority over

A nineteenth century wood engraving of Napoleon III at a hospital in Lyons, France, shows the typical warehouse approach to hospital design. *Courtesy Bettmann Archive.*

the physician as well as the treatment he prescribed. Moreover, physical examination involving actual contact between the doctor and his patient was a rarity discouraged by the social gulf that separated the practitioner from his client. Instead, the physician listened as the patient described his symptoms, observed what he could, and prescribed a course of treatment accordingly. In the hospital, however, where poor patients were more or less captive and, in any case, were of lower social caste than the physician, actual physical examination was possible. Since the physician had far more control over the patient in the hospital setting, medical *science* progressed more rapidly there.

With the gradual development of empirical medicine, made possible in large measure by the hospital setting, physicians, also gradually, gained a measure of respect and social position—as well as authority in decisions affecting hospital design. As early as 1752, Sir John Pringle, in his *Observations of Diseases of the Army in Camp and Garrison,* trumpeted the salutary effects of ample ventilation, an issue that soon came to figure in discussions of the design of hospitals as well as prisons. It was not until the mid nineteenth century, however, that medical theories of fresh air and ventilation to combat the evil effects of stagnant air and miasma began to exert practical influence over new hospital construction. But even before this time, physicians were concerned about cross-infection, which, they believed, resulted from massing patients in large, undifferentiated wards. Advanced hospitals, therefore, began to segregate surgical from non-surgical cases and even attempted to divide and isolate patients according to symptoms.

Along with smaller wards and segregation came ever-increasing control emanating directly from medical staff as opposed to the institutional administrators and governors. Forty cites an early nineteenth-century French observer on the state of Parisian hospitals:

> More or less severe punishments, such as privation of food or wine, even prison itself, are inflicted on those patients who disturb in some way the established order or who resist the will of the doctor, even when these demands are not immediately relevant to the treatment of their illness.

The physicians' power over patients was reinforced by architecture and by hospital furnishings, which became less generally institutional and more specifically clinical. Austerity of furnishings, which had been supported on moral grounds, was now endorsed for medical reasons: the fewer the items present in a ward, the fewer there would be to keep clean. Bed curtains, long regarded as a necessity in the drafty interiors of the days before central heating, were dispensed with in an effort to promote ventilation, despite the total sacrifice of privacy this entailed. Patients were also discouraged or prevented from bringing personal belongings into the hospital setting, since these were considered unhygienic. Thus hospital patients became wards of a "total institution," but less under the moral authority of a charitable board of governors than under the medical authority of physicians.

The mid nineteenth century saw the triumph of the pavilion-plan hospital in France and England. This hospital type, adumbrated in Stonehouse and the Hôtel Dieu (as rebuilt after a fire in the 1780s), consisted of what were in effect separate buildings joined by a single arcade or corridor. The design grew directly out of physicians' recommendations, as a means of providing maximum exposure to fresh air in an effort to dispel miasma.

During the height of the pavilion-plan hospital, the single most influential medical professional, in terms of hospital design, was neither a doctor nor an architect, but a nurse, Florence Nightingale. Her mission of reform, which encompassed the establishment of hygiene as well as the promotion of nursing as a respectable profession, dovetailed perfectly with the trend toward larger wards, ample ventilation, and interior austerity. Her design for the ideal ward, a long rectangular space with fifteen beds arranged along both long walls and a single entrance adjacent to the nurse's station, was widely adopted and christened the "Nightingale ward." Privacy was entirely sacrificed in the name of efficiency of nursing and the ability to regulate entry to and exit from the ward. Nightingale advocated plans that eliminated small spaces, including closets, sculleries, and lobby areas, which she believed were not only unhygienic but functioned as a "hiding or skulking place for patients or servants disposed to do wrong. And of such no hospital will ever be free."

The triumph of the pavilion plan may have been associated with the miasmic or zymotic theory of disease, but the continued dominance of this building style long outlasted belief in the scientific basis for it, persisting well after the zymotic theory was displaced by the modern germ theory and persisting even after numerous studies showed the pavilion plan to be no more conducive to patients' health than any other hospital layout. The persistence of the pavilion plan is even more remarkable when its disadvantages are taken into account. The footprint of such structures is very large, claiming extensive tracts of expensive urban real estate. Construction and maintenance costs are also considerable,

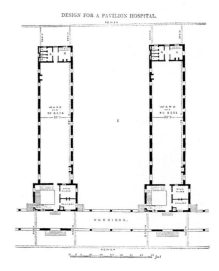

DESIGN FOR A PAVILION HOSPITAL.

The Nightingale ward, a rectangular space with fifteen beds arranged along both long walls, austere furnishings, and a single entrance adjacent to the nurse's station, sacrificed patient privacy for nursing efficiency.

Johns Hopkins University Hospital, Baltimore, Maryland. The impractical pavilion plan of hospital design long outlived the miasmatic or zymotic theory of disease that encouraged open arcades and maximum ventilation as a means of curing the sick. *Courtesy Bettmann Archive.*

New York Hospital, New York. Massive hospital buildings dominate the urban landscape. Imposing structures endowed the physician's role with a measure of magnificence, elevated his social position, and justified his increase in fees. *Courtesy Bettmann Archives.*

since the pavilion-style hospital is really a complex of individual structures linked together. Forty suggests that the building style persisted mainly because the imposing style endowed the physician's role with an added measure of magnificence, justifying his social elevation and providing a rationale for ever-increasing professional fees. Thus the dominant form of the general hospital at the end of the nineteenth century was more expressive of social, cultural, and professional-cultural values and motives than of perceived functional medical needs, let alone the human needs of the patient.

As physicians consolidated their prestige, both socially and scientifically, at the start of the twentieth century, the reputation of the hospital also greatly improved from its image as a place for the hopeless poor to linger before death to a center for possibly efficacious treatment. With this amelioration of image, the hospital began to attract paying patients from all social classes. In effect, this was the hospital's first brush with something conventionally definable as a marketplace, and, albeit slowly, hospitals began to cater to that marketplace. For the first time in the history of the institution, patients' needs were directly addressed and gestures toward creating a more humane environment were made. Among these gestures were improved food, more liberal visiting hours, and less arbitrary and absolute issuance of orders; patients were now routinely better informed. Design changes were not dramatic, but efforts were made to improve lighting, reduce noise, arrange beds more comfortably, and even to relieve the universal whitewash typical of the Nightingale ward with domestically toned color.

By the twentieth century, hospitals made attempts to address patient needs and create more humane environments. *Courtesy Bettmann Archives.*

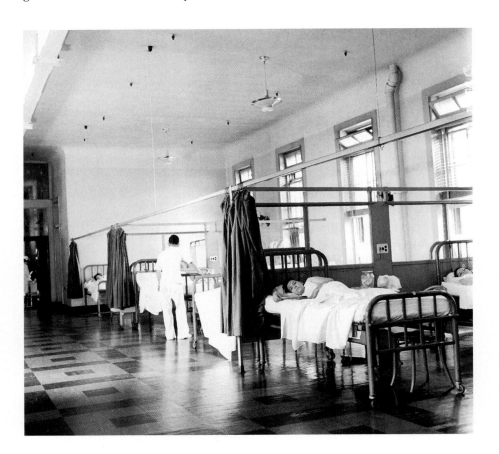

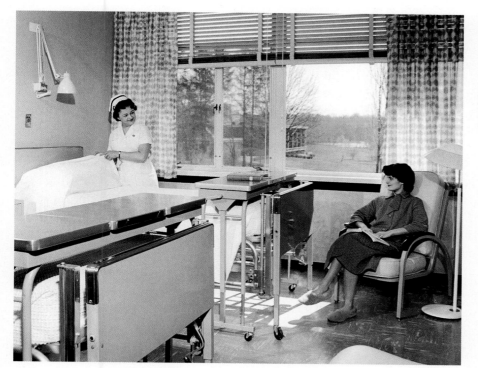

At about the time that patients gained a significant influence on hospital design, the apparatus of a growing medical technology also began to assert its demands. Up through the present, the needs of patients—once perceived as primarily emotional, now seen as psychosomatic, tightly bound to overall well-being—have come to coexist (often uneasily) with the design demands of technology, the design demands for the efficient working of personnel, and the institutional agenda that persists to a greater or lesser degree in most hospitals.

The growth of technology and the further development of the germ theory, antisepsis, and heroic surgical procedures coalesced with the modernist movement in architecture to create, by the early 1950s, sleek structures shorn of ornament and suggesting a hybrid between high-tech functionalism and a style suited to a downtown corporate headquarters. Many patients find such a style dehumanizing.

■ New Directions

Our object is not to condemn the majority of hospitals that exist today, but to understand the compelling cultural forces that have shaped them and, where appropriate, to suggest alternatives. It is also true that old-paradigm hospitals do address some still-useful and valid emotional needs. The monumental and ecclesiastical echoes in some of these structures are not only beautiful in and of themselves, but may actually inspire and encourage some patients rather than depress them or increase their level of anxiety. The functional modernist approach may not strike all users as inhuman, but may impress some as scientific and efficient, imparting confidence in the healing technology the hospital offers. Yet, as the paradigms enumerated in Chapter 1 continue the process of shifting, we believe these views will diminish in relevance commensurately.

It is not sufficient to change hospital design for the sake alone of improving the physical plant or even to accommodate new technologies, but to recognize that many of the *cultural* reasons for the old-paradigm hospital are no longer valid. Patients are still generally cast in a submissive role. Authoritarian—"institutional"—architecture is perceived as depressing, and depression is beyond doubt a negative influence on patient health. The depression may well be aggravated by the sense of isolation most old-paradigm hospitals foster. Even in institutions that encourage visitation by means of extended visiting hours, few make any design provision for family and companions. Finally, traditional designs tend to be rigid and difficult to adapt to expansion, renovation, and the installation of new equipment. It is clear from the literature of hospital design, patient care, and the sociology of medicine that ideas have changed. It is equally clear from most existing hospital and healthcare facilities that, unlike the ideas, the buildings have yet to change fundamentally.

3

New Markets, New Design Principles

We do not pretend to be voices in the wilderness. Judging from the many articles whose titles pose variations on the question "Can Hospitals Survive?", the healthcare industry is aware that old-paradigm services and structures do not merely fail to serve patients adequately, but fail in what even the most reluctant healthcare providers have come to recognize as a medical marketplace. This chapter outlines and describes the areas in which new design trends are aimed at addressing the emerging shape of the market for healthcare.

■ Flexibility

By this point in our discussion, at least one principle should have emerged clearly and unambiguously: Hospital and healthcare facility design must be sensitive to and responsive to the marketplace. But herein lies the rub. Retailers and manufacturers of consumer goods have always lived and died by the dictates of the marketplace. With luck, everyone will read the marketplace correctly and the company will be the first to come out with the hottest widgets. But what if the market for widgets suddenly shifts to a demand for dingbats? A flexible, responsive manufacturer will move heaven and earth to change production from widgets to dingbats. Depending on the product involved and the resources of the company, a manufacturer of consumer goods usually has that option, that degree of flexibility.

But what about healthcare providers, hospital administrators, facility planners, and architects? How feasible is it to be responsive to a marketplace when you are dealing with a multimillion-dollar building program?

It usually is not possible to start building one kind of facility, then change "production" to build another, let alone finish a building only to turn around, tear it down, and start over again.

The marketplace paradigm is seductive. Failure to anticipate or respond to the marketplace spells disaster. Yet it is also a fact that it is far more difficult productively to anticipate or respond to the terms of the market if your product is big, complex, culturally freighted, and staggeringly expensive than if your product is small, simple, culturally neutral, and relatively cheap. Even in view of this, we cannot abandon the paradigm of the marketplace. The simple fact is that the marketplace is real and will not go away. Instead, we need to develop designs that are not only responsive to the new paradigms that define today's emerging markets as we presently perceive them, but that are inherently flexible enough to anticipate and respond to market trends as yet uncertain or unforeseen.

The need for flexibility is further intensified by the technological nature of the healthcare industry. Not only must facilities adapt to changing patient populations and changing patient needs, but they must also anticipate the physical demands emerging technologies may make. Hospitals built in the age of the X-ray machine sometimes have difficulty accommodating the size of today's diagnostic and treatment capital equipment, including surgical gamma knife and MRI, let alone the controversial PET technology. Some trend predictors have suggested that such equipment may become even larger, for example as dedicated MRI units specifically built for operating rooms are developed. Brigham and Women's Hospital in Boston has a surgical MRI large enough that procedures can be performed in real time within the bore of the unit.

To be sure, it is possible, if costly, to anticipate such a technological contingency and to design and build accordingly. Yet other medical futurists predict that, during the next fifteen to twenty years, "space lab" technology and other trends toward electronic subminiaturization will actually *reduce* the structural space required for diagnostic hardware. Hence the need for flexibility in design, for spaces that can be expanded— or shrunk—as needed.

How fast are major technological changes moving? It is quite probable that, before the century ends, the useful life of equipment and

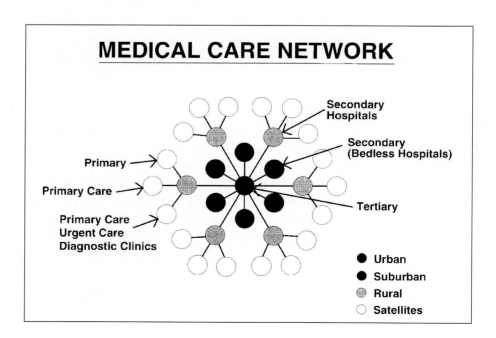

34

New Markets/New Design Principles

facilities will contract to as little as three years. Flexible design means creating facilities that can be quickly, economically, and repeatedly retrofitted and reconfigured—a design task challenging enough in and of itself, but that may be made the more difficult by outmoded building codes.

Flexible design has long been a hallmark of office and commercial spaces; for example, where it presents a relatively easy goal that is primarily a matter of erecting or eliminating partitions. In contrast, hospitals and healthcare facilities make more complex demands on electrical/mechanical systems and, therefore, present greater challenges to achieving flexible design. Moreover, as new monitoring and filtration technologies are developed and become desirable, perhaps even required, to ensure air quality and prevent toxicity, these demands will become even more complex.

In old-paradigm designs, the mechanical core was designed more rigidly than any other aspect of a building. It was perceived as a highly durable, virtually permanent component—a good thing, too, since, in hospitals, the mechanical core and electrical core accounts for 40 to 45 percent (or more) of construction costs. In sharp contrast, new-paradigm thinking calls for mobile, portable, and/or modular multiple HVAC systems designed in relatively small zones that can be easily changed and upgraded. Along with this, construction will use moment-resistant steel frames instead of braced frames or concrete, and floor systems will incorporate a systematic redundancy of penetrations to allow additional service chases as they may be called for in the future.

As early as the later 1960s, several architectural firms designing hospitals were developing variations on a basic structural-mechanical concept aimed at addressing what Eberhard Zeidler, of Craig, Zeidler & Strong, called "a fifth dimension in architecture—the change of space-function due to the lapse of time." Zeidler's firm designed the Health Sciences Center for McMaster University (Hamilton, Ontario), among the first hospital structures to use the principle of "interstitial space." The phrase was an apt one for hospital design, since *interstitial space* is a term borrowed from medicine itself, where it is used to describe the spaces between layers of the skin.

Interstitial spaces are intermediate service floors inserted between primary floors. Within these intermediate floors, which generally vary from a 6-foot height to heights approaching 8 feet, are all the mechanical, HVAC, and electrical components of the building. Granted their own space, these vital building elements become totally accessible for maintenance, upgrading, retrofitting, and other adaptations without having to invade or close down primary spaces. Not only is the mechanical core rendered more flexible, the primary spaces require fewer fixed vertical obstructions and therefore can be larger, more open, and more easily and quickly renovated and redesigned as needed.

By the late 1980s, the interstitial concept had evolved into the Integrated Building System (IBS), first developed for the Veterans Administration hospitals by the firm of Stone Marraccini and Patterson. In IBS designs, the intermediate service (or M/E, mechanical/electrical) floors,

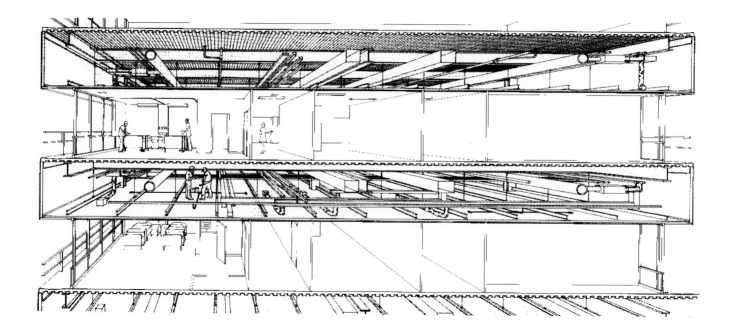

Interstitial Building System (IBS) Design. Mechanical and electrical runs can be reconfigured easily without disrupting the building's functions. *Courtesy of Stone Marraccini Patterson.*

separated from primary floors by a fireproof walking deck, are divided into repetitive M/E modules, each with its own utility room, to which all vertical utility runs go. The layout is duplicated on each floor, but each individual module is designed specifically to accommodate the particular department's needs, and, of course, each module can be readily altered or upgraded to meet changing needs.

Interstitial design has not been widely accepted because of the high cost of what is essentially a strategy of duplicating floors. The questions of cost raised by the interstitial concept speak to the heart of what it means to meet new markets with new design principles. Old-paradigm thinkers think in terms of immediate cost, whereas new-paradigm planners plan in terms of cost over the lifespan of a building. Even a relatively cheap building proves costly—usually disastrously so—if it is unable to change with a changing market, especially if the ultimate result is a three-year lifespan followed by oblivion and brand-new construction from scratch.

The interstitial concept is an extreme illustration of rethinking costs beyond initial outlay. The original proponents of this method have pointed out that the design saves operational costs through simplified maintenance and repair, and that ease of access encourages much preventive maintenance. M/E flexibility does make all renovation, retrofitting, and redesign programs less expensive, not only because working on the M/E system itself is easier and far less disruptive to primary areas, but because the intermediate floors reduce the number of fixed vertical obstacles traditional plans put in primary-use areas. Some architects have even argued that IBS can actually *reduce* some initial construction costs—despite the high consumption of material and labor. Construction, they say, can generally proceed faster, since the structural-mechanical grid is separated from primary-use spaces. The structural-mechanical aspects of the project can be bid and constructed before use-spaces, if necessary.

A compressed construction schedule is not only cost-saving in and of itself, getting the building into productive use sooner and reducing finance periods, but, especially in times of significant inflation, compressed construction schedules save additional significant sums. There is also the bonus of a gain in flexibility in the process of designing the primary-use spaces. Architects and planners have more time to work with clients, medical consultants, and others to plan these spaces more effectively. Additional costs may be saved by increasing the number of contractors who can bid on a single job that can now be divided into several. Smaller, more competitive firms, whose bond limitations might have precluded their undertaking a project as costly as an entire hospital, can be called on to bid individual aspects of the project—say, the M/E core alone.

Such arguments notwithstanding, at present the consensus among architects and their clients is that the interstitial strategy is simply too costly.

Who is right, and who is wrong? This may depend on how far one wants to anticipate the future. Even as soon as the first quarter of the twenty-first century, flexibility may loom as so crucial a design criterion that more administrators and planners will deem the initial capital costs of interstitial design justified. The point is that it is one thing to become aware that buildings exist in temporal as well as spatial dimensions, but, while it is a relatively straightforward planning task to decide how wide, deep, or high a building should be, it is far more difficult to determine how much capital should be invested now for gains that may be realized in ten or twenty or thirty years—or never realized at all.

If, nevertheless, as Zeidler suggested, architects have become aware that they build not only in spatial but in temporal dimensions, so cost planners and allocation managers must realize that they spend in this fifth dimension as well.

The interstitial strategy may or may not be cost-effective, but the principle that underlies it—flexibility of design—is emerging as increasingly vital in creating cost-effective healthcare facilities. Flexibility is crucial in planning the layout of the facility space. The traditional "racetrack" corridor design does have a certain flexibility, in that it can often be added to and modified with some ease. However, it is an inherently inefficient and often uncomfortable layout. Long corridors are difficult for nurses to monitor, and they mean many footsteps for physicians as well as nurses, who are obliged to spend more time walking than attending to patients. Similarly, supplies and equipment must be trundled up and down long distances. Patients' stress levels may also be increased by long corridors, which are, of necessity, active, bustling, and noisy. Finally, the racetrack plan is inefficient in terms of energy, difficult to heat, cool, and even to wire cost-effectively.

As noted earlier, circular plan alternatives to the racetrack enjoyed some popularity in the 1970s and were often welcomed by nurses, who saved steps and could more effectively attend to patients' needs. In the early 1980s, when Earl Swensson Associates (ESa) was assigned the task of creating a basic hospital plan for Hospital Corporation of America (HCA),

Fairview Park Hospital, Dublin, Georgia. The triangular design of the inpatient area allows the nursing staff to tend to patients efficiently. *Courtesy Earl Swensson Associates.*

1 Nurses' station
2 Dictation
3 Support
4 Patient rooms

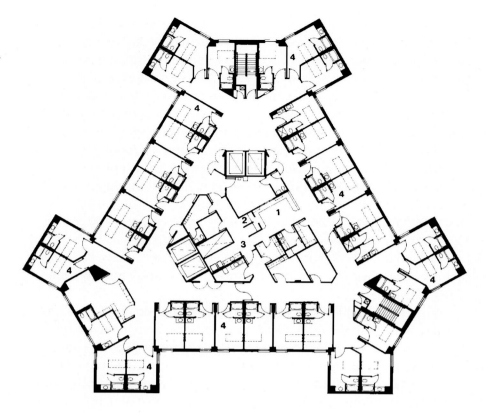

we considered the circular design, but found that it required too much square footage per bed and wasted space in the central nursing core. The size of the circular floor would ultimately have required provision of two nursing stations per floor, thereby increasing construction costs and multiplying staffing needs. Finally, the circular plan is inherently less flexible, less able to adapt to changing needs, than even the racetrack plan.

The solution ESa came up with was a triangle design, which shortens the distance between nursing stations and patient rooms, reduces the nursing unit's total square footage, cuts construction costs, reduces utility bills because of reduced outer wall areas, and still maintains flexibility for expansion and extension. The triangle design calls for no more than six patient rooms per straight corridor, in contrast to the racetrack's seventeen or eighteen rooms per corridor. Each point of the triangle has two sections extending from it, each holding three more rooms for a total of thirty-six patient rooms per nursing unit. The triangle design puts not only the nurses' station but the elevator and utility core at the center, as well as a visitor waiting area, food delivery area, housekeeping facility, and maintenance room. The design of the basic triangle can be varied and manipulated to suit different needs, such as the addition of more private rooms.

The idea of flexibility extends to the range of finishes chosen for buildings, with the most permanent infrastructures—pathways and vertical circulations, for example—finished in high-quality, long-lasting materials, and other areas, subject to shorter lifespans, finished with less expensive, less durable, even throwaway materials.

World War II made heroic demands upon the building industry, greatly accelerating the development of prefabricated structures. By the late 1960s, some hospitals were experimenting with prefabricated patient rooms created out of standard modular units developed by the Research and Graduate Center of Texas A&M's School of Architecture. The Adaptable Building System (ABS) was intended for loftlike spaces and consisted of four basic components: a raised floor, a modular partition panel system, a perforated suspended ceiling unit, and a one-piece molded glass-fiber "hygiene component."

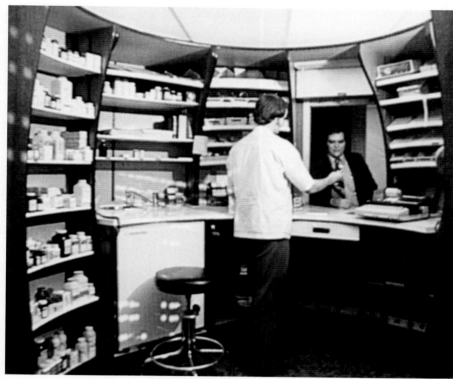

SystaModule. A highly efficient modular pharmacy, the SystaModule offers the flexibility of arranging a variety of modules in many configurations as needed. *Photo by Alan Karchmer. Courtesy Earl Swensson Associates.*

These experiments did not give rise to large-scale use of prefabricated hospital rooms, however. They had potential in situations where substantial undifferentiated and unimpeded open interior space was available, as in a handful of facilities built with deliberately unused expansion ("shell") areas. But few hospitals are planned this way, and therefore the market for prefabricated patient rooms remained small. However, the gains in cost-efficiency and in accuracy of fabrication offered by pre-manufactured building modules have shown promise in more specialized hospital and healthcare facility applications.

Beginning in 1969, Earl Swensson Associates collaborated with the Research Institute of Pharmaceutical Sciences at the University of Mississippi and General Equipment Manufacturers of Crystal Springs, Mississippi, to develop and manufacture what we called SystaModule, a self-contained, pre-manufactured pharmacy unit for a hospital setting.

The SystaModule was the result of listening to the needs of hospital pharmacists, a group of professionals whom traditional designs had largely ignored. The units ESa designed were task-oriented and based on human engineering principles, using Le Corbusier's "Modulor," a design concept by which man is made the measure in a system of rhythmic harmony, elegant proportion, and maximum efficiency. The modules were designed to accomplish specific tasks and could be assembled, as required, to create a complete pharmacy service unit. Tasks included outpatient dispensing, sterile extemporaneous preparation (including IV admixture), medication order review, and inpatient dispensing—basic, crucial tasks accommodated by no existing design.

SystaModule proved a highly efficient work environment. Whereas 28 seconds were required to prepare each medication in the traditional pharmacy work area, only 7.18 seconds were required per medication fill in the SystaModule environment. Beyond this gain in productivity—not only important for patient welfare, but vital to any industry operating in a competitive market—the SystaModule offers great flexibility, since the various modules can be configured and reconfigured as needed and as available space allows. Moreover, this flexibility makes the system specifically adaptable to very diverse pharmacy applications, from IV admixture to outpatient dispensing. Finally, the SystaModule is easily expandable and can grow—or, for that matter, shrink—as the need warrants.

■ Socially Responsible Design Is Dynamic Design

Flexible design begins at the planning stage, but it does not end there, nor even after construction is complete. Flexible design, by definition, is dynamic design, a process that is part of what Janet R. Carpman, writing in *Group Practice Journal* (July/August 1991), calls "socially responsible health facility design," which she identifies as a major new direction for the industry.

Socially responsible design has five characteristics:

1. It is based on an explicitly understood shared value system.
2. It is based on information.
3. It is the product of a participatory design process.
4. It incorporates periodic, systematic design review.
5. It incorporates periodic evaluation of the finished project.

The first three factors ensure that the proposed design is politically, economically, and physically feasible, while placing greatest emphasis on the social, psychological, and physical needs of patients, visitors, and staff. These needs are paramount in socially responsible health facility design. Before design work begins, information is gathered, based on review of pertinent literature, facility visits, interviews and surveys among facility users, and simulations (using models, computer-aided virtual reality techniques, videotape simulation, and so on). This information is used to formulate design guidelines or performance criteria.

During the design process itself, the participation of the users of the facility needs to be sought. This will help to clarify design objectives and to ensure that the objectives of the primary project planners, the architects, and the users mesh. Carefully considered and evaluated, participatory design leads to better design decisions while evoking positive behavior and attitudes from clients and users and creating a community of common interest. Insofar as participatory design averts errors and the necessity for costly modifications, it also has the potential for lowering construction costs. Finally, participatory design provides an opportunity for dynamically assessing design-related organizational policies.

The last two components of the socially responsible model of design are the most relevant to ensuring the ongoing flexibility of the design, because they establish a system in which design is subject to evaluation and reevaluation, both during the design process and after the project ostensibly has been completed. We say "ostensibly," since, in an environment as dynamic as that of the hospital or healthcare facility, the project is never really complete. In today's healthcare market, a completed project is, truly, a *finished* project: done for, and doomed to the briefest useful life. In contrast, a project in which process is built-in stands the greatest chance of enduring.

■ Dynamic Design Is Synergenial Design

The dynamic approach implied by the goal of socially responsible design is encompassed in what Earl Swensson Associates has called "Synergenial Design," a concept discussed in the opening chapter of this book. *Synergism* and *geniality*—the component terms of the concept—are the key elements of a design approach that acknowledges both the synergistic nature of the problem-solving process and the congenial, user-sensitive attributes of a successfully designed solution.

Synergenial buildings are functional environments that evoke positive responses from their users on physical, intellectual, and emotional levels. To achieve this level of *response* requires a high level of *responsiveness* from architects and designers. The trend in hospital and healthcare design is to allow architects and designers to become increasingly responsive by bringing them in at the earliest possible stages of a proposed project and then retaining them through the lifespan of the building. In this sense, the building is always a *project*, flexible and responsive to evolving physical, intellectual, and emotional needs.

■ Patient-Centered Design

Participatory design does have its limitations. Of necessity, those who have the opportunity to participate most fully in the process are planners, administrators, architects, and care providers, including physicians, nurses, and physical plant staff. It is possible and desirable also to gather information from and about the other users of the proposed structure, the patients, but, of course, this group is not likely to participate in the dynamic design process in any formal way.

This does not mean that patients fail to make their needs and preferences known. A retail establishment does not hire customers to serve as merchandise buyers, but the buyer who allows himself to get out of touch with the store's customers is soon out of a job. The successful retailer does not begin by asking what seems an obvious question: "What merchandise is proper and appropriate for a store to stock?" Instead, he begins by asking, "What do my customers want?" And it is a question he must ask and answer not once, but, dynamically, each and every day.

Hospitals and healthcare facilities of the old paradigm "establish" themselves by asking: "What services are proper and appropriate for a hospital to offer?" And this is a step made all the more rigid by being a question to which many planners and administrators believe they already have the answers. In contrast, new-paradigm medical facility planners begin by assessing what their patients want.

Once this kind of questioning begins, an important market distinction emerges. At the most basic level, the traditional general hospital serves two distinct markets:

1. Patients requiring acute care, which includes trauma (emergency); burns; high-risk obstetrical and neonatal care; intensive care; neurological or cardiac surgery; multi-organ failure; organ transplantation; and similarly life-threatening situations.

2. Patients with chronic conditions or subacute conditions requiring inpatient or ambulatory care. This includes such services as ambulatory diagnostics and surgery; chronic care screening and maintenance; day treatment and recovery care; routine childbirth; and routine inpatient surgery. Non-urgent emergency room services should be included in this market segment, which may (and, in many communities, should) be expanded to include the primary care network and private practice base. Other community-oriented services include health education and disease prevention and home-care networks.

Incredibly, by tradition, hospitals have failed to distinguish between these two basic markets. The result, in the days of full insurance reimbursement, was financial waste and inefficient, inconvenient, and often anxiety-generating care for the patient. In today's consumer-driven medical marketplace, where costs are contained through systems based on the DRG (Diagnosis-Related Groups) system introduced by Medicare in 1983, failure to understand the structure of the marketplace is likely to result in failure to survive.

The DRG system radically altered the way reimbursements are made. Under the old total-reimbursement system, insurance paid for virtually all tests and procedures a physician saw fit to order, and hospital stays were reimbursed on a per diem basis. The introduction of Diagnosis-Related Groups, however, has meant that, for the most part, insurance pays a lump sum for a given condition, based on the usual and customary cost of treatment for the problem. In cases where hospitals and physicians accept insurance assignment, the motive for increased efficiency is obvious. The less time and resources expended to resolve a problem, the greater the profit. The more expended, the less the profit—or the greater the loss. In cases where hospitals and care providers depend on the patient to pay, that individual, knowing that his reimbursement is capped, is likely to shop around for the best value.

In and of itself, the DRG system was a strong impetus to shorten hospital stays and to transfer as much care to ambulatory departments as possible. Yet, for hospitals designed under the old-total reimbursement rules, this kind of turnover created a problem in the form of empty beds. What does an industry do when supply exceeds demand? If you're a flexible manufacturer, you can shift your production to other product lines or you can simply reduce production and lay employees off. These

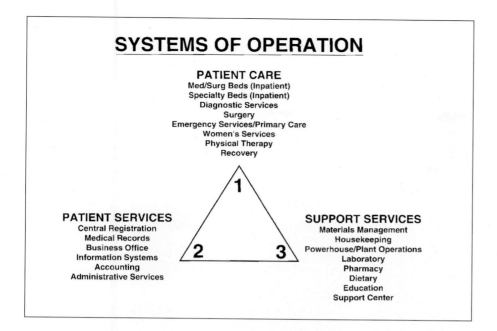

SYSTEMS OF OPERATION

PATIENT CARE
Med/Surg Beds (Inpatient)
Specialty Beds (Inpatient)
Diagnostic Services
Surgery
Emergency Services/Primary Care
Women's Services
Physical Therapy
Recovery

1

PATIENT SERVICES
Central Registration
Medical Records
Business Office
Information Systems
Accounting
Administrative Services

2   **3**

SUPPORT SERVICES
Materials Management
Housekeeping
Powerhouse/Plant Operations
Laboratory
Pharmacy
Dietary
Education
Support Center

steps are not as feasible for a hospital, however, and the better solution to empty beds is to fill them through aggressive marketing.

What does a hospital have to market? The most obvious product is excellence in healthcare, and, to be sure, a facility's reputation for excellence is a strong incentive to healthcare consumers to select that institution over another. However, in most geographical areas, consumers find it difficult to judge strictly medical standards. To put it most frankly, the greater direct influence on potential consumers is "packaging"—architectural design, and the patient amenities the design offers.

■ Vertical Integration

Patient focusing is a current trend that is likely to endure. An associated trend is vertical integration and work redesign, a way of rethinking the traditional departmental organization of the hospital so as to maximize caregiver contact with patients and to promote continuity of care by making a team of caregivers responsible for each patient from admission to discharge. In vertically integrated hospitals, the multiplicity of departments and bureaucratic fiefdoms is reduced to a few general, integrated areas of responsibility, such as *patient*

PineLake Medical Center, Mayfield, Kentucky. In this design of unbundled services, separate entrances lead patients and visitors directly to emergency, the MOB, and the women's center. Distinctive entrances minimize, to an extent, way-finding problems. *Photo by Gary Knight. Courtesy Earl Swensson Associates.*

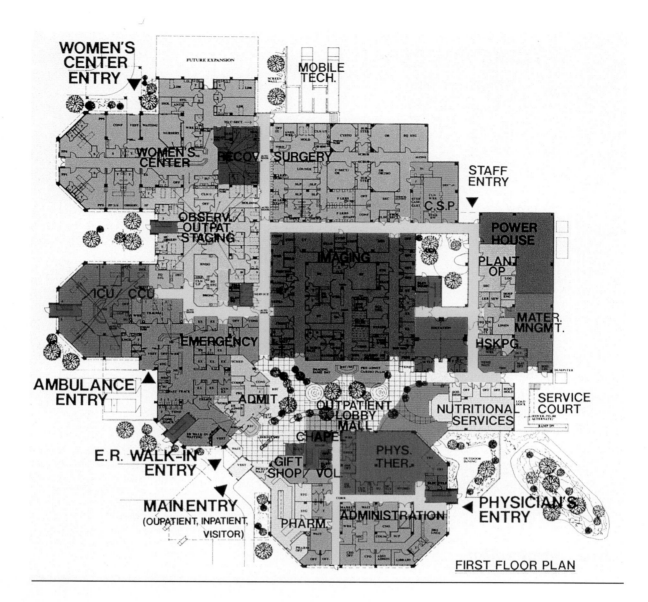

WOMEN'S CENTER ENTRY

FUTURE EXPANSION

MOBILE TECH.

WOMEN'S CENTER

RECOV.

SURGERY

STAFF ENTRY

C.S.P.

POWER HOUSE

PLANT OP

OBSERV. OUTPAT. STAGING

IMAGING

MATER. MNGMT.

ICU/CCU

HSKPG

EMERGENCY

AMBULANCE ENTRY

ADMIT

OUTPATIENT LOBBY MALL

NUTRITIONAL SERVICES

SERVICE COURT

CHAPEL

E.R. WALK-IN ENTRY

GIFT SHOP/ VOL

PHYS. THER.

PHYSICIAN'S ENTRY

MAIN ENTRY
(OUPATIENT, INPATIENT, VISITOR)

PHARM

ADMINISTRATION

FIRST FLOOR PLAN

McMinnville Community Hospital, McMinnville, Oregon. Plans reflect the vertical integration of services at a full-service community facility. Note: This drawing reflects an early plan for the hospital. When the facility was actually constructed, the plan was flopped. *Courtesy Earl Swensson Associates.*

services, support services, and *patient care.* Based on Earl Swennson Associates' design for the McMinnville Community Hospital in McMinnville, Oregon, the following outline is intended to suggest some of the work and design implications of such an organization in a smaller, rural facility, showing how facilities, equipment, and staff may be effectively shared across what once were the barriers of traditional departments:

Patient Services. The combination of business and administrative services allows cross-trained employees to work in a barrier-free environment to minimize duplication of effort and to maximize time efficiency. Design should help facilitate streamlining patient processing, facilitating a smoother flow of information, and reducing paperwork.

1. A single entry area, under a canopy and adjacent to parking, serves outpatients, inpatients, emergency walk-ins, and those visiting physicians' offices. It is convenient and facilitates way-finding.

Spring View Hospital, Spring View, Kentucky. Floor and ceiling materials define the admitting area, which features admitting cubicles designed for privacy. *Photo by Gary Knight. Courtesy Earl Swensson Associates.*

2. Registration is centralized at the main entry, and no effort is duplicated.
    a. Cross-trained personnel work among central scheduling, coding, emergency registration, and reception, helping to minimize duplication and assist in way-finding.
    b. Scheduling for all departments is centralized.
    c. Registration can also support physicians' offices.
    d. Having the PBX positioned adjacent to emergency department registration allows twenty-four-hour observation of security monitors without staff duplication.
    e. Fast-track registration (registration and cashier combined) allows for faster service. A sit-down area is provided for handicapped registration, and a private counseling office is provided for financial counseling.
    f. The role of receptionist is shared among volunteers, and a directory is available at reception to aid in way-finding.
3. Medical records/business office/accounting/information systems
    a. The area is designed in a modular setting with computer flooring to aid cross-training among staff and flexibillity to adapt to change; many times records staff can be cross-trained to back up registration.
    b. Medical records and business office records are combined in fixed files to allow several staff members to access the information at the same time.
    c. Information systems allow for decentralization and ready availability of records in the future. Social services are *decentralized*—located adjacent to inpatient beds on the nursing floor for the convenience of patients and their families.

Pevco-Pneumatic tube system. An example of "smart technology," the Pevco system reduces the time needed to send specimens to a laboratory for analysis. *Photo by Walter Larrimore. Courtesy Pevco System International, Inc.*

4. Administration/Nursing Administration/Medical Staff Lounge/ Human Resources
   a. Administration includes CEO, CFO, assistant administrator, marketing, director of nursing, and nursing supervisor.
   b. Work areas are efficiently shared. Human resources has an independent entry located near the main entry, which allows physicians and administration convenient access for communications.

Support Services. Support services create a center for all support requests (such as meals, supplies, mail service, housekeeping services, plant operations support, patient transport, etc.). This center improves communications as well as reduces duplication and supports nursing staff by providing proper training and cost-effective staff to assist in support duties, thereby keeping higher-paid nursing staff dealing with higher-level nursing issues.

1. Pharmacy
   a. Outpatient and inpatient is combined to minimize pharmacy staff. The outpatient dispensary is located near the front door, for the convenience of medical office patients, emergency department patients, and inpatient discharges.
   b. Modular shelving is used for flexibility.
   c. Pneumatic tubes reduce the need for couriers to deliver medications to inpatient locations, although some dispensers are located in the inpatient units.
2. Laboratory
   a. Modular design ensures future flexiblity.
   b. Pneumatic tubes connect to all patient areas, greatly reducing the need for couriers and expediting processing.
   c. Lab staff does not draw all blood; staff in patient-care areas are cross-trained to draw blood.
   d. Lab is located near materials management area for supply delivery.
   e. Frozen-section facility is adjacent to surgery.
3. Support Center
   a. Contains area for secretarial support and vendor waiting.
   b. "One-Stop-Shopping" distribution area for all support services.
   c. Housekeeping, plant operation, materials management, dietary, and mail distribution are based here, sharing secretarial support.
4. Materials Management
   a. Positioned ideally to receive and distribute materials.
5. Housekeeping
   a. Accessible to all areas, but separate from public traffic.
6. Plant Operation/Powerhouse
   a. Plant Operation is located adjacent to the powerhouse service area for equipment repair.
7. Dietary
   a. Serviced by support core.

b. Adjacent to conference center for ease of catering service.

   c. Located convenient to outpatient area for dietary counseling.

   d. Positioned to provide efficient inpatient service.

   e. Nourishment areas provided on patient floors.

   f. Pleasant dining area for inpatients, outpatients, and others located in outpatient mall.

   g. Outdoor dining is available.

8. Education

   a. Prominent position in outpatient mall for community education.

   b. Accessible for internal staff education as well as outpatient and inpatient education.

   c. Flexible, subdividable conference facility is available.

Patient Care. With facility-wide support systems provided by support services and patient services, optimal use of professional staff is possible. Many traditional areas are combined, both through physical construction and staff cross-training. Flexibility is the key design ingredient.

1. Diagnostic services

   a. Combines imaging, cardiopulmonary, preadmittance testing, lab testing, drug screening.

   b. Many support staff and areas are shared among the services.

   c. Staff work areas are separated in order to minimize patient/staff conflicts.

   d. Exam rooms for pre-admission and cardioplumonary are not designated for specific functions and are shared among both services for flexibility of use. Staff is cross-trained in multiple tasks.

   e. Imaging is located for easy accessibility from emergency, with heavy-use diagnostic (CT, chest X-ray, MRI, and ultrasound) near the emergency area, thus eliminating duplication.

2. Emergency Services/Primary Care

   a. Includes Emergency and ICU/CCU as a combined area.

   b. Emergency shares central registration with all other services.

   c. Triage adjacent to registration and visible from nurses' station.

   d. Fast-track expedites minor cases of emergency primary care.

   e. Emergency department walk-ins and primary care are separate from trauma cases for the patients, yet combined by staff.

   f. Two areas within the department, trauma and primary care, share support areas and staff.

   g. Trauma rooms and ICU/CCU rooms provide back-up for one another through adjacency.

   h. Emergency and ICU/CCU share support. Can overflow staff and rooms from ICU/CCU, if necessary.

   i. Outpatient pharmacy located near primary care portion of emergency department.

   j. Waiting area for ICU/CCU adjacent to patient mall, so that families can use dining facilities and overflow into more comfortable waiting and dining areas.

      k. Observation is shared with emergency department and obstetrics.

3. Recovery/Same-Day Surgery/Observation
    a. During daytime, same-day staff monitors the observation area as well as the same-day staging areas.
    b. Recovery cross-trains its staff to back-up area.

4. Obstetrics
    a. Distinct entry to department provides patient with a identity and purpose separate from the rest of the facility.
    b. Provides comforts of home in a residential setting.
    c. Offers one-room birthing (labor-delivery-recovery-postpartum rooms). Rooms include family.
    d. Shares its support areas (soiled utility, dietary, etc.) with recovery/same-day/observation.
    e. C-sections are performed in the adajacent surgery department.
    f. Dedicated education area for Lamaze classes, etc., are located in the obstetrics department.
    g. Nurses' station is positioned to monitor entry, nursery, corridors, and the observation unit.

5. Surgery
    a. Central sterile supply managed by support center.
    b. Anesthesia is accessible to surgery suite as well as obstetrics unit.

6. Physical Therapy
    a. Inpatient physical therapy is adjacent to skilled nursing unit as well as medical/surgical units.
    b. Outpatient physical therapy is located on the main level for easy access.
    c. Outpatient physical therapy is visible and accessible from the outpatient mall, for sports medicine and wellness marketing aspects.

7. Inpatient care: medical/surgical
    a. Visitor elevator is separate from service elevator.
    b. Patient services staff member acts as receptionist, coder, and unit secretary; monitors family waiting area.
    c. Nursing sub-stations within the units bring nursing staff and supplies closer to the patient.
    d. Patient rooms are designed in pods for closer, patient-focused monitoring. The pods are designed to be converted to special-care units. Their modularity facilitates adaptability. Visual contact to patient beds is possible as in the ICU/CCU.
    e. Rooms can be converted to intensive care units by placing toilets on the outside walls and adding glass at the corridor wall.
    f. Support core provides shared restocking areas and support for all pods. The key to this area is adaptability to whatever special-care needs might develop.

8. Physician Offices
   a. Offices are integrated with the hospital for convenient, one-stop access for both patient and physician.
   b. Minimizes the duplication of diagnostics.
   c. Uses the hospital's laboratory through an integrated pneumatics system.
   d. The offices share in the business/medical records/information systems functions of the hospital.
   e. Maximizes the use of the physicians' time through proximity to the hospital.

■ What Healthcare Consumers Look For

Studies conducted by Carpman Grant Associates, Environmental Design Consultants, Ann Arbor, Michigan, suggest that all hospital patients (and visitors) share four basic design-related needs: *physical comfort, social contact, symbolic meaning,* and *way-finding.*

At its most basic, physical comfort means such things as appropriate room temperature, pleasant lighting, comfortable furniture, a telephone located within easy reach of the bed, freedom from unpleasant odors and harsh or annoying noise, and so on.

Social contact encompasses personal privacy—limiting what others see and hear of you—as well as controlling what you see or hear of others. For example, if a design provides no place for physicians to consult with family members, a patient may overhear conversations in the hall outside his room. It is also demoralizing for a patient, attired in an open-backed hospital gown, to have to wait in a hallway for some test or other procedure.

Symbolic meaning encompasses the array of non-verbal messages embodied in design. For example, a cramped, uncomfortable waiting area with inadequate seating is not only physically offensive, but suggests to patients that "the powers that be" hold them in low regard.

Finally, among the most intimidating aspects of large hospitals are the obstacles they present to way-finding. Patients, already under stress, can easily feel buried or lost in a forbidding technological maze, while visitors are fearful of inadvertently wandering into some restricted, embarrassing, or even frightening space.

In 1984, Earl Swensson Associates conducted research with the assistance of Professor Ken Barker of the Department of Pharmacy Care Systems at Alabama's Auburn University to project the future of healthcare and the role of architecture in it. They posited a typical twenty-first-century patient, eighty-six-year-old Edna Johnson, and followed her through the healthcare system as she coped with a myocardial infarction. Many technological innovations were predicted, but a key feature of the hospital and healthcare facilities of the future was seen to be large, home-like patient rooms within structures that featured a similarly homelike scale with plenty of cues to way-finding and design features intended to make life easier for an aged, frail woman.

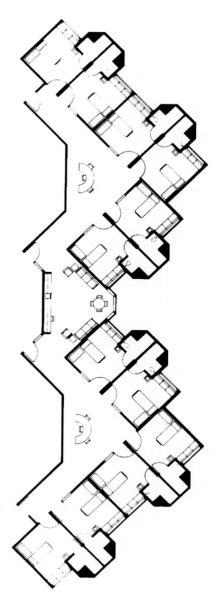

Floor plan of typical "care suites."
Courtesy Ratcliff Architects.

More recently, a 1992 survey by Press, Ganey Associates, Inc. (published in *U.S. News & World Report*, June 15, 1992) showed privacy to be the primary concern of 140,000 patients discharged from 225 hospitals. Accordingly, the Ratcliff Architects of Emeryville, California, and the H.O.M. Group, Inc., of San Francisco, developed a prototype of a patient-centered hospital that, in the interest of maximizing privacy, features all private rooms, each larger than what is typical of most community hospitals—the bed area is 35 percent larger—and each offering the option of family rooming-in. The enlarged rooms also make the space more flexible, assuming that technologies for bedside recording and medication will minimize patient movement from one department to another. Moreover, the patient rooms are grouped into "care suites," which accommodate a lounge, library, kitchenette, and conference area for patients, family, and caregivers. (Wanda J. Jones and Milton Bullard, "Translating Operational Change into Facility Design," *Healthcare Forum Journal*, January/February 1993.)

Designs that address the basic needs outlined above are of paramount importance in the pages that follow, and we shall explore them in detail. Generally, the overriding patient need that ties these four basics together is, in the phrase that futurist John Naisbitt made famous in his 1982 *Megatrends*, a desire for a "high-tech, high-touch" environment. Make no mistake, patients want the best that technology can offer administered by the best people, but with this high technology, they also want a humanized environment, comfortable and aesthetically pleasing.

Facilities that lure patients by their human warmth began to appear in the mid-to-late 1980s. The Portland-based firm of Broome, Oringdulph, O'Toole, Rudolf, Boles & Associates completed in 1985 the Kaiser Rockwood Clinic in Rockwood, Oregon, deliberately meant to counter the bland anonymity previously associated with that HMO's "no-nonsense" buildings. Set in a beautiful rural landscape and making many references to the area's wood-based architectural traditions, the Rockwood facility exemplifies what John W. Grigsby, a physician and ambulatory care center developer, described in 1987 as a consumer-driven trend "away

Kaiser-Rockwood Clinic, Rockwood, Oregon. A clinic in a rural setting, Kaiser-Rockwood takes a departure from the institutional image of a healthcare facility. The clinic's exterior makes effective use of color and owes its style to local, wood-based architectural traditions. *Photo by Ed Hershberger. Courtesy BOORA Architects.*

from stainless steel, metal doors, linoleum, insensitive lighting, and bland institutional color schemes. The emphasis on 'high touch' means that physician-administrators are asking their architectural consultants to help them de-institutionalize, de-stress, and dress up their waiting rooms, clinics, and hospital service areas. . . . We've even gone as far as trying to duplicate the living room in our very own homes."

The Rockwood facility is a good example of adding humanizing elements by thoughtful reference to the community. As Gideon Bosker relates in his discussion of the building ("Architecture as an Asset in Health Care," *Architecture,* January 1987), "The strong emphasis on squares, rectangles, and figural setbacks imparts a high-tech image, while the formidable port-cochère, with its large fir beams and seamed sheetmetal roof, conveys the high-touch ambiance of mountain lodges that dot Mt. Hood just down the road."

The health facility does not have to be in scenic Washington state to make meaningful and aesthetically pleasing references to familiar, "humanizing" surroundings. Two of the most popular models for new-paradigm hospitals and healthcare facilities are the retail mall and the hotel.

Kaiser-Rockwood Clinic, Rockwood, Oregon. The clinic's interiors feature custom detailing in warm wood hues and colors. Natural light provides an attractive, healthy atmosphere. *Photo by Ed Hershberger. Courtesy BOORA Architects.*

■ The Mall Model

Among the first departures from traditional pavilion-based hospital design was the concept of a medical campus, a hybrid between an academic and a parklike setting. In the mid 1970s, this notion, among forward-thinking, market-conscious designers, began to give way to the idea of the medical mall.

If familiarity is a key to humanizing and "de-stressing" healthcare facility design, perhaps only the home itself is a more familiar model to evoke than the shopping mall, ubiquitous in our culture today, not just as a place of retail exchange, but of amusement, and social exchange as well. Not only does the mall configuration offer patient comfort and reassurance, the spread-out, mall-like setting offers tremendous flexibility for laying out inpatient and outpatient facilities.

How did the medical mall evolve? H. Ralph Hawkins, writing in the *Journal of Health Care Interior Design* (vol. 2, 1990), traces its origin to hospital complexes in which the hospital proper is linked to a medical office building via a corridor or corridors. These became "main streets" for pedestrian traffic passing between the two buildings, and some hospitals developed this highly trafficked but non-critical area as retail space, leasing it to storefront operators offering health-related and more general consumer-related services (pharmacy, gift shop, news vending, and the like).

By the mid 1970s, healthcare providers had started to exploit the opportunities afforded by the existing circulation paths through certain healthcare complexes. In 1975, Bob Wright of Medical City, Inc., created a development called Medical City Dallas. This was an atrium around which spaces for public functions and amenities were provided on the

Mt. Sinai Integrated Medical Campus MOB, Beechwood, Ohio. The attractive atrium area, which links the MOB to a bedless hospital, features dining tables, sculpture, an outpatient pharmacy, and a gift shop. *Photo by Gary Knight. Courtesy Earl Swensson Associates.*

Rush-Copley Medical Center, Aurora, Illinois. A new facility, scheduled for completion in 1995, the center features a patient-focused model with unbundled services; all services are within 200 feet of one of five major entrances. The architects reconfigured patterns of service delivery and projected that the center can supply the same level of service as the facility it replaces but that it provides a 40 percent reduction in the number of beds needed, a 20 percent reduction in square footage, and a 33 percent reduction in staff. *Courtesy O'Donnell Wicklund Pigozzi & Peterson.*

lower level and physicians' offices on the upper level. Intersecting the atrium was a 356-bed hospital. In subsequent years, the facility proved highly successful and was greatly expanded.

It was not until 1982 that Jack Ryan, founder of the healthcare consulting firm of Ryan Advisory, coined the term *medical mall* to describe such installations as Medical City Dallas and a project Ryan himself had worked on in Milan, Italy—a diagnostic medical mall that featured a panoply of services, including a diagnostic imaging center, laboratory, CT scanner, multiphasic diagnostic center, and hemodialysis unit.

As it has subsequently developed, the medical mall usually centers around a major public-circulation atrium or spine that connects all public entrances to health service areas in a configuration quite deliberately recalling the neighborhood shopping mall. Indeed, the various services are housed in storefronts similar to the retail mall.

Here the retail analogy breaks down to a degree, however. The engine that drives the retail mall is impulse shopping. The typical mall customer may have a particular purchase or store in mind as his destination, but, on the way, is lured by many impulse opportunities. It is, of course, far less likely that a patient visiting a medical mall for laser corneal surgery will, on impulse, purchase another procedure on the way to the ophthalmic center. However, the storefront display of other services does suggest to the medical consumer the range of help that is available for future needs.

Furthermore, the analogy to shopping, a familiar and pleasant exercise of power and choice, can alleviate much of the apprehension and anxiety associated with medical procedures, which are often performed in settings that promote passivity, casting the user of the service in the role of "patient" rather than "client" or "consumer."

In addition to the specifically medical services offered in the mall, health-related (for example, pharmacy, optician, prosthetics shop, hearing-aid center, and the like) and other retail stores are available, as are dining facilities and even hotel accommodations.

In a culture that has accepted the retail mall as a community adjunct and part of the neighborhood, the medical mall also offers an opportunity to cater to and develop another growing segment of the healthcare market, community-oriented health maintenance, wellness programs, prevention, and health education. Sports medicine, gym, and spa facilities are also highly appropriate to the medical mall setting.

As the retail mall proved a formidable competitor to the traditional downtown shopping district by offering the convenience of one-stop

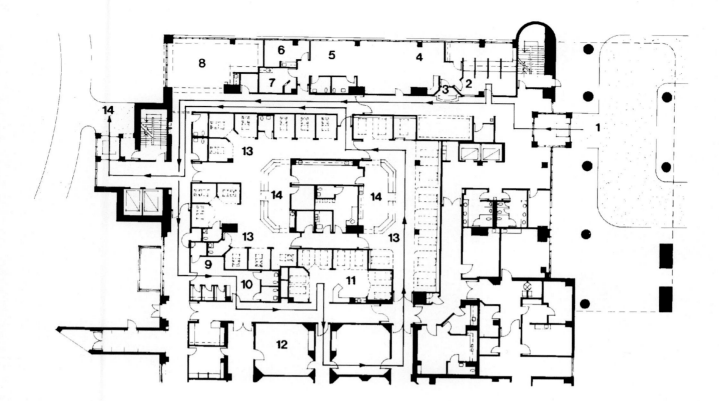

shopping, ease of access, and ample parking, so the medical mall enjoys similar advantages over the more traditional downtown hospital, particularly in the areas of parking and access. It is in the area of access that medical malls make perhaps their psychologically most compelling departure from the old-paradigm hospital. Like a retail mall, the medical mall embodies the multiple-entry concept. Gone is the single entrance that leads to the institutional ritual of admitting and that gives the traditional hospital the oppressive, quasi-penal aura of having only one way in and one way out.

Still taking off from the retail model, the medical mall is an excellent setting for the implementation of advanced electronic information systems. Patients—or consumers—could be issued credit card-sized magnetic-stripe data cards that allow access to complete medical history and insurance information, which they can take from one storefront treatment center to another.

As patient information can be centralized but readily accessed from a variety of remote points, so building support services can be shared, much as they are in a retail mall. For all their feeling of variety and individual identity, all medical services share a central mechanical plant as well as central receiving and shipping facilities.

The medical mall concept has already been applied in varying degrees throughout the nation. The Dartmouth-Hitchcock Medical Center in Lebanon, New Hampshire, is a very fully developed, full-service medical mall hospital. Completed in October 1991 at a cost of $218 million, it incorporates medical buildings and services configured like a shopping mall, surrounded by parking, and focused on a central atrium, which shelters a bank and thirteen retail shops and restaurants. The atrium

Pavilion, Reston Medical Center, Reston, Virginia. Floor plan. The arrows of this pre-admissions testing area indicate traffic flow through the facility, which has been designed to eliminate the need for cross-overs and back-tracking. Patients using the testing area need never enter the hospital proper. *Courtesy Earl Swensson Associates.*

1 Entrance/drop off
2 Outpaient admitting
3 Reception
4 Subwaiting
5 Interview
6 Blood draw
7 Chest X-ray
8 Waiting
9 Subwaiting
10 Patient dressing
11 Patient holding
12 Operating room
13 Recovery
14 Patient pick-up

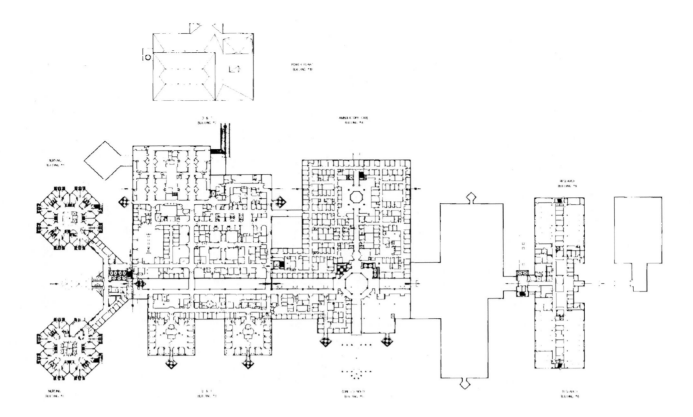

Dartmouth-Hitchcock Medical Center, Lebanon, New Hampshire. The medical mall and its relation to the center's other buildings. *Courtesy Shepley Bulfinch Richardson and Abbott.*

Dartmouth-Hitchcock Medical Center, Lebanon, New Hampshire. The design of this medical center takes its inspiration from a shopping mall, a facility familiar to all consumers—medical and otherwise. Medical services and stores are located along the center's central spine. *Photo by Jean M. Smith. Courtesy Shepley Bulfinch Richardson and Abbott.*

connects two five-story "patient-care buildings" with a separate diagnostic and treatment building. The complex also encompasses a research building and a planned conference and education facility. In 1993, Earl Swensson Associates replaced a forty-year-old Mayfield, Kentucky, hospital with the 107-bed, 170,000-square-foot PineLake Medical Center, which makes use of mall elements. It is discussed in Chapter 9.

■ The Hospitality Model

Some medical mall designs incorporate hotels either as part of the mall complex or adjacent to it. Hotels associated with hospitals serve two purposes. They provide convenient—and profit-generating—lodging for members of patient families, and, when thoughtfully configured in relation to the main hospital complex, they can also provide convalescent housing for patients who are not so acutely ill that they must occupy a hospital bed, yet for whom home care is impractical (for instance, because of distance from the healthcare facility) or inappropriate (no caregiver at home or a need for more medical supervision than is available in the home setting).

Even the inpatient hospital itself is learning from the hotel model. Hospitals and hotels share more than a linguistic root connoting the concept of "guest." They both take responsibility for the welfare of a great number of people. Hospitals are beginning to realize the market advantage in treating consumers as guests rather than patients. Houston's Methodist Hospital, for example, has developed a joint program with the

Jesse H. Jones Rotary House International, Houston, Texas. Managed by Marriott Conference Centers for its owner, the Texas Medical Center, the facility provides lodging for the out-of-town visitors of patients being treated for cancer at the medical center's M. D. Anderson Cancer Center. *Photo by Joe C. Aker. Courtesy Morris Architects.*

PineLake Medical Center, Mayfield, Kentucky. Waiting areas use the hospitality model of healthcare facility design, featuring attractive wood detailing, plants, and natural daylight. Light levels were designed to approximate those of a living room. Sitting groups of four to six chairs also recall a living room setting. *Photo by Gary Knight. Courtesy Earl Swensson Associates.*

Marriott Corporation to create a hybrid of hotel and hospital services. Incoming patients—or guests—are greeted by doormen, and a bellman is available to take the patient's luggage to his room. In most cases, the institutional formalities of admitting are handled by telephone, before the patient actually enters the hospital. As in a first-class hotel, the hospital is staffed by a concierge, who takes care of special needs and requests—though, in contrast to the conventional hotel, a large part of the concierge's job is to assist the patient's family. Valet parking and laundry services are available, as are upgraded rooms, which include gourmet-quality food service.

Even conventionally designed hospitals can, to a degree, incorporate operational policies based on the hospitality model. But these policies are greatly enhanced by design features based on hospitality rather than conventional hospital models, not only in patient rooms, but in waiting and lobby areas.

■ Residential Models

The next logical leap from the hospitality-based model of patient-centered design is to make aspects of the hospital—particularly the patient room—look like home. The origin of the homelike design movement is the Planetree organization, founded in 1978 by Angelica Thieriot, a medical lay person—that is, a medical consumer—who was so horrified by her experience with conventional hospitalization that she created a non-profit organization to provide the public with medical information and to improve, to *humanize,* the quality of patient care. Called Planetree, after the plane tree under which Hippocrates was supposed to have sat as he lectured his students, the organization developed a thirteen-bed model unit at San Francisco's Pacific Medical Center in 1985.

In addition to such policy innovations as open charts (patients have total access to their own records), an active give-and-take exchange of questions with caregivers, unlimited visitation, and so on, rooms are designed like domestic environments, with plenty of wood, subtle lighting, plants, and even paintings on loan from a local museum. There is a patient lounge, with a VCR, videocassette library, and a library of books, and there is a kitchenette, where patients can prepare their own food if they wish. Other hospitals across the country have implemented the Planetree idea.

Hill Rom. The decor of the patient rooms offers a residential feel. Even the tell-tale medical gases unit has been hidden. *Photo by Tom Westerkamp. Courtesy Hensler Westerkamp Giles.*

Hospitality- and home-inspired design programs spring from a conviction that familiar environments are less stressful than unfamiliar environments and, therefore, promote healing. Such programs, however, also make marketing sense, as hospitals use elements of hotel and home to retain medical consumers who might choose a competitor or, under certain circumstances, opt for home care.

■ The Need for Balance and the Use of Demographics

Hospitality and domestic design models do have their critics. At the very least, objections have been raised that materials and finishes appropriate to hotels and homes do not stand up well to the heavy-duty use they receive in a hospital setting. In some cases, hospitals that have contracted with outside providers for upgraded food service, ranging from familiar fast foods to gourmet dinners, have found their non-profit tax status in jeopardy.

There are also more profound objections. Architect Henry Stolzman, writing in *Aesclepius* (2, no. 3 [Summer 1993] p.3) has objected that it is a mistake to "disguise" hospitals as "places we associate with comfort":

> At worst, this has produced hospitals as sterile and disorienting as ever, with a few cosmetic trappings. At best, it has produced facilities that are well decorated and cleverly planned, but are based on the wrong proto-types.
>
> Hospitals should not look like homes. People are often reluctant to leave their homes for hospitals, but when they do, it is to get a level of technical expertise and intense care that they cannot get at home. A "homey" design, standardized to fill thousands of square feet of rooms and corridors, is never going to be close to what a patient thinks of as home; it will be more hotel or motel. And hotel/motel-like hospitals are antithetical to the idea of home. . . .

Stolzman also criticizes the "shopping center concept" as "inherently impersonal . . . as cold as a freeway-side mall. From the doctor, nurse, or pharmacist's point of view, it seems to take dignity and warmth out of care giving."

Stolzman suggests that it is wrong to "conceal and demean" the realities of caregiving and suggests that a better alternative to either the retail mall or hospitality models is to be found in the tradition of the sanitarium and spa of the nineteenth century, which suggest a "more majestic stature, serenity, solidity, and honesty toward function."

Whether one agrees with Stolzman or not, it is clear that there is a danger of thoughtlessly flocking to design strategies, including the medical mall, hospitality, and residential models, without regard for the community—the community of healthcare providers, of patients, and of neighbors. It is important to strive for a sense of balance, in which the needs of no group of users are slighted. It is also important to see beyond the general market trends—the trends to which the approaches outlined

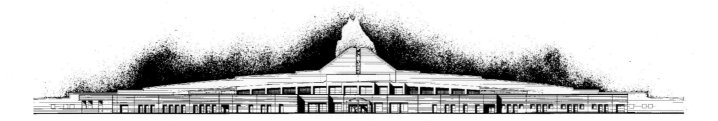

Shiprock Comprehensive Health Care Facility, Shiprock, New Mexico. A full-service, acute-care facility in the Navaho Nation, Shiprock's design combines the needs of modern medicine with the cultural beliefs, regional geography, and medical practices of the Navaho people. *Courtesy Anderson DeBartolo Pan.*

The Heart Center of Fort Wayne, Indiana. This center squarely emphasizes the patient in it all its services and operations. It locates in one facility a full range of cardiac services, including patient education programs that stress wellness and prevention. *Photo by James E. Miller/ Envisions. Courtesy MSKTD and Associates/Architects Engineers Interior Design.*

Centennial: The Women's Hospital, Centennial Medical Center, Nashville, Tennessee. Patient rooms in this facility offer a pleasant, feminine atmosphere, custom millwork, and furnishings of a timeless quality. *Photo by Bill LaFevor. Courtesy Earl Swensson Associates.*

above are responses—and examine the more immediate and particular community the hospital or healthcare facility is intended to serve.

Computer-aided demographic studies can be used to assess the nature of the market in the community surrounding the facility. Demographic studies identify communities that are medically underserved and detail such factors as age, incidence of injury, traffic accidents, violent crime, and, using mortality and morbidity data, the incidence and nature of disease. When this medical data is correlated with socioeconomic and environmental conditions, a profile of the type of healthcare facilities required in a community emerges.

In specific circumstances, planners may determine that a given market is strongest for specialized medical services, including birthing centers, clinics that treat stress and related disorders, emergency care centers, immediate care centers (freestanding facilities popularly called "doc-in-a-box"), sports medicine facilities, eating disorder units, long-term care facilities, and home health services.

By the late 1980s, the phrase "Centers of Excellence" had become a buzz word to describe service and design development programs that certain, usually community-based, hospitals undertake in response to a perceived market need in order to concentrate on providing particular medical services. The idea is to create a facility of a caliber that will attract the best and most productive specialists in the field, whose presence will, in turn, draw a specifically defined segment of the medical consumer population.

In the Salt Lake Valley of Utah, Cottonwood Hospital assessed community interest in the alternative birthing movement and commissioned the firm of Kaplan McLaughlin Diaz to design a Center for Women's Health, which rapidly increased Cottonwood's market share by 30 percent. West Side Hospital, in Nashville, Tennessee, had no births before 1985, the year it inaugurated a new women's services program, when West Side became part of the new Centennial Medical Center campus. Ultimately, Earl Swensson Associates transformed West Side into Centennial: The Women's Hospital, a center of excellence for women's care. The hospital, which offers a full range of women's services, with particular emphasis on education and a family-oriented, homelike birthing environment, is described in Chapter 11; its neonatal intensive care unit (NICU) is described in Chapter 8. By 1989, the number of births had risen to 2,000; in 1993, it was 2,645; and by the first half of 1994, there were some 3,000 births.

■ Aging Population

Direction of design and services offered must, of course, be determined on a community-by-community basis. However, certain market trends are general. Chief among these are the decline in inpatient population and a concomitant rise in demand for outpatient or ambulatory services. Additionally, for inpatients, the length of stay has been steadily decreasing. Demographically, the population of North America is aging, with important implications for the healthcare market and for the design of healthcare—and, for that matter, many other—facilities.

One of the strongest of the old paradigms consciously or unconsciously governing design in many areas, hospitals and healthcare facilities included, is the standard of the healthy thirty-year-old man. Traditionally, he has been the yardstick against which architectural design has been measured; he has been the envisioned ideal user of any given facility. The demographic trend toward an aging population, coupled with new building codes stemming in large part from federal legislation in the form of the Americans with Disabilities Act, means that architects should be standardizing public facilities on the ideal of a seventy-year-old woman.

This is especially important in healthcare-related design, since an aging population will make increasingly extensive use of health and hospital facilities. Guidelines include:

1. Using large, clear letters for signage
2. Avoiding lighting the background of signs
3. If hospital floors are color-coded, avoiding blues, greens, and neutral colors, which the aging eye may have trouble distinguishing among
4. Providing higher illumination levels and diminishing glare

Veterans Administration Medical Center, Castle Point, New York. The designers of the facility made the nurses station accessible to wheelchair-bound patients. *Photo by Whitney Cox. Courtesy Norman Rosenfield Architects.*

5. Avoiding uneven lighting
6. Designing acoustically optimal environments that incorporate sound-absorbing materials; acuity of hearing tends to diminish with age, and some persons have difficulty distinguishing speech from background noise
7. Providing ample seating, with arms for ease in sitting and rising
8. Enhancing way-finding and orientation
9. Providing ample handrails
10. Providing adequate door widths for wheelchair use
11. Using easily operated lever-type door hardware
12. Ensuring adequate wheelchair turnaround space in small rooms
13. Ramping throughout for wheelchair access
14. Using surface texture changes on walks adjacent to hazard areas (tactile warning strips)

Design for an aging population is a vast area, which we will explore in a later chapter. As a design principle, however, it should be recognized that this population trend poses challenges yet also presents medical market opportunities and, therefore, market opportunities for designers and architects as well.

Susan Behar, an interior designer with the firm Universal Design, describes design for aging (and/or disabled) users as "universal design (UD)" (see Behar, "Universal Design Blends Function with Form," *Group Practice Journal,* July/August 1991). The objective of UD is to "enhance and promote independence" by emphasizing the "Four A's": aesthetics, accessibility, adaptability, and affordability.

For example, the Morton Plant Hospital Family Care Center, Clearwater, Florida, includes a 2,400-square-foot outpatient clinic with wide, 36-inch doorways and 5-foot-wide hallways to accommodate wheelchair users. Similarly, all offices provide a 60-inch turning area for wheelchairs. Door hardware consists of lever handles and U-pulls. Signage, at eye level, is large and clear, carpeting reduces noise, and, where carpeting butts with tile, the two are installed at the same level for easier mobility. Grab bars are provided throughout—which means that walls must be properly reinforced—and the bars are brightly colored, not only to enhance visibility, but to make them aesthetically attractive design elements rather than clinical-looking additions. Lighting is designed to help define surfaces more clearly for persons with visual disabilities. In varying degrees, such aspects of universal design are becoming the norm for hospitals and healthcare facilities.

"God," Mies van der Rohe said, "is in the details," and this is, to a great extent, true of design for an aging population. However, with retirement communities a well-established building and development market, design for an aging population also presents some of the most exciting prospects for creating community-integrated healthcare facilities and for designing entire communities around healthcare, achieving a level of coordination and integration impossible in the traditional hospital setting and in the context of the traditional relations between hospital and community.

Making Yesterday's Hospitals Work Today

■ Hard Choices

In business, we have said, if you want to be heard, you must speak the language of business. The ideological, technical, and marketing reasons for rethinking hospital design are manifest and ample, but how do you translate these reasons into action?

Speak the language of business. Older hospitals were built when the main purpose of a hospital was to house and treat inpatients. What that means—*today and now*—is that one-third of all hospital *beds* in the United States are empty: 300,000 every night. This translates into a collective loss among hospitals of between $6 and $8 billion in unreimbursed *overhead* costs alone. Doubtless, as federally mandated cost-containment measures become even more stringent, the figure will rise.

The point is that these losses are not exclusively the result of science, society, and policy, and they will not be reversed by changes in science, society, and policy. They are, in large part, a function of architecture, of old-paradigm buildings struggling to survive in a world swept by new paradigms, and the losses will be reversed, in significant measure, by architecture. Either existing buildings must be reconfigured to serve the new markets and new realities, or new construction, along the lines laid out in the preceding chapter, must be planned. There is no third choice.

The problem is, the choice between the first two alternatives can be, in and of itself, a difficult enough one to make. Under what conditions does it make sense to renovate an existing facility as opposed to building a new one? Is it even possible—or, at least, economically feasible—to bring an old-paradigm hospital to the level of value and cost-effectiveness required to survive, let alone compete profitably, in the emerging market-place?

Of course, this decision has to be made on a case-by-case basis, and we will provide some guidelines. However, it is our opinion that, as a general principle, hospitals built before 1960 should be replaced. In terms of cost-

1 Existing 3-story facility

2 Steel trusses are constructed above the existing facility, which remains in operation.

3 Four levels are built above the trusses. Stairs and elevators extend to grade.

4 Hospital functions move to the upper levels from the existing facility, which is demolished. The parking and lower levels are completed.

Shriners Hospital for Crippled Children Burns Institute, Boston, Massachusetts. In some instances, renovations must be squeezed into a very tight site. *Photo by Odell Associates. Courtesy Odell Associates.*

effectiveness, of achieving efficiency for people and for energy, pre-1960 hospitals usually cannot be made to deliver adequate value.

Some hospitals are virtually impossible to renovate. Since old-paradigm facilities have most of their now-vacant space in areas designed for acute care, it is difficult to expand these areas logically as outpatient facilities. A great many existing hospitals suffer from an insufficiency of land, so expansion is impossible, difficult, haphazard, or clumsy. Few older hospitals were built with vertical expansion in mind. Many also have structural limitations, such as load-bearing walls, low floor-to-ceiling heights, intrusive support columns, and so on, which obstruct major renovation.

Attempting to patch up and remodel buildings like these is a symptom of old-paradigm thinking. What is needed is the boldness and resolve to break out of inefficient, non-cost-effective, and inadequate policies. The hard fact is that realizing new ideas, building according to new paradigms, creating new responses to emerging markets, and creating new markets where none now exist all require new designs, new buildings. Some older hospitals may be deemed *obsolescent* and can, quite possibly, be satisfactorily renovated. The vast majority of those built before 1960, however, are frankly *obsolete,* and no amount of patchwork is likely to achieve a satisfactory, profitable result.

This may mean demolishing old hospitals and building anew on the vacant land, or it may mean finding alternative uses for "hopeless" facilities and building new ones elsewhere. Such uses may be medical, as in the renovation of a part of St. Leonard's Hospital, an 1862 facility in the East End of London. Grossly inadequate to house the functions of a modern hospital, the aged building was transformed into a primary healthcare facility for the "GP unit" (general practice). The renovation process is documented by Ann Noble in the *International Hospital Federation 1988 Official Yearbook* (London: Sabrecrown Publishers, 1988). It would also be possible to adapt outmoded hospitals to nursing home use, psychiatric use, and such non-medical purposes as prime or secondary (back-office) office space.

Women's Center, North Florida Regional Medical Center, Gainesville, Florida. To complement the addition of the Women's Center, the most visible parts of the existing facility were reclad. Clients enter the Women's Center through a designated main entrance. *Photo by K. D. Lawson. Courtesy Earl Swensson Associates.*

■ To Build or to Renovate?

If pre-1960 hospital facilities are likely candidates for demolition or alternative use, what about later facilities or more questionable cases? What factors enter into the decision to build new or to renovate?

Begin with the most basic question: Which is cheaper, renovation or new construction?

The answer can be surprising. If markedly new services are to be offered—say, significantly expanded ambulatory services and/or a long-term care facility to accommodate an aging community of consumers—it

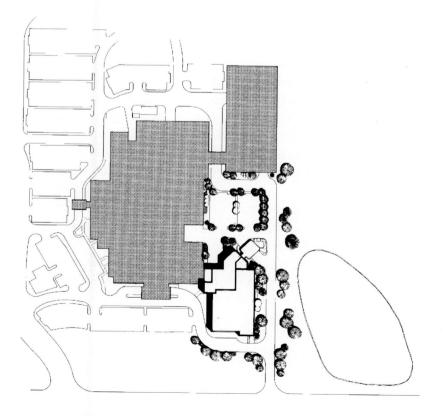

Women's Center, North Florida Regional Medical Center, Gainesville, Florida. This site plan shows the extent of the center's new construction and its relation to the existing facility (represented in screened portion). *Courtesy Earl Swensson Associates.*

Sharon Hospital, Sharon, Connecticut. A new building skin unites the disparate styles of successive additions to the original facility. *Photo of renovation by Bill Maris/Semarco. Courtesy Stecker LaBau Arneill McManus.*

may well be more costly to renovate and expand present facilities than it is to build new structures. Other pressures that push toward new construction are the enhancing of professional prestige and employee appeal. A new, state-of-the-art, aesthetically pleasing facility may go a long way toward attracting the best physicians and excellent support staff. Hospitals have learned that they must compete for the former, and even more for the latter, in a chronically crisis-ridden support staff market. Moreover, as the preceding chapters have demonstrated, new facilities featuring patient-centered amenities attract savvy healthcare consumers.

To determine, in a general sense, whether renovation or new construction will be more cost-effective, you must address the following issues:

1. Determine if the renovation is cosmetic or functional. Cosmetic upgrades rarely require anything more than simple renovation and can improve a hospital's image. Functional renovation is, of course, more extensive. First, determine if the functional renovation can be accomplished without major alteration to the building's core and shell: foundations, structural elements, and exterior walls. On average, if most of the core and shell remain untouched, renovation realizes an 80 percent savings—in core and shell costs only—over new construction. However, functional renovation projects save little if anything over new construction costs in other parts of the building.

2. Consider how old the facility is. This consideration may seem obvious to the point of being self-evident, but it is useful to view the age of the facility in question in relation to three landmark years: 1947, 1967, and 1972.

    Nineteen forty-seven marked implementation of the Hill-Burton Act, which defined and mandated certain environmental standards for hospitals. Renovation projects in hospitals built prior to this date may be very expensive or even impracticable because of code compliance requirements. For example, after Hill-Burton, hospitals were required to have forced fresh-air ventilation, which meant floor-to-floor heights of 12 1/2 to 16 feet in order to carry overhead ventilation ducts. Prior to Hill-Burton, floor-to-floor height was often in the 10-foot range. This alone may preclude functional renovation.

Nineteen sixty-seven saw the introduction of an extensive update of the National Electrical Code. Renovation of pre-1967 hospitals may well require major upgrading of electrical systems, including the establishment of three separate emergency-power branches: critical, life-safety, and emergency.

Finally, it was not until 1972 that asbestos was identified as a major environmental hazard and prohibited as a building material. Prior to that year, of course, the material was very widely used. The presence of asbestos is not an insurmountable problem, but the cost of asbestos abatement is very high, and the process is time-consuming. Abatement also takes precedence over the work of other trades, so it is often necessary to essentially shut down a job until asbestos has been cleared.

Note that unanticipated inadequacies of infrastructure add substantially to the cost of a renovation project. Duane Mariotti, a consultant in facilities management at ECRI, Plymouth Meeting, Pennsylvania, was quoted in *Modern Healthcare* (Elizabeth Gardner, "Revamping Hospitals' Approach to Renovation," April 14, 1989): "I can't think of a hospital I've been in that doesn't have problems with its infrastructure."

Finally, it is vitally important that all renovation projects, especially those done "inhouse," be carefully documented. This will avoid nasty—and costly—surprises that emerge during demolition.

3. Evaluate the different levels of use that affect the choice to renovate versus to commission new construction. Lawrence C. Bacher, an estimating executive for Gilbane Building Co., Providence, Rhode Island, writing in *Health Facilities Management* (July 1991), introduces a useful distinction among low- , mid- , and high-tech space. Renovating existing facilities to create low-tech space— offices, storage, and the like—requires little in the way of sophisticated M/E engineering and is relatively unconstrained by code requirements. Renovation of such areas ranges very widely from $10 to $135 per square foot versus new construction costs of anywhere from $59 to $291.

Mid-tech renovation introduces more constraints and expense, especially in the area of air-exchange systems. Renovation costs of such areas rise to the range of $55 to $183 per square foot, whereas new-construction costs begin at $105 and range to $267. High-tech areas, which include such spaces as operating suites, ICUs, radiology, imaging facilities, and the like, are expensive to design and build new, but when renovation is technically feasible

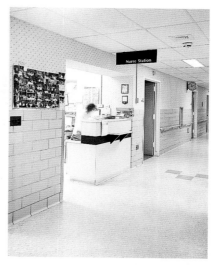

Baystate Medical Center, Springfield, Massachusetts. New floor, wall, and ceiling finishes enliven the center's interiors. The distinctive use of light and ceiling treatment define the nursing station. TRO supplied architectural and interior design services. *Photos by Robert Mikrut. Courtesy TRO/The Ritchie Organization.*

(which is not always the case), they are also expensive to renovate. The range for renovation is $56 to $273 per square foot, versus new construction costs of $110 to $279 per square foot.

4. Determine what impact a renovation project will have on the building's code status. In some jurisdictions, renovating a certain percentage of the square footage of a building requires that the *entire* building be brought up to code. This might raise costs substantially enough to make renovation less cost-effective than new construction.

5. Consider how the renovation projects will disrupt day-to-day operations, ranging from the creation of annoyance to periodic utility disruption to forced temporary departmental relocations. The concessions that staff must make to construction-worker intrusions may raise costs by reducing productivity, while the concessions that construction workers must make to minimize disruption will likely raise construction costs 15 to 20 percent. Dirt, noise, and the perception of chaos wear on staff members and may well impact negatively on patient welfare, discouraging some consumers from patronizing the facility while it is "under construction." Such potentially substantial costs are difficult to calculate. The demolition phase is often the most disruptive, disquieting, and least adequately appreciated by planners.

Hospitals routinely opt for renovation over new construction. In 1989, for example, architects reported 1,025 hospital renovations, 477 extension projects, and only 65 new hospitals. In 1991, renovation accounted for 72 percent of hospital construction projects. Wholesale gutting of a facility brings renovation costs to as much as 85 percent of new construction costs. Factor in the "hidden costs" of disruption of services and reduced productivity, and it is possible that renovation may be costlier than new construction. Moreover, as Ronald Skaggs, of Harwood K. Smith & Partners, Dallas, pointed out in *Modern Healthcare* (in Gardner, April 14, 1989), "It takes 10 to 15 percent more space to put the same amount of function into renovated space" because of the necessity of building around existing column supports and other immovable obstacles. This significant *loss* in available space can easily cut into the savings renovation seems to offer over new construction.

Finally, renovation is all too often a departmental project rather than a system-wide project. Old-paradigm thinking is, by its nature, departmental and piecemeal, whereas new-paradigm thinking looks at the entire system and the potential for future expansion and change. Renovation of even a single department should not be undertaken without considering its impact on and role within the institution as a whole. Furthermore, renovation, no matter how reasonable the initial construction costs, should not be made at the expense of existing efficient and successful operations, and it should not cannibalize existing facilities in such a way as to inhibit continued development.

■ The Renovation Process

If, after careful evaluation of facility needs and goals—and this should be undertaken with the assistance and advice of experienced architects and engineers—it is determined that a renovation project is more appropriate than new construction, the project must be planned carefully and strategically.

Funding

Depending on the age of the facility and the construction documentation available, major renovation projects are subject to more unpleasant surprises than new construction. Blueprints and engineering diagrams may tell planners, architects, and engineers what is *supposed* to be in a wall, but, unfortunately, it is only when the wall is demolished or dismantled that the whole truth emerges. If some part of that truth consists of immovable obstacles or unanticipated electrical/mechanical components, plans may have to be altered accordingly. The master renovation proposal must allow for such contingencies, and funds must be available to cover unanticipated overruns in order to keep a project from stalling with disastrous results.

While construction costs will almost certainly be the largest item on the renovation shopping list, funding must also cover the costs of the following:

▲ *The financing itself*
▲ *Specialized studies*
▲ *Medical and non-medical equipment that may be temporarily required while permanent equipment is unavailable due to renovation*
▲ *Temporary facilities*
▲ *Additional staff time, including reduced productivity due to renovation activity*
▲ *Moving and occupancy start-up costs*
▲ *Loss of revenue during the renovation period*
▲ *Cost of soils and materials testing, surveys, legal costs, costs of securing Certificate of Need (CON)*

As with any construction project, inflation can play a highly significant role in cost overruns, especially if the work falls behind planned schedule because (for example) of unanticipated structural obstacles.

Consultants

Except for very large corporate or federal institutions, hospitals and healthcare facilities generally cannot support full-time architectural staff, although many development-minded institutions do now keep an architectural consultant on tap through some form of retainer. For renovation, administrators should seek professional consultants with wide experience in specifically medical renovation. Such consultants include:

- ▲ *Marketing specialists*
- ▲ *Business strategy experts*
- ▲ *Financial consultants*
- ▲ *Workflow and organizational experts*
- ▲ *Medical programming/planning consultants*
- ▲ *Cost-estimating consultants*
- ▲ *Architects and engineers*

Depending on the preliminary assessment performed by these experts, it may be necessary or desirable also to consult:

- ▲ *Soils engineer (in sites subject to instability or seismic activity)*
- ▲ *Civil engineer*
- ▲ *Waterproofing specialist*
- ▲ *Certified industrial hygienist (a CIH—especially where the presence of asbestos or other environmental hazards is a possibility)*
- ▲ *Medical equipment consultant*
- ▲ *Communications consultants*
- ▲ *Laboratory/pharmacy design specialist*
- ▲ *Interior designer*
- ▲ *Graphics consultant (for signage)*
- ▲ *Food service specialist*
- ▲ *Lighting consultant*

Planning

Planning begins with a detailed survey of existing conditions, including

- ▲ *Structural frame*
- ▲ *Accessibility to the disabled (A.D.A. and other code compliance issues)*
- ▲ *Utilities, including underground utilities*
- ▲ *Roof*
- ▲ *Elevators*
- ▲ *Fire exits and other life-safety considerations*
- ▲ *Floor-to-floor heights*
- ▲ *Ventilation*
- ▲ *Electrical capacity*
- ▲ *Existing and usable space*

If the project involves site modifications, including additional access, new entrances, and parking, site studies are called for.

Of course, the renovation plan must include an assessment of just what services and activities will suffer disruption and how this may be minimized through the identification of swing space for temporary relocation. It may be necessary to rent space off-site or to bring in portable spaces, including prefab units and trailers. It may also be necessary to plan construction in smaller phases in order to minimize the scope and duration of disruptions. Such decisions require careful analysis of the cost of disruption versus the added costs (and delays) incurred by multiple small construction phases.

In consultation with key staff involved in the renovation, a needs assessment should be carried out simultaneously with the facility survey.

It may be desirable to encourage the creation of a comprehensive "wish list," which then can be prioritized and refined in order to establish the project's scope.

In consultation with architects and other consultants, and following analysis of the facility survey and needs assessment, a master plan should be developed. Obviously, the plan cannot be established without a full awareness of regulatory requirements; however, the impact of some of these cannot be assessed *until* the master plan has been completed.

Hazards and Safety Considerations

Administrators and the renovation team must anticipate the following hazards and contingencies:

- ▲ *Asbestos and its abatement*
- ▲ *Presence of PCBs*
- ▲ *Adverse effects of construction noise on patients and staff*
- ▲ *Heightened risk of infection and contamination of wounds due to airborne construction dust*
- ▲ *Coordination of construction and occupancy-phasing*
- ▲ *Disruption of critical medical activities*
- ▲ *Disruption of utility service*
- ▲ *Seismic safety*
- ▲ *Security—of construction areas as well as the institution as a whole during renovation exposure; this includes security in narcotics and biological hazard areas*
- ▲ *Maintenance of all fire-exiting routes, fire-rated occupancy separations, fire-alarm and -suppression (sprinkler) systems*
- ▲ *Unanticipated structural defects or obstacles*
- ▲ *Impact on productivity caused by relocation; productivity may suffer as much as a 30 percent reduction due to relocation during renovation*

Depending on the nature, extent, and site of the renovation, the prevention of surgical wound infections from environmental contamination may well become a significant consideration. A case report of a contamination prevention program during renovation at Chicago's Grant Hospital appears in *Hospital Topics* 55, no. 1 (Paul Stiffler and Jean Matousek, "Preventing Surgical Wound Infections Due to Environmental Contamination During Hospital Reconstruction"). The program, outlined in the report, consisted of

- ▲ Controlling construction traffic
- ▲ Sealing off construction areas from areas in use
- ▲ Maintaining housekeeping at a fastidious level
- ▲ Maintaining an ongoing environmental culturing program

Construction workers were assigned exclusive use of an elevator, and the construction area was sealed off from the operating room area using half-inch dry wall nailed to 2 x 4 framing, with all butt joints taped using air-conditioning tape. Ventilation systems into the operating area were rerouted to avoid construction areas.

One other hazard that cannot be ignored is the impact of renovation on patient relations. Good public relations, based on communicating the extent and purpose of the renovations, will help to address patient concerns, head off patient grievances, and keep patients from seeking services elsewhere. A typical patient relations program undertaken during a $30 million renovation project at Redding, California's Mercy Medical Center was reported by John S. Jacobson in *Health Progress* ("Patient Relations Program Eases Construction's Inconvenience," vol 76, no. 10, December 1986).

Elements of the program included a brochure entitled "Pardon our Dust . . . Mercy on the Move," which briefly described the hospital's history, present goals, and future plans, explaining the purpose of the renovation construction. Every patient admitted to the hospital received a copy of the brochure. A poster program was also introduced, and, as an additional gracious touch, a fresh flower was included on patient breakfast trays with a card reading "We hope your day is as fresh as a daisy!" and text explaining the reason for renovation. Pediatric patients were each given a plastic hard hat that said "Junior Foreman, Facilities Improvement Project, Mercy Medical Center Redding."

■ "Fast-Tracking" Renovations

In 1982, while much of American business and industry was in the depths of a malaise fueled by inferiority feelings over invidious comparisons between the progressive prosperity of "Japan, Inc." and the high quality and high value of its technology and consumer products, Tom Peters and Robert Waterman published their best-selling and highly influential *In Search of Excellence,* a survey and analysis of successful strategies of entrepreneurship, inventiveness, and management. One of the concepts that emerged from Peters and Waterman's book is "fast-tracking," a process that works across established bureaucratic barriers and departmental partitions to accomplish an institution-wide common goal quickly, efficiently, and with high-quality, high-value results.

The fast-tracking concept is an inviting and seductive one, alluring in the same way as the story of Alexander the Great's using the blade of his sword to resolve the puzzle of the Gordian Knot. Many consultants, architects, and other planning and design professionals believe, however, that major renovation projects do not lend themselves well to fast-tracking. Too many individuals and individual needs and agendas must be meshed with long-range institutional needs and goals and too many pitfalls (as outlined above) exist to make the fast-tracking process a comfortable alternative.

This said, a thought-provoking instance of fast-tracking in a renovation project was documented by Deborah Spector and Carole Runyan Price, writing in *Healthcare Forum Journal* ("Fast-Tracking in Hospitals," January/February 1988). The authors discuss the "bleak outlook" for Stanford University Hospital's proposed same-day surgery unit, which had been stalled for two years after planning had been authorized. The need for the unit was universally recognized. In 1982, the four-bed ambulatory care unit performed 12 percent of the hospital's surgeries. In 1985, that figure had increased to 25 percent, and the facility was clearly overburdened. To make matters worse, the unit was located adjacent to the hospital's morgue! Despite these incentives, motives, and pressures to get the project under way, it apparently floundered in hospital bureaucracy.

Finally, inspired by Peters and Waterman's fast-tracking concept, management appointed an individual to serve as what Peters and Waterman call an "executive champion . . . cloaked with clear authority by the CEO and chief operating officer." Armed with concept approval, the "champion" was freed from having to seek approval of each step and became a fully empowered project leader. Her first step was to recruit a representative cross-section of staff from the surgical department, admitting, clinical laboratories, facilities, and medical staff. This relatively small group became what Peters and Waterman call a "skunkworks"—a "band of eight or ten zealots off in a corner [who] often outproduce product development groups that number in the hundreds."

The Stanford "skunkworks" teams reexamined all previous proposals and set as their goal the short-term objective of producing an interim solution to the need for expanded ambulatory surgery facilities. Long-term goals would be left to a later, larger hospital modernization project. The teams agreed that the short-term focus was necessary, because revamping ambulatory facilities had become critical to the financial viability of the hospital. It was perceived less as a matter of improvement of services than as an issue of survival.

Contrary to traditional planning methods, the skunkworks teams functioned in small clusters coordinated by the leader. In this way, there was no need to coordinate the changeable schedules of a large number of hospital staff. Tasks were "chunked," broken into mini-action plans, each of which was designed to meet some set of needs of a particular constituency. The leadership approach was deliberately "loose-tight," meaning that the leader encouraged individual autonomy and "intrapreneuring" while also maintaining goal-directed overall focus.

The soul of fast-tracking is a leader—champion—who works one-on-one, up-close and personal, with the various teams and individuals involved in the project. For example, rather than rely on questionnaires, formal studies, and policy statements, the project leader personally walked the director of anesthesiology through a draft of the plan. The anesthesiologist pointed out that a repositioning of recovery beds would avert what could have been a critical and costly traffic-flow problem. This was something no one else had seen before, and, in a more rigid planning environment, the input of this professional might not have been solicited, might have been shunted aside, or might have been delayed in implementation, requiring more expensive and complicated revision.

In this particular project, fast-tracking techniques resulted in a six-month turnaround time, from the beginning of the skunkworks meetings to the start-up of the facility. During the first year of operation, the facility treated 6,368 patients, an increase of 1,530 patients from the previous year. Between November 1986 and July 1987, the number of patients treated monthly rose 35 percent, from 858 to 1,168, and, whereas revenues had been $891,300 in 1984–85, they climbed to $1,336,690 during 1986–87.

The story at Stanford University Hospital is one of success, and, under compelling fiscal circumstances, fast-tracking may well have been the best available option—although it could be argued that two years of apparent floundering should not have been permitted to delay the project in the first place. Whenever possible, renovation should be planned in the context of long-term institutional goals, and in such a way that provides sufficient flexibility for further, as yet unplanned, expansion and modification. We are not in favor of bureaucratic red tape, but we find reason to be concerned about the ability of any project leader, using such techniques as mini-meetings and "chunking," to appreciate all aspects and details of the big picture, a picture whose dimensions are defined not only by space but by human action and interaction, as well as by time itself. Yet, in this very real world, human needs and financial pressures do not always afford the luxury of long planning schedules. Fast-tracking is likely to be increasingly relied upon as a means of making buildings more flexible and rapidly responsive to changing needs.

■ A Range of Renovation Projects

SCRIPPS MEMORIAL HOSPITAL
Encinitas, California

Many, perhaps most, renovation projects are essentially cosmetic, attempts to upgrade the facility's image in order to attract more patients, to attract and retain the best professional staff, and to enhance the institution's image within the community, thereby generating greater levels of community and financial support. An example of this was published in *Hospitality Design* (14, no. 8., 1992), which featured a $13.2 million project commissioned by the Scripps Memorial Hospital in Encinitas, California. The original structure was described as a "dour-looking, single-story structure that blended in with the industrial buildings set along the freeway of this north San Diego suburb." Renovation consisted of updating the facade, creating a double-height atrium lobby, expanding the rehabilitation center, and refurbishing interior furnishings and finishes. The look that BGRP Architecture and Planning of San Diego, and interior designer Jain Malkin, Inc., achieved, was evocative of a hotel rather than a traditional hospital.

The new look started with the exterior, which was given a new porte-cochère and a rich, multi-colored facade, while the lobby was transformed into a skylit atrium and furnished with seating and drapery appropriate to the lobby of a first-class hotel. Instead of the anonymous vinyl and chrome-tubular-steel lobby seating found in traditional hospitals, the Scripps facility was furnished with comfortable, fabric-upholstered armchairs. Harsh overhead lighting was replaced by elegant table lamps.

Patient rooms featured enlarged windows and coordinated finishes. Patients were also encouraged to bring in their own items, such as comforters, favorite pillows, and other personal items. Even the hydrotherapy facilities, which, as in many traditional hospitals, occupied a dreary basement setting, were cheerily upgraded with mosaic tile work evocative of a classic spa. Other features of the expanded rehabilitation department include a furnished apartment known as an ADL (Activities of Daily Living) suite, which provides a realistic environment in which recovering patients can practice skills they will need before returning home.

In addition to the spacious lobby, the renovated hospital includes a spacious second-floor gallery/lounge. Overlooking the lobby and admitting area, it is a public space in which patients are encouraged to walk or sit, thereby gaining respite from the nursing floor and contact with "the outside world." While patients can observe activities in the lobby, they themselves cannot be viewed from the lower vantage point of the lobby, thereby reducing self-consciousness over being seen in pajamas or bathrobes.

ROCKLAND PSYCHIATRIC CENTER
Orangeburg, New York

Another dramatic, but essentially cosmetic makeover project was completed in 1989 at New York State's Rockland Psychiatric Center. Profiled in *Health Facilities Management* (Andrew Freireich, "Renovation Cuts Cost, Speeds Construction of Psych Group Home," vol. 3, no. 4, April 1990), this project is a good example of the cost-effectiveness of renovating "low-tech" spaces.

In the early 1980s, the Rockland Psychiatric Center, Orangeburg, New York, was designated to be renovated from a traditional and outmoded psychiatric hospital built in the 1930s to a "deinstitutionalized" group home for patients requiring congregate transitional housing. The $6.46 million project, completed in 1989, was the result of a decision to renovate rather than to rebuild based on the following factors:

▲ *The candidate buildings were vacant.*
▲ *The candidate buildings were located on state-owned land, thereby obviating the need to acquire new property.*
▲ *The existing facilities were structurally sound, and renovation would save 25 percent over the cost of new construction.*
▲ *Renovation would save one year over new construction time requirements.*

While structurally sound, the renovation task was a formidable one: to transform an institutional dormitory void of all privacy into a cheerful, aesthetically pleasing living complex. A principal goal was to provide for a modicum of patient supervision while accommodating patients' need for privacy.

The 67,000-square-foot building designated for renovation was built in the 1930s to house 400 patients. Architects Howie, Freireich, and Gardner set out to transform it into a modern residence for 131 patients. This entailed the removal of some interior partitions and ceilings and the enlargement of the existing small windows to admit a maximum of natural light. Since the original structure lacked a ventilation system, the entire building required a retrofit for a modern HVAC system as well as communication and fire-alarm systems.

As a state facility, Rockland did not have to be renovated to compete in a given marketplace. However, the alterations were designed not merely to lift patients' spirits, but to reinforce the facility's role as a transitional environment from life in a hospital to life in "the real world." The institutional facade was domesticated to the appearance of a Spanish villa, and, inside, the renovation was structured around an urban design metaphor, including good-humored street signage suggesting a community (the central corridor is "Main Street," a meeting room is designated as "Town Hall," and so on).

The living spaces, dormitories that had been a classic warehouse for the mentally ill, became a collection of twelve large suites, each differentiated by an individual color scheme and designated by names evocative of the world outside ("Hickory Haven," "Ivy Arch Apartments," and so on). Each of the suites has a private bathroom, kitchenette, and laundry room. Renovation cost was $96 per square foot, positioning it toward the high end of low-tech renovation projects, which generally range from $10 to $135 per square foot (versus new construction costs of $59 to $291).

NORTHWEST HOSPITAL
Seattle, Washington

Sam G. Deliganis, director of support services for Northwest Hospital, Seattle, profiled the renovation of the maternity wing of his institution in *Health Facilities Management* ("Maternity-Wing 'Face-lift' Becomes Big Renovation to Recoup Market Share," vol. 3, no. 12, December 1990). The project came about in response to a decline in market share among women who were interested in alternatives to the labor and delivery rooms of traditional hospitals. Indeed, in 1984, Northwest had been the first hospital to introduce the alternate birthing room concept to the Seattle area, an idea that caught on so rapidly that other area facilities soon provided more "BirthSuites" than Northwest, which, by 1987, was seeing a slight decline in maternity-wing patient census.

The most apparent shortcoming of the maternity unit was, despite the progressive BirthSuites, outmoded and unappealing postpartum and nursery environments. In response, administrators proposed a cosmetic renovation consisting primarily of new carpeting and wall coverings. Further study, however, resulted in a plan to add six more BirthSuites and renovate eight private postpartum rooms.

As Deliganis observes, one of the hospital's greatest challenges during the renovation period was simply to stay open. This is a central hurdle of all major remodeling projects. During the project, maternity was relocated to the orthopedic department, which, fortunately, was located near C-section delivery rooms and surgical facilities. Orthopedics was obliged to share space in the medical/surgical wing.

The hospital and architect Christina A. Johnson, of Design Plus, Inc., Seattle, also faced another challenge typical of renovation: the mechanical/electrical limitations of the original structure and unpleasant surprises in the form of deteriorated M/E components. Installation of air conditioning in one area required the installation of a rooftop chiller and new ducting to patient rooms. In another portion of the space, the existing HVAC unit was found to be corroded beyond repair and had to be replaced. New ductwork was also required. Some two weeks were lost in the renovation schedule, and between 70 and 80 percent of the original project budget had to be devoted to M/E upgrades before work began on a single room. However, the replacement of the rooftop HVAC unit did make it possible to create a 16-foot skylight at the child-birth center's nursing station—an unlooked-for dividend from an unlooked-for expense.

Design of the BirthSuites themselves relied heavily on nurse and physician input, even to the extent of mocking up a BirthSuite in a trailer, transporting it to the hospital, and allowing staff members to "test-drive" the facility and make suggestions for modifications.

Despite the cost overruns, the $114-per-square-foot renovation was successful, as evidenced by a survey revealing that 64 percent of new mothers chose Northwest first. One survey respondent remarked, "I heard it's the 'baby hospital' in Seattle."

SOUTHERN HILLS MEDICAL CENTER
Nashville, Tennessee

Southern Hills Medical Center, built during the early 1980s, faced a characteristic problem in the 1990s. Designed primarily as an inpatient

Southern Hills Medical Center, Nashville, Tennessee. Master site plan. *Sketch by Earl S. Swensson. Courtesy Earl Swensson Associates.*

1 Existing hospital
2 Future hospital/MOB expansion
3 Future hospital/MOB expansion
4 Medical Office A
5 Medical Office B
6 Medical Office C
7 Future sub-surface parking garage

Screened portion represents new construction

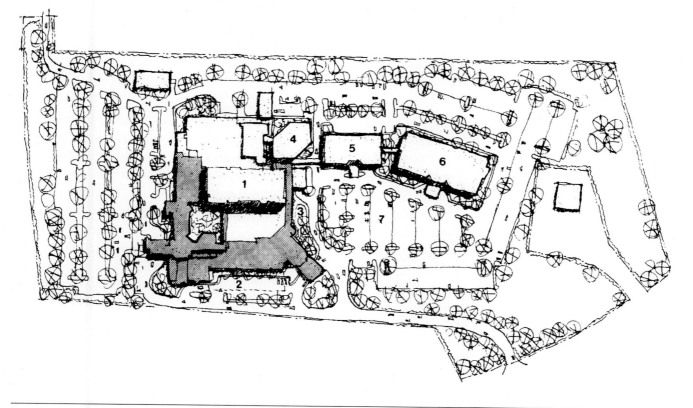

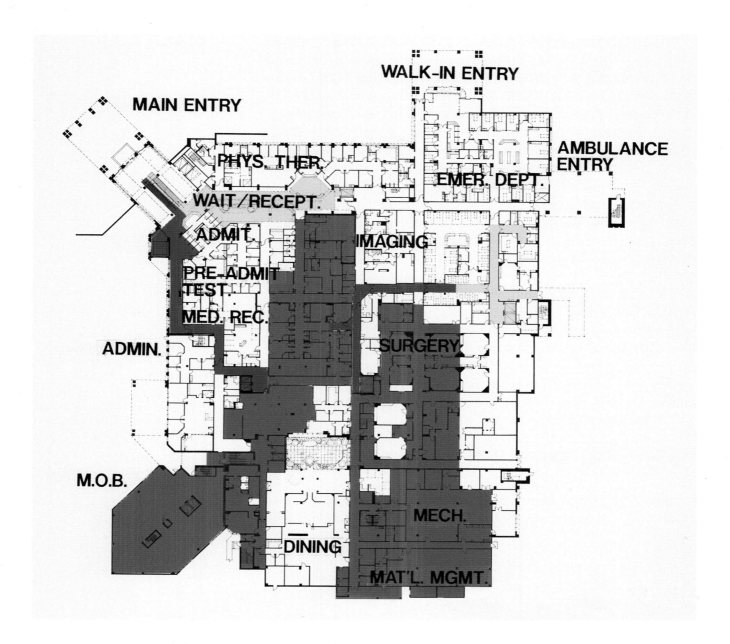

WALK-IN ENTRY

MAIN ENTRY

PHYS. THER.

WAIT/RECEPT.

ADMIT.

PRE-ADMIT TEST

MED. REC.

ADMIN.

M.O.B.

AMBULANCE ENTRY

EMER. DEPT.

IMAGING

SURGERY

MECH.

DINING

MAT'L. MGMT.

Southern Hills Medical Center, Nashville, Tennessee. First-floor plan. The area in red represents the existing building. Yellow areas designate movement through inpatient services. Green indicates areas of outpatient services. *Courtesy Earl Swensson Associates.*

facility, it found itself in a medical marketplace in which the inpatient population was flat while the demand for outpatient care was growing beyond the facility's capacity to accommodate it effectively. In addition, surgical volume had also increased beyond original anticipations. The hospital also faced some typical "real-world" problems, including a tight site that was further hemmed in by sloping topography and strict zoning regulations.

Accommodating the outpatient market is not simply a matter of providing space for facilities. In the case of Southern Hills, as in many outpatient-oriented hospitals throughout the country, the main entrance was buried in the center of the facility and was hard to find, creating a confusing situation for outpatients. Also discouraging were the parking facilities, which were spread out over the site, inefficient, and poorly utilized—a bad combination in any facility, but particularly problematic in a facility reorienting itself for the ambulatory market.

Earl Swensson Associates created a master plan for renovation, which identified the problem areas, proposed solutions, and established a phased construction schedule in order to minimize disruption of ongoing activities during renovation and new construction. The existing ICU was temporarily moved to a fifth-floor location, Recovery was moved to the existing Ambulatory Surgery Recovery area, and Outpatient Staging was temporarily relocated to upper-floor patient rooms. The existing operating rooms remained active during construction. Priority was given to relocating the Emergency Room, so that the new lobby could be constructed. While that work was under way, the original lobby remained in operation. Construction of Laboratory and Administration areas was phased in after the Outpatient and new Lobby areas were complete. Finally, newly

Southern Hills Medical Center, Nashville, Tennessee. Second-floor plan. Red shows the existing building. Yellow indicates areas of inpatient services. Outpatient areas appear in green. *Courtesy Earl Swensson Associates.*

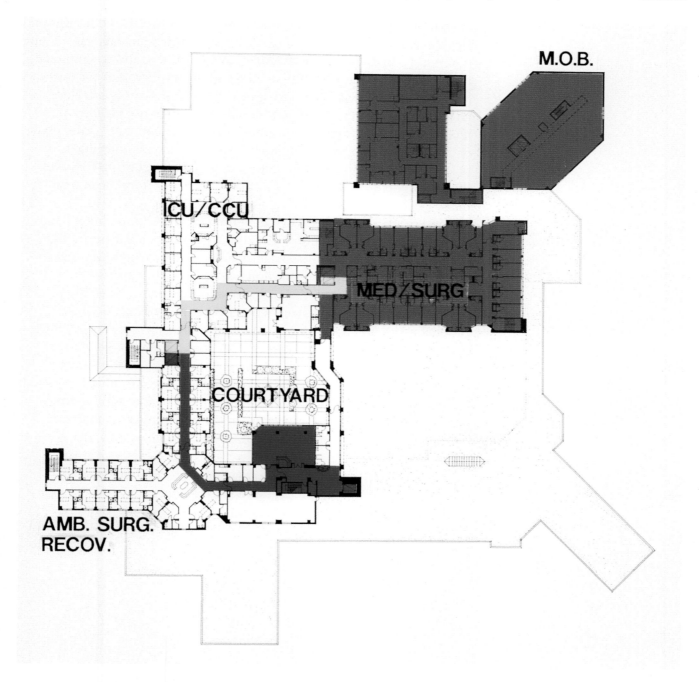

rationalized and additional parking facilities were planned as the final phase of renovation for 1995.

The main entry of the hospital was moved to the front corner of the site, so that there could be no mistaking the entry location. Strategic siting of a well-designed entrance can be a momentous step in renovation, doing much to reclad a hospital's image. Anyone who has ever spruced up his house to make it more attractive to buyers knows the importance of cleaning up, painting, and repairing a shabby front door. It creates, after all, the potential buyer's first impression of the house. The same holds true for potential users of a healthcare facility. For the patient, the architectural greeting provided by an entrance proclaims volumes about the kind and quality of care he may anticipate.

The new front entrance, located near the parking area, was designed to accommodate valet parking. Valet parking for hospitals and healthcare facilities is an important recent trend. It may at first seem extravagant, but it is in fact a highly cost-effective solution to attracting and accommodating patients. To conform to the sloping site, the front entry is at a lower level than the existing first floor. Inside the lobby, escalators and elevators go to the existing main level. But the new lobby does not *feel* low. It is illuminated by a skylight, which leads to an outpatient mall. A later phase of construction calls for a split-level parking deck and an integrated medical office building on top of the parking garage. The upper level of the future parking facilities will be directly accessible from the outpatient mall.

One of the cardinal rules of redesigning for ambulatory care is to separate outpatient from inpatient traffic. Not only is inpatient traffic somewhat intimidating to ambulatory patients, they tend to get the feeling that the hospital is more "interested" in the inpatients—the "regulars"—and that they, the mere outpatients, will be treated like second-class citizens. In all likelihood, this has no bearing on actual hospital policy, but it *is* a feeling, and good design should work to diminish it. The Imaging Department was redesigned to ensure separation of inpatient from outpatient traffic. However, there is no reason to locate inpatient and outpatient registration separately. All registration is handled at a central location, which is adjacent to a new pre-admission testing area, so that patients do not have to wander an intimidating maze of corridors for tests or suffer the redundancy of sign-in, waiting, filling out forms, then changing clothes.

In addition to expanding surgery facilities—to accommodate increased loads—dietary facilities also were expanded and renovated so that the existing pleasant courtyard became the focal point of the dining room.

LANIER PARK HOSPITAL
Medical Office Building
Gainesville, Georgia

The existing medical office building (MOB) at this facility was determined to be inadequate to the new emphasis on outpatient care. The old building was situated in a depression about 25 feet deep, so that a prospective patient's initial view of the facility was of its roof and mechanical equipment—hardly inviting, especially in the competitive outpatient market. To compound this problem, patients entered through the *rear* of the building, which is where the (very inadequate) parking facilities were located. Earl Swensson Associates created a masterplan that called for a new "front door" and a new image.

Three stories were added to the existing MOB, and the new entry was thereby raised to the same level as the approach to the building in 1992.

Lanier Park Hospital, MOB, Gainesville, Georgia. The building's new facility uses the same vocabulary as the existing hospital, giving the complex a unified and updated look. *Photo by Gary Knight. Courtesy Earl Swensson Associates.*

Lanier Park Hospital, MOB, Gainesville, Georgia. The two-story front lobby gives a new look to the existing hospital. The contemporary feel of the design features a monumental staircase leading to the second floor, and the lobby's open spaces serve as a prefunction area to the hospital conference center. *Photo by Gary Knight. Courtesy Earl Swensson Associates.*

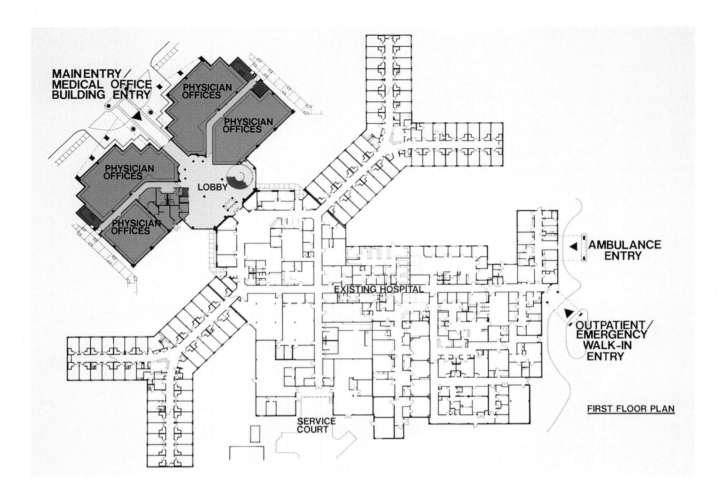

Lanier Park Hospital, MOB, Gainesville, Georgia. Floor plan. *Courtesy Earl Swensson Associates.*

Extra parking was located in the front of the building, with valet service provided. Patients are now met at their car with a golf cart and are driven to the front door. The entrance is marked by a two-story canopy, which leads into a two-story lobby. The MOB as well as the hospital are accessed from this lobby, which also contains a gift shop. Separate entrances are provided for physicians and for mail and deliveries.

The MOB is joined to the hospital through a 40-foot courtyard connecting to an outpatient mall. In this way, the hospital and MOB are integrated, yet remain distinct, and no patient-room windows are blocked off.

The Lanier Park project is a good example of renovation with future needs in mind. The MOB was built to hospital specifications, and the structure was designed to allow for vertical expansion. The mechanical systems, too, are easily adaptable in case of future changes.

EASTERN MAINE MEDICAL CENTER
Bangor

The final renovation example we will look at illustrates the patchwork approach to renovation and its negative impact on access and circulation patterns. The Eastern Maine Medical Center, Bangor, was founded in 1892 as a sixteen-bed hospital located in a mansion. In 1896, a tent had to be erected on hospital grounds to accommodate summer patient overflow. From that time on, at roughly twenty-year intervals, ad hoc expansions were made until 1968, resulting in a sprawling, chaotic complex of buildings, including an emergency room that was *not* directly accessible from the adjacent highway.

In 1970, Payette Associates, Architects, were engaged to plan and execute a ten-year renovation and expansion program, which is documented in the *Architectural Record* (May 1984).

What made renovation feasible at all was an ample (and beautiful) site, which provided not only room for expansion but views of the Penobscot River.

The first phase of this massive project was to determine which buildings were still usable, then to take steps to rationalize circulation by defining zones of utilization and establishing a circulatory spine to connect the existing usable buildings with the proposed new construc-

Eastern Maine Medical Center, Bangor, Maine. The center's renovation illustrates a successful solution to rationalizing earlier additions and to allowing sufficient flexibility for future expansions. *Photo by Paul Ferrino. Courtesy Payette Associates.*

tion. Outside the buildings, public parking was regrouped to relate to a new main entrance, and emergency service entrances were relocated for access to the highway.

A 275,000-square-foot addition formed the new heart of the complex, containing 190 medical/surgical beds on three floors, plus a fourth-floor shell for future expansion. The addition also provided emergency and outpatient facilities, surgery, radiology, pathology, ICU and CCU services, as well as stores, food service, and an education division. The new facility, designed with future expansion in mind, incorporated vertical zoning and circulation, as well as an oversized, reinforced, concrete structural system for ease of upward expansion through the addition of floors. The potential for upward expansion was intended to reduce the sprawl of the already widely distributed complex.

The design's inherent flexibility was put to the test in 1980, when it was found that existing shell space was insufficient to accommodate a state-of-the-art radiation therapy unit. Both technology and the market for this service made demands on the building that were entirely unanticipated. Planners were able to insert the facility on a site underlying a courtyard off the east-west pedestrian spine. The site not only provided adjacency to an existing basement cobalt unit, but was accessible via a dedicated elevator, and allowed for the required shielding by means of earth fill above. Since the facility lay beneath the east-west court, this important aspect of circulation and aesthetics remained undisturbed. The project is an excellent example of how renovation can redress the sins of earlier, ad hoc efforts at expansion, and also of the ways in which renovation can be left open-ended, allowing sufficient flexibility for future, rational expansion.

5

The Emergency Unit

■ Emergency!

With an aggregate occupancy rate of about 68.5 percent in 1992 (according to AHA statistics)—another year of decline in a period of virtually steady decline since 1950—American hospitals are learning the value of marketing their products, and architects are learning to sell design to hospitals as a marketing asset—indeed, as a means of economic survival. How bizarre, or at least ironic, this must seem to the professional staff of the nation's emergency rooms.

AHA figures report 30 million emergency department visits to the 92.8 percent of short-term acute hospitals with emergency departments in 1965. In 1980, the figures were 82 million visits to the 81.5 percent of hospitals with emergency departments. In 1990: 92 million visits to the 93.4 percent of short-term acute hospitals with EDs. In 1992: 95.8 million visits to the 81.9 percent of short-term acute hospitals operating emergency departments. Moreover, in 1965, the United States had, overall, 7,123 hospitals; in 1990, the figure dropped to 6,649; and, for 1992, the AHA reported 6,539 hospitals.

An informal 1989 poll by the American College of Emergency Physicians found that overcrowding in hospital emergency departments was a problem in 41 states, and an Emergency Nurses Association poll that same year found overcrowding in all 50 states.

What does this overcrowding mean?

A 1988 National Public Health and Hospital Institute joint study with the Association of American Medical Colleges/Council of Teaching Hospitals revealed that, of 277 urban hospitals responding, 38 percent experienced emergency-room crowding so severe that patients were sometimes forced to wait twelve hours for a bed. A report on emergency care at the Harbor-UCLA Medical Center (Torrance, California) in the *Journal of the American Medical Association* (August 28, 1991) revealed that 8.2 percent of patients who visited that facility's ED left without being seen by a physician. How long did they wait before they left? On average, 6.4 hours. Of those who left, 46 percent were evaluated as requiring immediate medical attention, and 29 percent were evaluated as needing care within forty-eight hours. Three patients who left later required emergency surgery, and 11 percent were hospitalized within a week.

Here is another snapshot: On January 7, 1992, in New York City's hospitals with emergency departments, 646 patients waited for ED beds. In the last half of 1991, 90.4 percent of Chicago hospitals reported that patients had to wait *more than* four hours before being placed in ED beds. Not only are such conditions inhumane and medically dangerous, they lead to litigation exposure for hospitals. Stephen A. Frew, a Rockford, Illinois, attorney with expertise in ED issues, stated in a *Hospitals* cover story (February 20, 1992) that emergency department waiting times and the general atmosphere in the ED are big factors in litigation.

The overburdening of the emergency department is not exclusively an urban crisis. Rural ED admissions rose 21 percent in the decade of 1980-1990, while urban ED admissions rose 16.2 percent. However, to anyone who observes the activity and atmosphere that prevail in most emergency departments, the violence, pain, and squalor evident in many inner city facilities make a dramatic and horrifying impression that recalls nothing more vividly than combat in a war zone.

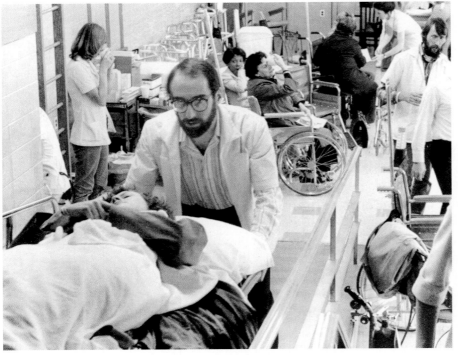

The pressures on emergency departments, especially in the nation's cities, and particularly in the inner cities, are many. To the casual observer, the emergency care crisis is most obviously linked to the explosion of violent crime, especially drug-related crime, in cities, suburbs, and even rural areas. Indeed, this has seriously strained EDs.

The hospital emergency room bustles with activity following a disaster. In addition to meeting the emergent-care needs of the community, emergency departments have become overburdened by a large segment of the American population who use emergency rooms in place of family physicians or alterative primary-care facilities they cannot afford. *Courtesy UPI/Bettmann.*

Modern Healthcare reported (February 5, 1990) that the number of ED admissions in which cocaine was mentioned increased from 8,831 in 1984 to 46,020 in 1988, according to a U.S. Department of Health and Human Services National Institute on Drug Abuse study. The same article reported on a study of 80,529 trauma cases between 1982 and 1987, showing that 21.1 percent (about 17,000) involved "penetrating trauma"—that is, stab or gunshot wounds.

These numbers in themselves are sufficient to suggest the magnitude of the workload weighing on emergency departments. The financial impact of this workload can be appreciated by noting that penetrating trauma is generally very expensive to treat. Each case costs $15,000 to $20,000 on average, and, as Dr. Vincent Markovchick, director of emergency medical services at Denver Health and Hospitals, observed in the *Modern Healthcare* article, "The general consensus is that 90 percent of penetrating trauma patients are uninsured and the hospital doesn't recover anything. We lose big on penetrating trauma."

But burgeoning violence—and victims who cannot pay for care—is just one part of the problem. The hospital emergency department has become a care provider of last resort—of *only* resort—for a large segment of the American population, which, uninsured or underinsured, cannot afford to pay for the services of a family physician or alternative primary-care providers such as ambulatory care centers. The ED bears much of the burden of our society's literal and figurative ills, and the state of crisis under which so many EDs operate is a symptom of the long-standing failure to reform the U.S. healthcare system.

The number of individuals who cannot afford "private" healthcare has grown and includes far more than the indigent and the homeless, who, however, do make great demands on many emergency departments. Moreover, a large proportion of ED patients, whether uninsured, so-called "working poor," or abjectly indigent, have special needs, which many EDs are poorly equipped to serve. These groups include patients with AIDS and the aging.

As overwhelming as the problems facing emergency departments seem, they are, in large part, a function of a disparity between paradigms. Most emergency departments remain what they were originally designed to be: *emergency* departments, facilities set up to treat sudden life- or limb-threatening illness and injury. Given today's social realities, however, a large proportion of patients visit the ED not for "emergent" conditions, which pose a threat to life and limb, but for "urgent" conditions— conditions that require prompt treatment but pose no threat to life and limb—and for "non-urgent" conditions.

In a profile of the ED at Mary Immaculate Hospital, in a lower-income area of Queens, New York, *Health Progress* (May 1991) noted that "Of every 10 people treated here, 8 to 9 have colds, the flu, a rash—'Cases that should be treated in a doctor's office,' as one physician put it. Unfortunately for many of these people, as that physician knows well, there is no doctor's office."

■ New Directions

The architect or medical facilities planner looking at this situation readily arrives at design and space utilization solutions aimed at facilitating triage and distinguishing among patients requiring emergent care and those who fall into the urgent and non-urgent categories. The most obvious design solution is to plan ED facilities as a true "front door" to the hospital, a point at which the patient can be admitted directly for emergent care or given the urgent and/or non-urgent care she requires—not in the traditional "emergency room" but in an adjacent or nearby ambulatory care center.

Unfortunately, the crisis cannot be resolved by design measures alone. For the reasons outlined above, emergency departments are expensive to run, and realize little, if any, revenue. The community mission of the ED, as well as its revenue situation, could be improved by providing facilities that segregate emergent from non-emergent cases. The situation can be further improved by community-oriented hospital programs and facilities that emphasize prevention of disease and, especially, prevention of injury. However, a great many emergency departments are caught in a kind of gridlock. Hospital administrators understandably find it difficult to fund expansion of centers of deficit rather than profit. Without such funding, of course, emergency departments are doomed to remain centers of deficit and will, therefore, fail to receive adequate funding.

For all too many hospitals, then, the answer has not been to rethink and redesign the emergency department, but to close it down. *Hospitals* reported in its February 20, 1992, issue that a June 1990 survey of hospital executives by Deloitte & Touche revealed that 53 percent of respondents cited emergency departments as the "most unprofitable" service they provided, and ED was the only service—out of eighteen—so named by a majority of the respondents. Ten percent of these respondents said they would stop offering emergency service in order for the hospital to survive. In bottom-line financial terms, that percentage is quite small—a testament to the sense of community responsibility by which most hospitals operate. In human terms, however, even 10 percent is a frightening figure.

A more indicative measure of the trend toward reducing emergency care, however, is the number of hospitals that have opted out of programs of state certification as trauma centers. In the 1970s and 1980s, hospitals rushed to attain certification as trauma centers, seeing this as a mark of prestige likely to attract more patients of all kinds. By 1987, about 1,000 adult general hospitals in the United States had certified trauma centers. By the next year, 1988, the figure had declined 30 percent to 700. In 1989, about 600 hospitals were certified. By 1992, however, 881 hospitals reported certification, perhaps a hopeful sign of reversal of the trend toward abandonment of emergency care.

What, then, are the new directions in emergency unit design? Given the prevailing trends, it is quite possible that, for a significant number of hospitals, the new direction will be toward no emergency department at all. For new construction, architects may be asked to design ambulatory care centers and primary care centers to compete with the freestanding ambulatory ("immediate") care centers currently popular in many parts of the country. But the trauma-oriented emergent-care facility will likely be absent from a significant number of new facilities. Likewise, in renovating existing construction, plans may well call for converting the emergency department to some other use—such as ambulatory/primary care.

■ Impact of Universal Health Insurance

As we write this, it seems to us inevitable that some form of universal health insurance will be created as part of a total federal health reform package. How extensive and effective it will be we do not know. We do expect that it will work to ease the crisis that besets a great many of the nation's emergency departments, but a shortage of primary healthcare providers in many communities will continue to prevent EDs from totally segregating emergent and primary care functions.

That is, in all likelihood, emergency departments will still be called upon to render primary care for a significant segment of the community. It may well be that this role will be given official sanction by an evolving national healthcare plan; certain EDs will be designated primary care providers for their communities. While the managed-care insurance programs likely to proliferate in the "pay-or-play" insurance climate that universal health insurance is expected to create will tend to discourage use of the ED as a primary care provider, it is also likely that efforts at cost containment will prompt many providers to negotiate with EDs to provide after-hours care. Particularly in heavily populated urban areas, this may lead to volume expansion in non-emergent care.

The emergent function of the emergency unit will certainly continue well into the twenty-first century. The non-emergent component may well decrease in volume for conditions traditionally treated by the family physician. However, as payer trends continue to shift toward outpatient services, and to the degree that hospitals and healthcare facilities fail to develop ambulatory services distinct from emergency departments, ED volumes are likely to rise. As states and localities continue to cut funding for social services, ED volume in such areas as acute infection, psychiatric disorders, and conditions related to social distress (chiefly homelessness) also will rise.

For hospitals that choose (or must) provide emergency services, it is and will continue to be essential to adequately fund forward-looking design and building of the emergency department to promote quality, productivity, flexibility, and safety. This is easily said, but in reality difficult for many hospitals, whose administrators are faced with allocating funds that may be disproportionate to revenue generated. The design strategies we outline next are intended to suggest ways in which ED operations can be made more cost-efficient and can even be made to generate revenue, particularly from the non-emergent care provided.

■ Principal Design Issues

For any number of reasons—ranging from a sense of mission to meeting community licensing requirements—the majority of hospitals will continue to provide certain levels of emergent care. For these, design issue areas will include

- ▲ *Helicopter access*
- ▲ *Access and evaluation (triage)*
- ▲ *The waiting area*
- ▲ *Treatment spaces*
- ▲ *Staff and support spaces*
- ▲ *Accommodation of data and diagnostic technologies*
- ▲ *Flexible design for flexible response*

▲ *Specialty emergency treatment spaces/units*
▲ *Security*
▲ *Nearby parking*
▲ *Prominent signage and access*

Access and Evaluation (Triage)

One of the new-paradigm realities hospitals must face is that, for many patients, the emergency room is the "front door" to the facility. In traditional emergency departments, triage for walk-in patients is rudimentary at best, and little attempt, beyond the ad hoc, is made to separate urgencies from dire emergencies. The new-direction departure from this may be illustrated by two projects, one at South Shore Hospital, South Weymouth, Massachusetts, the other at St. Joseph's Hospital, Tampa, Florida.

EMERGENCY CENTER
SOUTH SHORE HOSPITAL
South Weymouth, Massachusetts

TRO Architects designed an award-winning (First Place, New Construction Category, National Healthcare Environment Award Competition) 20,000-

South Shore Hospital, Emergency Center, South Weymouth, Massachusetts. Dominating the main lobby of the hospital's walk-in entry, the information desk serves as a beacon to patients and visitors. Personnel at the desk direct patients, dispense information, and aid in the hospital's security. *Photo by R. Mikrut. Courtesy TRO/The Ritchie Organization.*

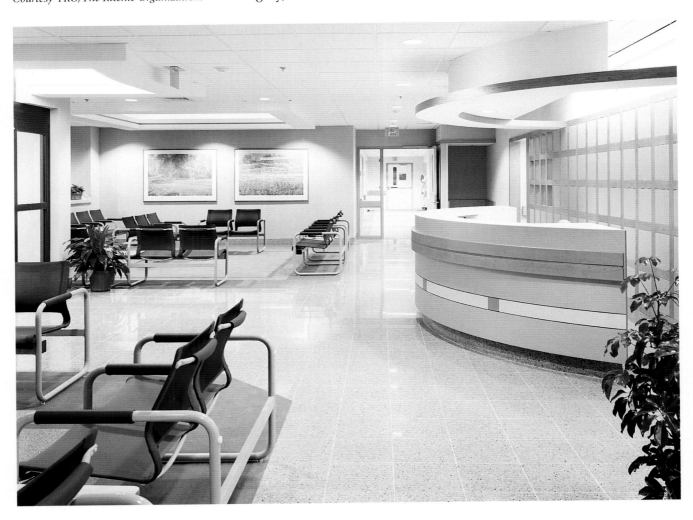

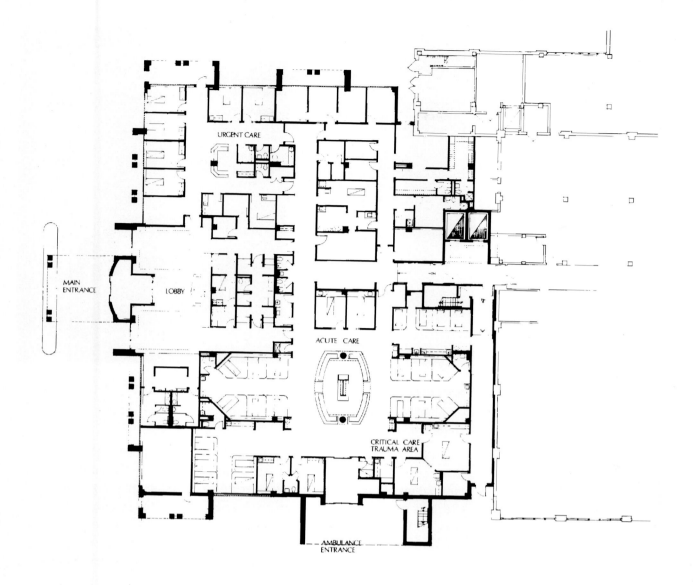

square-foot Emergency Center to accommodate 75,000 patients a year. The center features separate entrances for ambulances and walk-in patients and includes six "fast-track" treatment rooms for less serious cases, as well as twenty-five acute care stations. Central registration and triage areas are prominent, the radiology suite is within the department, and the expanded waiting facility includes a play area for children.

In an emergency facility this large, flexibility is especially important. TRO designed the general exam rooms for easy convertibility to psychiatric treatment rooms by means of pull-down walls that shield casework and equipment. Two trauma rooms can convert to a single, large, critical care area. In addition to designing for maximum utility, the Emergency Center was finished and furnished in tones of sea blue-green, which harmonizes with the hospital's shoreline setting.

South Shore Hospital, Emergency Center, South Weymouth, Massachusetts. The floor plan for the emergency department features separate entrances for ambulances and walk-in patients, "fast track" treatment rooms for less serious cases, twenty-five acute care stations, and prominently located registration and triage areas. *Courtesy TRO/The Ritchie Organization.*

St. Joseph's Hospital, Emergency Department, Tampa, Florida. The information and waiting area of the emergency department offers registration facilities designed for privacy. Sections of the department feature different finish materials, such as the carpeting in the waiting area, and the areas suffering the heaviest traffic have been finished in hard, easily maintained surfaces. *Photo by George Cott. Courtesy Hansen Lind Meyer.*

EMERGENCY DEPARTMENT
ST. JOSEPH'S HOSPITAL
Tampa, Florida

Leon Floerchinger, a partner in the architectural firm of Matthei & Colin Associates, Chicago, observes that "once a hospital reaches about 20,000 annual visits to its ED, it needs to create separate facilities" to serve patients with varying needs and reduce the time it takes to provide service. St. Joseph's Hospital rejected its original plans to renovate its ED, which was designed to handle 25,000 annual visits, because, with an actual patient load of 60,000, it became clear that a whole new facility was required.

In 1993, the firm of Hansen Lind Meyer designed a 25,000-square-foot department with forty-eight exam rooms distinctly divided into specialized areas, including "express care" for minor emergencies, pediatrics, trauma, and 23-hour observation. Each of these areas is contained within a "pod" that has its own nurses' station and waiting area. In addition, the pediatric pod has its own triage area so that pediatric patients are thoroughly segregated from adults. The St. Joseph ED has its own radiology department and is connected to pharmacy and laboratory facilities elsewhere in the hospital via pneumatic tubes to transport laboratory specimens and medications.

The St. Joseph ED is planned to become integral with an entire "critical care" wing, which will include intensive care and coronary care units. While maintaining a separate identity as an ambulatory and emergency facility, the St. Joseph ED will be able to move patients quickly and efficiently into the more intensive acute-care areas of the hospital.

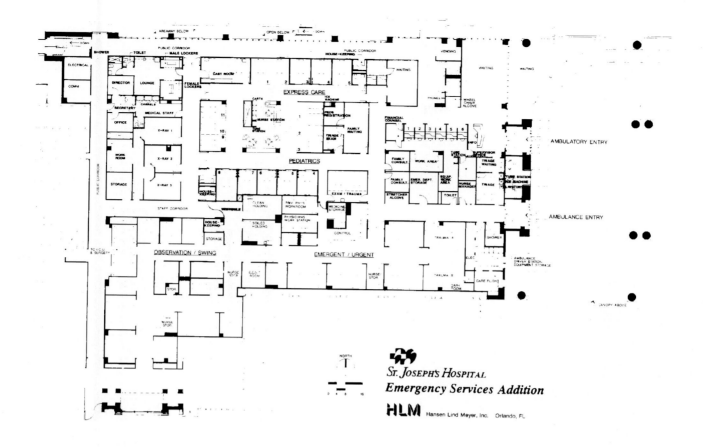

St. Joseph's Hospital
Emergency Services Addition

HLM Hansen Lind Meyer, Inc. Orlando, FL

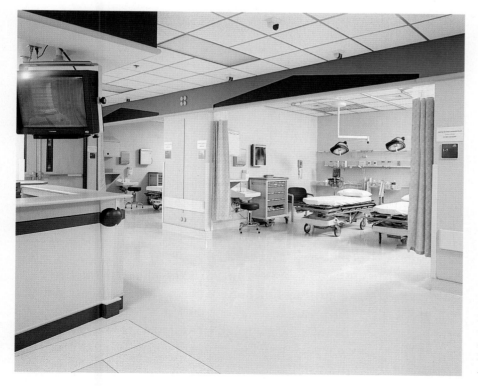

St. Joseph's Hospital, Emergency Department, Tampa, Florida. Floor plan. *Courtesy of Hansen Lind Meyer.*

St. Joseph's Hospital, Emergency Department, Tampa, Florida. The department offers forty-eight examination rooms in a 25,000-square-foot facility. Trauma rooms are situated conveniently near the department's nursing station so that patients in the rooms are constantly under the nursing staff's observation. The department's design allows ready access to mobile equipment when it is needed. *Photo by George Cott. Courtesy Hansen Lind Meyer.*

Thomas Jefferson University Hospital, Emergency Department, Philadelphia, Pennsylvania. Floor plan of first floor. *Courtesy MPB Architects.*

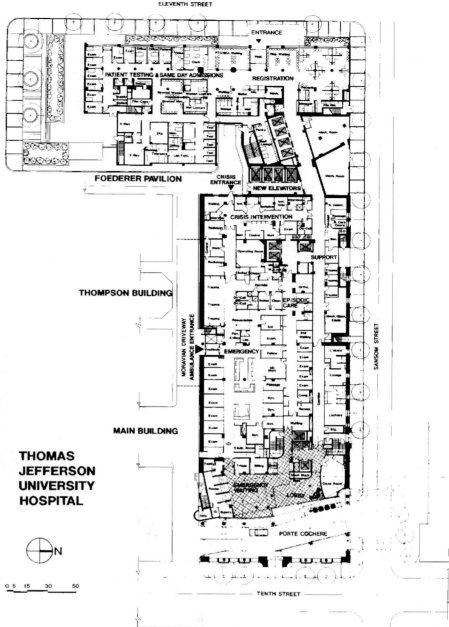

Thomas Jefferson University Hospital, Emergency Department, Philadelphia, Pennsylvania. The walk-in emergency entrance required a unique treatment: the lower portion of the building was cut away to provide a covered drive-through. The department offers valet parking as a extra customer convenience. *Photo by Matt Wargo/Matt Wargo Photography. Courtesy MPB Architects.*

Additional Access Considerations

As it is essential to make entry crystal-clear, that clarity should begin at the "pre-entry" stage as well, with prominent highway or street signage and bold, lighted departmental entry signage. The walk-in and ambulance entrances should be covered, and, for large facilities, a garage-type ambulance entrance should be considered.

Special parking facilities are essential to access and to promoting the ambulatory and primary-care functions of the department. Traffic patterns must not conflict with driveways for emergency vehicles, and parking spaces for patients, ED staff, and law enforcement officers should be very clearly designated. It is important that there be no confusion concerning the location of the ED parking area.

The same clarity should carry over seamlessly into the entrance and reception area, with a clearly marked and strategically positioned reception desk and a triage area adjacent to it. It is advisable to position the security office so that security personnel can readily monitor the reception area. Security is discussed in greater detail later in the chapter.

The ambulance entrance must also be clearly and unmistakably marked, and a nurses' station area should be included at the entrance, with an ample alcove for stretchers, gurneys, and wheelchairs, so that these may be kept clear of the entrance. It is advisable, wherever possible, to equip the ambulance entry area with automatic sliding doors, as opposed to manually operated swinging doors. Care should be taken to prevent walk-ins from using the ambulance or trauma entry in lieu of the walk-in entry. This can be achieved architecturally by plantings, the use of berms, and other measures. Clear designation of parking areas also separates trauma from walk-in entry.

St. Luke's Medical Center, Milwaukee, Wisconsin. The design of the entrance to the emergency department clearly distinguishes it from the entrances to the center. *Photo © 1993 Wayne Cable. Courtesy Bobrow/Thomas and Associates*

PineLake Medical Center, Mayfield, Kentucky. The emergency department features separate, clearly designated entrances for walk-in patients and ambulances. Parking for walk-in patients is convenient to their entrance and is located away from ambulance traffic patterns. *Photo by Jonathan Hillyer. Courtesy Earl Swensson Associates.*

Helicopter Access

Virtually all hospitals with emergency facilities should plan for helicopter access. In the case of emergency departments that handle significant volumes of "Life Flight" and other helicopter-ambulance traffic, the landing facility should be located to give as direct access as possible to the ED. In other large hospitals that customarily receive patients by helicopter, the landing area may be positioned to share access among the ED and other departments (such as pediatrics, a burn unit, and so on). Urban campuses, likely to be surrounded by tall structures, must coordinate with the Federal Aviation Authority the safest flight path into the heliport. Emergency departments in smaller hospitals also benefit from a strategically placed helicopter landing pad for rapid transfer out of patients whose condition requires the advanced facilities of a larger medical center. The complexity of the landing pad design will depend on the amount of anticipated usage.

In remote areas, it is conceivable that an airstrip for fixed-wing aircraft will be part of the emergency department's system of access.

The Waiting Area

One measure of the success of an emergency department is how *little* the waiting area is used. The object is to make an ambulatory patient's stay in this area as brief as possible. Still, even in the most efficient emergency facility, the waiting area is a very important element that, traditionally, has been slighted or treated as an afterthought.

The waiting area communicates very powerful non-verbal messages. If the ED is a hospital's alternative "front door," the ED waiting area is, in large measure, the place where patients form their first impressions about the hospital as a whole. Old-paradigm design treated the waiting area as a space-consuming necessary evil. New-paradigm, patient-centered design regards it as an opportunity to express concern for the healthcare consumer's comfort. Colors should be cheerful, with an emphasis on timeless rather than trendy hues. Furniture should, of course, be comfortable. Modular seating groups are available that approximate a soft, residential appearance yet provide durability, including field-changeable upholstery covers. The anti-institutional, patient-oriented image of the facility can be further enhanced by individual chairs arranged in attractive groups rather than in bus station-style rows. If possible, a certain number of high-backed chairs should be reserved for geriatric patients, who may have difficulty sitting and rising.

It is also important to ensure that an adequate amount of seating is provided. Some authorities suggest a convenient formula for determining how many seats are sufficient:

$$2P - E = S$$

P is the average number of patients treated per hour; *E* the number of exam rooms; and *S* the seating required. This formula assumes that each patient is accompanied by a friend or relative. An added margin of safety

Thomas Jefferson University Hospital, Emergency Department, Philadelphia, Pennsylvania. Areas such as the waiting room should be inviting and pleasant to patients and visitors. The artificial skylight simulates the feel of natural daylight in a space that would otherwise be very dark. *Photo by Matt Wargo/Maytt Wargo Photography. Courtesy MPB Architects.*

can be attained by including a "late factor," derived by substituting $3P$ for $2P$. Simple as it is, such a formula may be used as a convenient starting place for planning, but it is no substitute for careful, "real-life" study. Not only should design provide a sufficient number of seats, but they should be deployed so as to avoid putting a large a number of waiting patients "on display." Such a sight may send patients off to a competing facility, if one is available.

Next to adequate and comfortable seating, lighting conveys the most critical of psychological messages. If possible, a combination of overhead, recessed, and indirect lighting is desirable to enliven and humanize what might otherwise be a threatening institutional space. Table lamps secured on coffee tables or side tables add a residential feeling and interest. The coffee tables should not have decorative reveals, which act as containment areas for spilled liquids and blood. If possible, natural light—especially from windows with a pleasant view—should be fully exploited. If artwork is used to decorate walls, track-lighting spots may be used to highlight it. Such lighting might also be used to highlight wall-mounted magazine racks.

Just as natural lighting has a soothing effect by allowing the patient to make contact with the outside, so well-kept and attractive plants help to maintain a sense of the presence of the familiar, pleasurable natural world. At least one television set should also be available, preferably in a corner or alcove where it will not disturb patients who desire quiet.

Carpeting is a very controversial feature in some new ED waiting areas. It has the advantages of lending a feeling of warmth to the area, greatly reducing noise, and reducing the chance of accidental slipping and falling. Type 6.6 nylon fiber is very durable, and antimicrobial treatment with such products as Sylgard inhibits growth of microorganisms, including those that cause infection, create odors, or provoke allergic reactions. A level loop pile is most appropriate in a heavily trafficked waiting area and will not pose an obstacle to wheelchair maneuvering. It is this latter consideration that must be most carefully thought out before installing carpet. The higher-pile carpets should be avoided, because they can make maneuvering wheelchairs difficult. Alternatives to carpeting include attractively patterned vinyl tile and tile with border designs.

The waiting area should have ample trash receptacles and vending machines available; it is preferable that the latter be assigned to a dedicated space or alcove. It is also desirable to make provision for smokers. Although a great many hospitals are entirely smoke free, this rule may be difficult to enforce in a high-stress area. One strategy is to provide some outdoor waiting areas, to which smokers—and others—may retreat.

Other waiting-area amenities include access to an adequate number of public telephones and restrooms, and a coat-hanging area. In situations where theft may be a problem, small lockers may be provided. The waiting area should be in full view of the reception desk, and in the children's waiting area, a play area should be designated. Here a somewhat higher-pile carpet than that in the adult waiting area is appropriate. If a play area is included, provision should be made for adult supervision, either by hospital volunteers or family members.

Where conditions permit, outdoor waiting areas are popular supplements to the indoor waiting room. Not only do such spaces afford a break from crowds and relief from anxiety, they are popular with smokers, who are increasingly hard-pressed to find areas that permit smoking.

Treatment Spaces

Treatment spaces can be divided into trauma rooms, general examination/treatment rooms, and specialized rooms. The trend is toward a multiplicity of specialized rooms—and, indeed, even toward specialized emergency departments. Based on an American Hospital Association checklist (1992), the following treatment spaces should be available in virtually any emergency department:

▲ *Triage area*
▲ *Trauma room(s)*
▲ *Cardiac resuscitation room(s)*
▲ *Urgent examination/treatment room(s)*
▲ *Non-urgent examination/treatment room(s)*
▲ *Geriatric treatment room(s)*
▲ *Suture/minor treatment room(s)*
▲ *Seclusion/quiet room(s)*
▲ *Secure isolation room(s) for psychiatric emergencies*
▲ *Pediatric treatment room(s)*
▲ *OB-GYN room(s)*
▲ *Eye room(s)*
▲ *Cast/ortho room*
▲ *Decontamination room(s)*

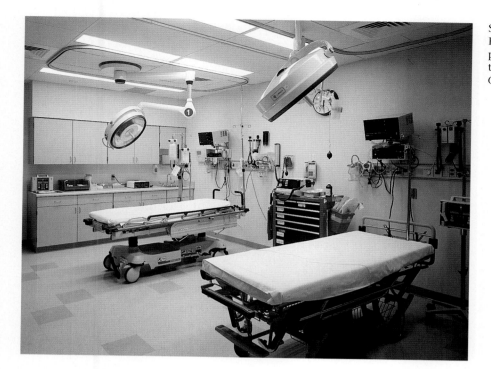

Spring View Hospital, Spring View, Kentucky. Simple things like a floor pattern can relieve the sterile feel of a trauma room. *Photo by Gary Knight. Courtesy Earl Swensson Associates.*

▲ *Observation room(s)*

▲ *Chest-pain observation room(s)*

▲ *Fast-track room(s) (for primary care: sore throats, minor injuries, etc.)*

▲ *Emergency dental treatment room(s)*

It should be noted that observation rooms are a rather controversial issue, with some authorities believing they are not only a waste of space but promote the holding of patients unnecessarily in the emergency department. Other authorities believe they are a valuable component of any emergency department.

The cast/ortho room is among the least-used specialized treatment areas in any ED, and for that reason many older EDs dispense with the room entirely, repairing fractures in any available general treatment room. This is a cumbersome, inefficient arrangement, and a dedicated cast/ortho room is far preferable. In the vast majority of EDs, a single such room is sufficient.

Special design consideration must be given to decontamination rooms, whose drainage systems and sewer connections must be designed specifically to handle hazardous material. Usually a holding tank system must be included in the design to collect hazardous waste for later safe disposal. Provisions should be made for handling biological and radioactive hazards, and the decontamination room should also have an independent, filtered ventilation and exhaust system.

In addition to the treatment spaces, provision must be made for a nurses' station and workstation.

Depending on the size of the hospital and the ED, diagnostic, laboratory, and medication facilities may be fully shared with other departments or may, in varying degrees, be available within the ED. The trend is to include at least X-ray facilities within or adjacent to the department and perhaps a stat laboratory as well as a modest pharmacy. In the absence of a departmental laboratory and/or pharmacy, a fast, efficient transport (pneumatic tube system) and data communication system must be in place, which is discussed shortly, along with design provisions to accommodate major diagnostic and other equipment. It needs to be observed here, however, that even in emergency departments where the inclusion of major diagnostic hardware is not anticipated, adequate space, electrical, and data transmission provisions need to be made for the bedside telemetry and diagnostic equipment presently available and for emerging remote telemetry technologies. Treatment rooms should be designed with sufficient space to accommodate computer terminals.

The following are minimum square footages *required* per AHA standards for treatment areas. The *preferred* square footages follow Department of Health and Human Services guidelines:

Room	Required	Preferred
Trauma	240 sq ft/per	300 sq ft/per
		250 sq ft/multiple
Cardiac resuscitation	240 sq ft/per	300 sq ft/per
		250 sq ft/multiple
Treatment (major)	100 sq ft/per	120 sq ft/per
	80 sq ft/multiple	100 sq ft/multiple
Treatment (minor)	80 sq ft/per	80-100 sq ft/per
Observation	80-100 sq ft/per	80-100 sq ft/per
Specialized treatment	100-150 sq ft/per	100-200 sq ft/per
Decontamination	250-300 sq ft/per	300 sq ft/per

Additional examination rooms may be required in emergency departments that are marketing so-called "fast-track" care: quick service for uncomplicated, non-urgent cases. Some emergency departments also dedicate a portion of their facility to industrial medicine, perhaps serving a local employer. These design issues are addressed in Chapter 10, "Ambulatory Care Design and Professional Offices."

Staff and Support Spaces

The basic staff and support areas required for virtually any emergency department include

- ▲ *Admissions*
- ▲ *Grief counselors/bereavement room*
- ▲ *Physician offices*
- ▲ *Nurse manager office*
- ▲ *Security station/office*
- ▲ *On-call room (with toilet and shower adjacent)*
- ▲ *Patient restrooms*
- ▲ *Staff restrooms/lockers/showers*
- ▲ *Staff lounge/canteen*
- ▲ *Physician/family consultation room*
- ▲ *Staff conference*

▲ Communications/disaster coordination room
▲ Physician dictation/computer workstation
▲ Chart/record room
▲ Patient tub/shower
▲ Library
▲ Soiled utility
▲ Clean utility
▲ Stretcher/wheelchair storage
▲ Supply room
▲ EMS equipment room
▲ Pharmacy/medication area
▲ Biohazard waste-holding (red bags)
▲ Housekeeping closet
▲ Communications/electrical equipment rooms

Space allocation for staff and support areas is more variable than for treatment areas; however, the following guidelines represent acceptable *minimums* only:

Room/area	Minimum
Clean utility	80-150 sq ft/per
Soiled utility	40-100 sq ft/per
Housekeeping closets	30-40 sq ft
Staff conference	200 sq ft
Equipment storage	200 sq ft

In planning emergency departments flexible enough to accommodate the current state of the art and to adapt to evolving technologies, support areas should be designed with telecommunication and data processing/ transfer requirements in mind. It is also important to approach such staff areas as lounges and conference rooms with the same humanity that is devoted to creating pleasant patient waiting areas. A quiet, restful oasis is crucial to maintaining staff morale and contributes greatly to staff performance and retention. Note that the staff conference room can be designed with sufficient flexibility to double as a disaster services coordination area.

■ Accommodation of Data and Diagnostic Technologies

Many EDs currently maintain their own departmental X-ray equipment. Proper shielding and reinforcement must be integrated into the design to accommodate this equipment. In smaller facilities, the ED may share X-ray equipment with another department, in which case it is very desirable to locate the ED adjacent to the department that has the X-ray equipment.

Beginning in the 1970s, many additional imaging technologies have joined X-ray as diagnostic tools. Some of these technologies, because of their size, are currently inappropriate for most emergency department situations, but even CT scanners and magnetic resonance imaging (MRI) devices may be incorporated in some settings where diagnostic services are offered on an outpatient basis.

Ultra-Fast CT, one of the fastest growing areas in diagnostic imaging, is easily installed and well suited to the outpatient setting. It may well commonly find a place in the ED. Ultrasound has many emergency applications, and the equipment is sufficiently portable as to require little in the way of special design considerations.

Surgical laser technology, which is already spurring great growth in outpatient surgery, may find a place in emergency departments that offer specialized ophthalmological treatment. Usage must be weighed against the cost of duplicating the equipment and staff of other departments.

Another imaging technology that is almost certain to play an increasingly large role not only in the emergency department but throughout the hospital, is the Picture Archiving and Communication System (PACS). PACS is a system for digitizing, archiving, and transmitting medical imaging data. Some X-ray equipment, for example, already uses directly digitized images rather than photographic film, and such images could be instantly transmitted via telephone or some dedicated transmission lines to specialists elsewhere in the hospital or at another institution so as to obtain an instant consultation.

It is difficult to predict whether emerging technologies will make the kind of design demands made by large X-ray, CT scanning, and MRI installations. While whole-body, real-time imaging devices may become very large, it is more likely that equipment suitable to an emergency setting will become smaller and more portable. In ED design, then, it is best to provide the M/E flexibility for installation and expansion of data communication lines, and to provide space, with the appropriate data and electrical connections, for computer and terminal equipment, preferably in each treatment room. Today and for the immediate future, the standard bedside requirements for ED treatment rooms include

- ▲ *Oxygen*
- ▲ *Compressed air*
- ▲ *Vacuum system*
- ▲ *Nurse call system*
- ▲ *Emergency call system*
- ▲ *Direct (work) and indirect lighting fixtures*
- ▲ *Airway supply rack, for airway and suction equipment*
- ▲ *Bedside work space and countertop*
- ▲ *Computer terminal space, with electrical and network/data transmission connections*
- ▲ *Monitoring equipment space, with electrical and data transmission connections*
- ▲ *Portable monitoring*
- ▲ *Electrical outlets, including those required for the computer terminal, plus 220-volt access*
- ▲ *Emergency generator*

▲ *Closed storage space*

▲ *Trash and sharps containers*

Larger treatment rooms should also include

▲ *Oto/ophthalmoscope*

▲ *Ceiling track IV*

▲ *Handwashing sink*

▲ *Monitoring equipment*

■ Flexible Design for Flexible Response

A design may be flexible in two ways. It may allow for ease of expansion, alteration, and renovation. It may also allow for varied use as conditions demand. In the design examples just discussed under "Access," we have seen some instances of both types of flexibility. Flexibility of use will be of increasing importance in emergency department design, especially in an era of uncertainty about the impact of medical policy reform.

Designers will be asked to create emergency departments in which the proportion of emergent versus urgent versus non-urgent patient care can be readily and easily varied. In effect, administrators will want EDs that can be converted to revenue-producing primary care centers and converted back again to provide emergent care.

In some settings the ED may be designed chiefly as an ambulatory primary care center with a relatively small emergency area located near areas that can be readily transformed into additional emergency care space in time of high demand, mass accident, or natural disaster. Added flexibility can be achieved by designs that provide for "special care" beds adjacent to the ED to expedite patient flow. These beds may also serve as a recovery area when the ED is adjacent to ambulatory surgery.

Among the leading motifs of advanced hospital design are strategies for reducing patient transportation. Thus, where possible, X-ray and other imaging equipment should be available in the ED itself. It is preferable not to have to transport the patient to radiology. Emergency departments of the near future may feature large critical care rooms that transform into an x-ray suite without having to move the patient at all. Portable walls can be opened up to accommodate a crash team, and the room can also serve as a limited operating theater by means of a mechanical system that provides for the correct air exchange and sterile conditions.

Such strategies take the emergency-department-as-front-door concept to the extreme of becoming a "front door" that does not so much admit the patient into the hospital as admit the hospital to the patient.

■ Specialty Emergency Treatment Spaces/Units

Old-paradigm hospital administrators had to decide how extensive an emergency department to design. The new paradigm calls for this decision to be made in relation to provisions for ambulatory primary care, which, for the vast majority of hospitals, is becoming an important means of generating revenue. One issue that planners must resolve is the degree of specialization to introduce into the emergency department as opposed to a separate ambulatory care facility. This issue aside, in larger EDs, the trend is toward incorporating specialized treatment rooms into the facility's design or even providing individual, specialized emergency facilities for certain conditions.

The most commonly found specialized emergency department is the pediatric ED. Treatment areas need not differ significantly from those found in the adult emergency area, except that, if possible, examination tables should be higher and (where funding permits) equipment should be scaled to pediatric applications. Waiting areas, however, present opportunities for imaginative design and decoration. Individual seating is not necessary in these areas, and continuous seating (common seat and back) for parents saves room to create a play area or even a "play pit" for children. Carpeting is an excellent floor covering choice for the children's waiting area and may be of a pile higher than that used in the adult waiting area. Toys and television may be provided, and it is also a good idea to decorate some wall space with a bulletin board to display children's artwork. This establishes an emotionally reassuring bond between present visitors to the pediatric ED and other children who have had the same experience.

Other specialty EDs, or rooms within general EDs, include cardiac, ophthalmic, ear-nose-throat (ENT), OB/GYN, and psychiatric. Ophthalmic and ENT rooms require special chairs, lights, and other equipment. OB/GYN facilities should communicate directly with the hospital's inpatient OB/GYN department. Psychiatric emergency facilities require special security rooms, as well as rooms that are quiet and relatively isolated from other patients—particularly critically ill or injured patients, whose presence may aggravate emotional distress.

■ Security

An issue of sharply increasing concern in emergency departments in recent years is security. Psychiatric emergencies have always presented special security problems, with violent patients who must be prevented from hurting themselves and others. However, EDs are also vulnerable to criminal violence, chiefly from two sources: substance abusers in search of narcotics, and gang members seeking revenge on rivals who are being treated—usually for gunshot wounds.

Ideally, the ED—as a hospital's alternative "front door"—should be a place of welcome, offering the promise of care, comfort, aid, and solace. The reality is that contemporary emergency department design must provide for adequate security. A security office should be located adjacent to the reception desk and should command a controlling view of the principal ambulatory entrance. More remote areas of the ED, including the ambulance entrance area, should be monitored in the security office by strategically positioned closed-circuit television cameras. The pharmacy or medication room, which should be equipped with appropriate locks on narcotic storage only, should be alarmed as well as monitored by closed-circuit television. The narcotics secure area might be accessed by electronic combination or magnetic-stripe card locks, and each entry recorded by computer, along with the name or code of the person accessing the medication.

If security facilities are designed as integral elements of the ED, they will do little to defeat the "user-friendly" image of the department. Indeed, they may add to the patients' sense of well-being, of having placed themselves in the capable hands of those concerned for their welfare and safety. Given the necessarily exposed location of the emergency department, the security presence—as part of a deliberate design strategy—also improves staff morale and promotes retention of skilled personnel.

■ Hospital-Based Emergency Departments

EMERGENCY DEPARTMENT
LYNCHBURG GENERAL HOSPITAL
Lynchburg, Virginia

Earl Swensson Associates was asked to design a new emergency department—opened in 1994—for this major regional trauma center, which handles approximately 60,000 cases per year. The existing department was physically too small to handle the caseload and could not deliver the level of patient care the administration wanted. Moreover, there was only a single entrance to the department, for walk-ins as well as trauma cases. Finally, the problem was also one of image. "Because of our role in the community as the hospital that treats more acutely ill patients," explains Darrell Powers, the hospital's administrator, "we handle a high volume of cases in our emergency department. About 75 percent of our admissions come through the emegency department, and it is here that one gets his first impression of Lynchburg General Hospital. We want this impression to be a favorable one."

Work was carried out without closing the existing department. Since the hospital is located in a transitional area between commercial and residential use, landscaping—berms—were employed to help reduce the apparent scale of the building. The landscaping also helped to minimize noise from high-traffic areas.

Square footage was dramatically increased by 8,000 square feet from the original 12,000, and, while walk-ins and ambulance admissions share registration and triage, they have completely separate traffic patterns, which never cross. Adjacency issues were addressed more effectively than they had been in the original department. As before, the facility was located near the diagnostic imaging department, but the mental health outpatient area was moved in order to be adjacent to the emergency department. The mental health department contains

Lynchburg General Hospital, Emergency Department, Lynchburg, Virginia. To service the 60,000 patients using the emergency department each year, the Lynchburg General Hospital required an expansion of its facilities, evident in comparing these two plans, one of the existing facilities, the other of the expansion. The expansion included separate entries for walk-in patients and ambulances, more efficient traffic patterns, and expanded services. *Courtesy Earl Swensson Associates.*

1   Entry
2   Security
3   Triage
4   Waiting
5   Reception
6   Nurses' station
7   Treatment
8   Heart room
9   OB/GYN
10 Lounge
11 Cast room
12 Emergency care
13 Isolation

1   Walk-in entrance
2   Waiting
3   Patient records
4   Triage
5   Trauma
6   Security
7   Cardiac room
8   Ambulance entry
9   Nurses' station
10 Treatment
11 OB/gyn
12 Cast room
13 Lounge
14 Emergency care
15 Eye room
16 Mental health area

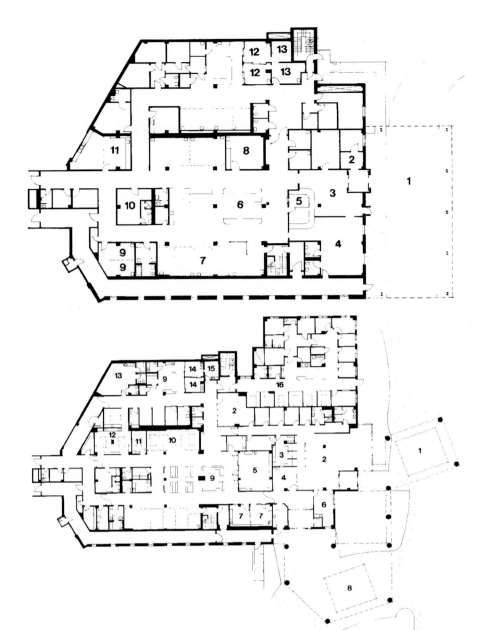

eighteen beds, which can now be used for emergency department over-flow in the event of a disaster.

EMERGENCY DEPARTMENT
MᴄMɪɴɴᴠɪʟʟᴇ Cᴏᴍᴍᴜɴɪᴛʏ Hᴏsᴘɪᴛᴀʟ
McMinnville, Oregon

Completed in 1995, the emergency department at McMinnville Community Hospital serves a small, rural market. However, this means that the ED is often used as a principal provider of primary care in this rural community. Access to the walk-in/primary care side of the emergency room is at the hospital front door and shares a canopy with the main entrance. There are two distinct entries for walk-in and trauma. Parking is adjacent to the walk-in vestibule, facilitating appropriate use of the

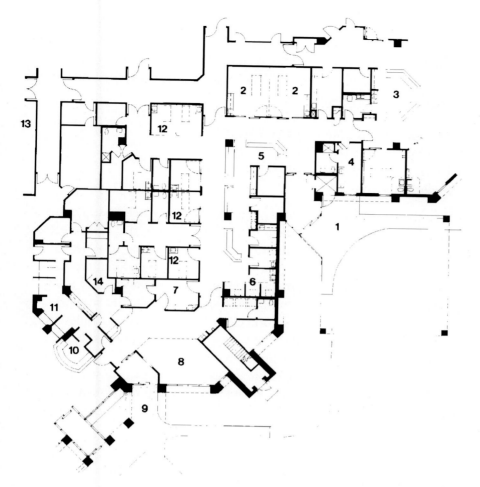

McMinnville Community Hospital,
Emergency Department, McMinnville,
Oregon. Floor plan. *Courtesy Earl
Swensson Associates.*

1   Ambulance entry
2   Trauma room
3   ICU/CCU
4   Lounge
5   Nurses' station
6   Fast track
7   Triage
8   Walk-in waiting
9   Walk-in entry
10 Reception
11 ER admitting
12 Exam room
13 Diagnostic department
14 PBX/security

designated entrances. Once inside the walk-in area, patients and families find a comfortable waiting room and easy access to the nearby outpatient mall.

Cross-training is essential in this small hospital, and emergency department registration is shared with central registration for the entire hospital. Triage is immediately accessible from the nurses' station, as well as from the registration area. The ED waiting room is adjacent to an outpatient mall, which offers appropriate waiting for outpatient services as well as dining facilities and a gift shop. Nearby, an outpatient pharmacy is available for filling prescriptions not only for the ED, but also for the integrated hospital and physicians offces.

The emergency department is flexible, with all primary care areas sized for overflow from the adjacent ambulatory surgery area. Fast-track care is available, and pneumatic tubes link the ED to the lab and pharmacy.

Although McMinnville is not a large facility, its provisions for trauma treatment are sophisticated. A decontamination shower and EMT area are located at the ambulance vestibule. All trauma units have breakaway glass fronts for easy access to trauma patients. ICU and CCU are adjacent to the trauma rooms, allowing intensive functions to be combined. All areas—primary, trauma, and ICU/CCU—share support areas: lounge, soiled utility, clean utility, and so on.

The emergency department is linked to an observation area and respiratory therapy unit, as well as the same-day surgery area. Although volume at McMinnville does not warrant imaging facilities within the emergency department, the imaging department is adjacent, and surgery is likewise in close proximity.

FREE-STANDING EMERGENCY FACILITY
SATELLITE DIAGNOSTIC/EMERGENCY DEPARTMENT
SEQUATCHIE VALLEY DIAGNOSTIC CENTER
Dunlap, Tennessee

When the local hospital in rural Sequatchie County, Tennessee, closed its doors, South Pittsburgh Hospital, in a neighboring community, created a diagnostic and emergency satellite center to serve the county. Sequatchie Valley Diagnostic Center is typical of the patterns of regional rationalization of healthcare delivery that are emerging across the country in response to cost containment. Sequatchie is a satellite facility supported by South Pittsburgh Hospital, a secondary facility about twenty miles away, and these two facilities are parts of a larger network supported by St. Thomas Hospital, a tertiary facility in Nashville.

Completed in 1994, Sequatchie Valley has the first licensed free-standing emergency facility in Tennessee. The idea was to create a facility to deliver primary, diagnostic, and emergency healthcare services and to

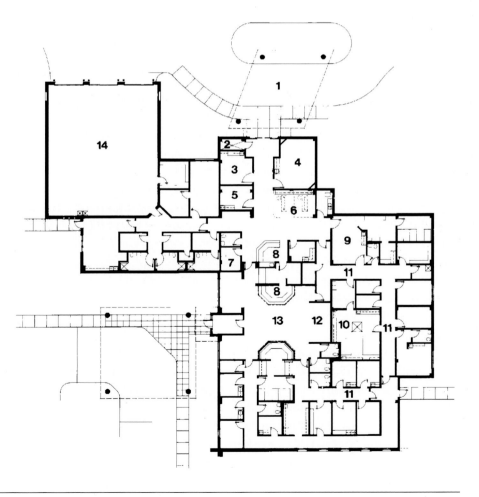

Sequatchie Valley Diagnostic Center, Satellite Diagnostic/Emergency Department, Dunlap, Tennessee. Floor plan. *Courtesy Earl Swensson Associates.*

1 Ambulance entry
2 Decontamination
3 Cast room
4 Trauma
5 Exam
6 Treatment
7 Triage
8 Nurses' station
9 Radiology
10 Lab
11 Diagnostic department
12 Diagnostics waiting
13 Lobby
14 Helicopter landing
15 Walk-in entry

integrate these with medical offices. Entering the facility through the main entrance, one finds a waiting area for emergency department walk-ins and primary care patients. Located off the emergency waiting area is waiting for physician offices and the diagnostic department, which includes a radiographic and fluoroscopic (R/F) lab, draw, pre-admission, EKG, and cardiopulmonary area. The principal thrust of the facility is primary care. Trauma patients would be stabilized and transported to the secondary or tertiary facility in the network. A helicopter landing pad facilitates rapid transport, but the Sequatchie center is also linked to the other facilities in the network through communication and data-transmission systems. The labs are linked electronically to those at South Pittsburgh. Registration is also linked to South Pittsburgh. Physicians' offices—designed for two doctors—share support areas with the emergency and diagnostic areas.

Since this area of rural Tennessee is growing, Sequatchie was designed for easy expansion, most likely to accommodate augmented diagnostic facilities. It is designed as a steel structure with an exterior insulation finish system (EIFS) skin, which brings expansion costs into the $90-per-square-foot range.

6

Diagnostic Imaging

■ High Cost, High Profit, Difficult Design Decisions

Diagnostics areas are the most expensive hospital and healthcare facility spaces to design and to equip. Not only are the initial capital outlays high, technology tends to evolve so rapidly that upgrading, retrofitting, and redesigning are inevitable and must be planned for. On the positive side are the extraordinary diagnostic—indeed, life-saving—benefits of state-of-the-art imaging technology and the potential for generation of revenue. "Imaging has always been a key profit area for hospitals. It will probably remain so," said medical consultant Greg Freiherr in a November 5, 1990 *Hospital* article ("Imaging").

The field of contemporary diagnostic imaging technology has evolved into a welter of modalities identified by an alphabet soup of acronyms:

▲ *CT (Computed Tomography—"CAT scanner")*
▲ *MRI (Magnetic Resonance Imaging)*
▲ *US (Ultrasonography)*
▲ *DSA (Digital Subtraction Angiography)*
▲ *PET (Positron Emission Tomography)*
▲ *SPECT (Single-Photon Emission Computed Tomography)*

And these, added to X-ray—the "conventional weapon" in the arsenal of diagnostic imaging—are just the most prominent contemporary and contemporarily emerging technologies. CT technology is becoming more specialized, particularly with the development of ultrafast CT, which allows effective real-time imaging. MRI equipment will also become increasingly specialized, with different machines used to diagnose different problems. Lay persons, architects, and even planners and physicians themselves are hard-pressed to assess precisely all the applications and benefits of each modality. For example, in recent years, requests for routine radiographic and fluoroscopic procedures decreased while nuclear medicine, ultrasound, and CT sharply increased. According to James B. Conway, radiology administrator at Children's Hospital, Boston (*Radiology Management* 4, no. 3 [June 1982]), a familiar comment in radiology departments is "The number of examinations we perform are decreasing, yet the staff is busier than ever." The reason for this is the decline in relatively brief radiographic and fluoroscopic examinations and the increase in longer, more staff-intensive CT, ultrasound, and nuclear medicine procedures.

This trend also has a profound impact on design. "It is not uncommon," Conway reports, "for 50 to 70 percent of a department's total examination volume (routine radiography) to be performed in 20 or 25 percent of its examining room space, since all of the new modalities require a considerable amount of space for a proportionally small number of examinations."

How much space? A typical CT installation requires 700 to 1,000 net square feet for 3,000 to 4,000 examinations per year, whereas only 250 square feet are required for 10,000 to 20,000 annual radiographic examinations.

Nor is it absolutely clear which among the state-of-the-art and emerging technologies to plan for—or plan most extensively for. As reported in *Hospitals* (Laura Souhrada, "Imaging Devices' Shifting Uses Affect Market," November 5, 1990), as the new technologies produce clearer diagnostic images, the boundaries between the various modalities and their appropriate applications blur. More and more, CT, MRI, and ultrasound are crossing over into what had once been designated the exclusive domain of one or the other. In the early 1980s, for example, CT was judged the ideal modality for studying the central nervous system. Now the more expensive, space- and design-intensive MRI has taken the lead in that role. CT is used extensively in studies of the abdomen and joints, but continued improvements in MRI—shorter scanning time and enhanced image contrast—are prompting many physicians to order MRI work for cardiovascular, abdominal, and orthopedic studies. Yet MRI examination in these areas requires the introduction of contrast agents, which turn the MRI examination into an invasive procedure, thereby introducing an element of added risk (and cost) not present in minimally invasive CT examinations. According to Jeff Cressy, M.D., assistant professor of radiology and director of neuro-MRI and neuro-CT at Vanderbilt University Medical Center, Nashville, CT is actually preferable to MRI for studying trauma cases, for stereotactic location of brain lesions, and for imaging areas of the head that are primarily bony (Souhrada). Furthermore, the development of ultra-fast CT allows for direct, real-time visualization of heart function without catheterization or the use of contrast agents. Various studies have documented that ultra-fast CT provides more specific diagnostic information in cardiology applications than MRI, and the technology is being scrutinized for non-cardiac applications as well. Ultra-fast CT may well come to displace angiography and cardiac catheterization as well as certain ultrasound and nuclear medicine applications. (See Theodore A. Matson, "Technological Considerations," in

Matson, ed., *Restructuring for Ambulatory Care: A Guide to Reorganization,* Chicago: AHA, 1990.)

Further complicating the choice among modalities are questions of cost. State-of-the-art MRI equipment costs about $2.2 million and requires extensive, elaborate, and space-consuming facilities to house it, whereas the most sophisticated CT equipment costs about $1.5 million and makes far less of a demand on space, construction materials, and design. These costs, of course, are reflected in the costs of the procedures, and, in an era of greater and greater cost-containment, the pressure is on to continue to develop CT as a first-choice imaging modality, despite the advantages of MRI.

In clinical terms, the choice is not a simple one. While Cressy points out that "there are times when MRI's diagnostic yield doesn't pay for the higher cost," William Bradley, M.D., director, MRI and radiology research, Long Beach (California) Memorial Medical Center, observes that "as many as 40 percent of patients with suspected disease of the brain will have normal CT scans but abnormal MRI scans" (Souhrada).

The likelihood for the next ten years is that MRI systems will be acquired by more hospitals, but that CT will not become obsolete during this period. Facilities that can afford both modalities will purchase both. Facilities that cannot afford both will face difficult decisions and will ultimately have to supplement their diagnostic capability by referral and outsourcing.

While physicians, administrators, planners, and architects puzzle over which big-ticket systems to specify and design for, ultrasound, wholly non-invasive (except for the emerging field of intravascular ultrasound), far less expensive, and far less design-intensive than either CT or MRI, is competing with these two modalities for some of the same diagnostic territory.

Ultrasound equipment was owned by 84 percent (and leased by 9 percent) of all U.S. hospitals in 1992, and, according to 1993 AHA figures, almost 76 percent of U.S. hospitals offered full ultrasound diagnostic services. The 1993 survey revealed that almost 66 percent of responding hospitals had CT scanners, while only 21.3 percent offered MRI. Nuclear medicine facilities (diagnostic radioisotope facilities) were operated by 54.8 percent of responding hospitals. About 82 percent of U.S. hospitals operate radiography and fluoroscopy rooms.

While ultrasound, CT, and MRI are the current mainstream state-of-the-art modalities, Single-Photon Emission Computed Tomography (SPECT) facilities are reported by 24 percent of hospitals responding to the 1993 AHA survey. SPECT provides three-dimensional radionuclide imaging information, estimates regional blood flow, and measures organ volumes. SPECT competes with another emerging technology, Positron Emission Tomography (PET). SPECT is two to three times less sensitive than PET, but it provides continuous data sampling of the heart in action, whereas PET requires frequent repositionings of the patient and recordings of several sets of data. SPECT also has the advantage in certain liver and bone-imaging applications. PET, however, provides some information SPECT and other technologies cannot provide, including the detection of metabolic activity in heart muscles that otherwise appear dead and the detection of brain abnormalities that elude other diagnostic methods, providing precise information on whether or not a tumor is responding to treatment.

The most significant difference between PET and SPECT is in cost. SPECT systems can be purchased for as little as $400,000-$450,000 (multi-head systems, which are more accurate, cost $650,000), whereas PET, which requires a cyclotron to make the radioactive isotopes used as tracers, costs from $2 to $5 million for the equipment and the installation. Approximately 2 percent of U.S. hospitals owned PET facilities in 1992, and the value of the technology (especially versus its cost) remains a hotly debated topic.

What are hospitals' motives for investing in expensive new technology?

A 1992 AHA survey cited in *Hospitals* (September 20, 1992) received limited response, but, of the 246 hospitals that responded to the question, "Why will equipment budget increase?" 80 percent replied that the spending was justified in order to remain up to date. Other important reasons were to improve the quality of care (74 percent), response to physicians' requests (70 percent), meet community needs (61 percent), prepare for expected demand (54 percent), remain competitive (50 percent), create new revenue sources (44 percent), provide more cost-efficient service (43 percent), and improve financial viability (36 percent).

Hospital diagnostic imaging departments must also deal with the rapid emergence of freestanding diagnostic imaging centers. A 1989 *Modern Healthcare* survey revealed that freestanding ambulatory care centers had increased 18.2 percent over 1987 levels. Freestanding centers that housed CT, MRI, and other radiologic modalities increased 25.4 percent during this same period. Individual hospitals, whether expanding, renovating, or building anew, will have to decide whether to compete with these facilities or cooperate with them. One technological development that may play a role in determining the number of hospitals that will invest in full on-site imaging facilities is Picture Archiving and Communication Systems (PACS). PACS is a system for storing as well as transmitting digitized diagnostic images. At the very least, PACS will facilitate medical consultation, allowing, for example, physicians in Chicago to discuss, in unprecedented detail and with real-time immediacy, a case in a hospital in Little Rock. Of greater long-term consequence is the potential impact of PACS on the regionalization of high-tech, high-ticket diagnostic modalities. It may be possible for smaller hospitals to own and maintain scaled-down versions of certain diagnostic equipment, perform diagnostic procedures on-site, and transmit the data to a larger regional facility for processing and consultation. PACS opens up possibilities for technology sharing among hospitals, among freestanding facilities, and among freestanding and hospital facilities.

Whatever the long-term trends may be, in the shorter term, indications are that hospitals will continue to invest heavily in diagnostic equipment and the building design that goes with the equipment. It is also likely that freestanding diagnostic facilities will continue to proliferate, which means that both hospitals and freestanding centers will have to realize the importance not only of providing for design that meets the technical and logistical demands of the diagnostic hardware, but that promotes the marketing of diagnostic services through a patient-centered orientation. As in the hospital as a whole, patients want to feel that they are benefitting from the best technology available, but they do not want to feel as if they are being swallowed up by a machine.

■ Hospital Diagnostic Imaging Departments: General Considerations

Designing space for diagnostic equipment requires specialized knowledge of the technical requirements of the equipment and effective, ongoing liaison with technical representatives of the manufacturers of the equipment being installed. Many architectural firms sub-contract equipment consultants. In some cases, the hospital or healthcare facility contracts these experts directly. A few architectural firms command the in-house expertise to specify equipment as part of the total design package. The discussion that follows is intended to outline new directions in the design of these facilities and deliberately avoids extensive technical detail.

Design for conventional radiography is relatively straightforward because the space required is self-contained. To be sure, the planner and architect must ensure that the facilities meet state and federal codes for radiation protection, and a certified physicist should be consulted regarding the type, location, and amount of protection required. But conventional radiography does not require the scope of "support facilities"—control rooms, equipment rooms, computer rooms, and patient-holding areas—that more advanced imaging technologies, principally CT and MRI, demand. CT and, even more, MRI equipment also require more space than conventional radiography just to accommodate the apparatus. While designers must cope with radiation protection in the case of conventional radiography equipment, they must design safely for high-energy magnetic fields in the case of MRI, the dangers of which are not as clearly understood, and the "minor" effects—such as interference with computer monitors (CRTs) on floors above the MRI or in other locations relatively remote from it—are likewise hard to predict.

Even in the conventional radiography facility, designers will want to create a patient-friendly environment—although in a conventional setting, even this is not as critical an issue as it is in more advanced radiography suites. Conventional X-ray and fluoroscope equipment is inherently less psychologically threatening to patients than formidable CT scan machinery or claustrophobic MRI equipment. For reasons of marketing and general reduction of patient stress, it is important to devote thought and resources to design issues of patient reassurance and comfort.

Another general design rule is to specify as much additional space in the technical areas of the "imaging suite" (the term architects now generally use to refer to the radiography facilities they design) as practical

Covington Medical Park, Tacoma, Washington. This medical center's design accommodates the use of mobile diagnostic units that can be added to the building's facilities as needed. This design element allows the center to provide more efficient use of and a greater range of services. *Photo by Gary Knight. Courtesy Earl Swensson Associates.*

to allow for cost-effective upgrading of equipment over time. While it is true that, in general, electronic devices are getting smaller, advances in diagnostic imaging will likely result in larger, more complex equipment, particularly in the case of equipment for whole-body imaging.

Particularly careful thought must be devoted to integrating the diagnostic suite within the overall plan of the hospital. The suite should be readily accessible to outpatients as well as to patients in various hospital departments, including surgery, cystoscopy, and emergency. All other things being equal, the most practical location for the imaging suite is on the ground floor. Here the equipment is most readily accessible to outpatients, floor load bearing and shielding are easier and less expensive to manage, and ceiling height requirements are usually easier to meet. In addition to engineering floors for the heavy loads of MRI and other imaging equipment and shielding, ceilings must be engineered with the appropriate supports and shielding for ceiling-mounted equipment. Ample raceways or interstitial floor space needs to be provided for ducts and wiring.

The imaging suite may accommodate the following imaging modalities:

▲ *Angiography*
▲ *CT scanning*
▲ *Diagnostic X-ray*
▲ *MRI*
▲ *Ultrasound*

■ Support Spaces

As mentioned above, advanced imaging technology requires an array of support spaces in addition to the rooms that actually house the diagnostic apparatus. We will discuss the special support facilities required for each diagnostic modality as we discuss the individual modalities. Certain support areas, however, are common to the entire imaging suite. These include:

- ▲ *Waiting and reception area*
- ▲ *Holding area*
- ▲ *Toilet rooms*
- ▲ *Dressing rooms*
- ▲ *Staff facilities*
- ▲ *Film files (active)*
- ▲ *Film files (inactive)*
- ▲ *Unexposed film storage*
- ▲ *Offices for radiologist(s) and assistant(s)*
- ▲ *Clerical area*
- ▲ *Consultation area*
- ▲ *Contrast media preparation area*
- ▲ *Film processing room*
- ▲ *Quality control area*
- ▲ *Clean utility*
- ▲ *Soiled utility*
- ▲ *Secure storage of drugs and medication*

Some of the above require discussion.

Waiting and Reception Area

The machinery of diagnostic imaging is truly among the wonders of modern medicine, and most patients realize this and are grateful for the existence of the equipment. That said, except for surgery, no other medical procedure creates more apprehension, fear of the unknown, and expectation of pain and discomfort than major diagnostic procedures. Even when these procedures don't cause actual physical pain, they do often involve prodding, poking, and probing by strangers, the forced ingestion of large quantities of fluids (as in barium studies), full-bladder discomfort (as in certain ultrasound studies), and similar emotional "insults." Add to this the overshadowing presence of heavy machinery made of cold stainless steel, capable of generating high dosages of radiation, and you have the makings of a very intimidating, certainly stressful experience.

Thoughtful design of the waiting area can help to alleviate some of the stress. Carpeting, upholstered, residential-style seating, grouped rather than arranged bench-style, pleasant wall coverings, and artwork all contribute to a feeling of well being. If possible, windows and skylights providing natural light should figure into the design to maintain contact with the outside.

It is important to keep the ambulatory waiting room entirely separate from the patient-holding area, which is for inpatients, many of whom will be attired in hospital gowns and lying prone on gurneys or sitting in wheelchairs. However, to the degree that it is possible and practical to do so, carry through as many of the "residential" design features of the waiting room into the dressing area and even into the actual procedure rooms. Avoid sharp transitions from the "outside world" to the "clinical world."

Holding Area

This area, strictly separated from the ambulatory waiting room, is designed as a waiting area for inpatients undergoing diagnostic procedures. It should include chairs, but also plenty of space for gurneys and wheelchairs. The name "holding area" unfortunately suggests an impersonal, even rather inhumane space —so much so that some architects, planners, and caregivers prefer to call the area "sub-waiting." The same degree of sensitivity to feeling that goes into the design of the ambulatory waiting area should be applied here as well. If natural light is available, exploit it. Wallcoverings should be cheerful and non-clinical. Artwork on the walls has a soothing effect. Since many patients here will be lying on their backs, consider the inclusion of a ceiling mural. If the design of what is most likely a ground-floor facility permits, consider a skylight.

At the very least, the holding area should be designed to minimize the disquieting effect of bustling activity. Gurney patients should also always have access to communication with staff, either through a call button or by being within view of a control area.

Dressing Area

Like the holding area, the dressing area should be entirely segregated from the ambulatory waiting area. Each dressing room should be equipped with comfortable seating and a *secure* place to hang or store clothing. Carpeting is desirable, and a mirror is a must. A magazine rack and, perhaps, a small-scale print or other artwork lend welcome touches of humanity and make any additional waiting required more comfortable. Once the patient is in a gown, it is highly desirable to allow him or her to wait in the privacy of the dressing room.

Staff Facilities, Offices for Radiologist(s) and Assistant(s), Consultation Area

These important support areas of the imaging suite should not be afterthoughts. As patient-centered design has become a key issue, so have staff amenities. A pleasant and humane working environment is not only vital for efficiency and cost-effective operation on a day-to-day basis, it improves staff morale, and serves to attract and retain top-quality staff.

The work of the imaging department is intensive and exacting. It is important to provide facilities for personnel to take breaks at prescribed intervals. Depending on the size of the imaging department, staff facilities may include rest rooms and a lounge with lockers. Nurses and techs often find precious little time to leave for meals. A token dining space within the lounge to accommodate "brown baggers" is appreciated. It is

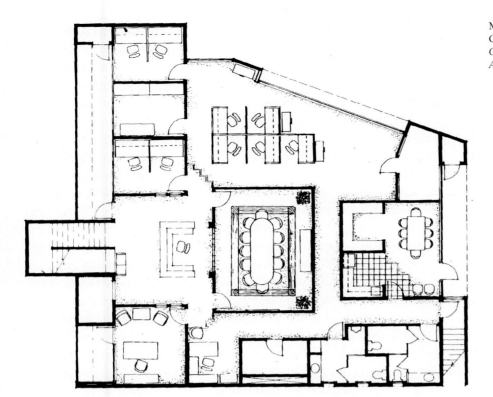

Modesto Imaging Center, Modesto, California. Floor plan, second floor. *Courtesy Anthony C. Pings and Associates.*

also important to provide an area specifically designed for consultation with referring physicians and others. This room should be located away from direct patient activity areas and should be private so that conversations will not be overheard. It must be furnished with equipment for viewing X-ray film and for studying the results of other imaging modalities.

■ General Considerations for Procedure Rooms

Different imaging modalities require differing M/E and structural support; however, two principles generally apply to all of these areas. The first is to plan for more space in each procedure room than may be thought *absolutely* necessary. The general trend is toward subminiaturization in high technology, but, as we have observed, it is impossible to declare with certainty that diagnostic hardware will likewise shrink. It may, in fact, continue to make greater demands on building space. The hardware and the people require space. A letter published in the July 28, 1977, *New England Journal of Medicine* is still relevant as a caution to designers today:

> In the haste to set up CAT scanners in hospitals and offices many have forgotten that these units were designed to serve patients. Because of inadequate planning . . . too many CAT scanners have been installed almost anywhere, generally being located in areas too small for the medical teams to care for the patient adequately. As a result many patients undergoing CAT scans have suffered inconveniences and even needless risks.

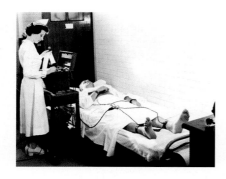

Fifty years ago, the dictum "form follows function" produced procedure rooms that served the activities conducted within. To our eyes, such environments seem hostile and sterile. *Courtesy Bettmann Archive.*

The second general principle is that the necessarily high-tech clinical areas of the imaging suite do not have to *look* uncompromisingly clinical. Some architects and designers bred on the form-follows-function dictum have expressed backlash sentiments about the trend toward introducing ideas from retail mall, hospitality, and even residential design into the hospital environment, protesting that these elements are merely feeble attempts to disguise the hospital's true function. Poorly done, such design gestures are, in fact, feeble. But, thoughtfully and imaginatively designed and executed, architectural elements that humanize the hospital environment do have a positive impact on healthcare, including patient well-being, staff morale and retention, and the facility's financial viability. Nor does the introduction of these elements violate the concept of form following function—if architects, planners, and administrators agree that the ultimate function of the hospital is to maintain or restore the health of the patients who use it. Architectural environments that separate mind and emotion from the physical body partake of the outmoded paradigm that also regards patients as sets of organs or physical disorders rather than whole human beings. It is not that one view is wrong and the other right, but that the former paradigm has shifted toward the latter. It is not a question of wrong or right, but of the reality in which architecture and healthcare currently exist or are trending toward.

Therefore, even at the "business end" of the imaging suite, design should be humane. Waiting room amenities such as carpeting are impractical in the imaging rooms themselves, but variable lighting, pleasant seating, cheerful but dignified wall coverings, and even artwork are not only feasible, but desirable. Since some imaging modalities require thick concrete walls and shielding, windows in these spaces are usually an impossibility. However, serene artificially backlit stained-glass "windows" (large transparencies) have been used to introduce an element of color, light, and interest into imaging rooms. Used in ceilings, such dramatic decorative elements provide a welcome focus for patients who must remain motionless on their backs while undergoing CT scans or MRI work. Backlit photo murals are another means of introducing an element of the outdoors into these necessarily isolated and "buried" spaces.

As a practical and humane consideration, patient toilet facilities should be clearly marked and available immediately adjacent to the imaging room. To promote efficient traffic flow, the toilet should have an exit to the area outside the imaging room. Ready availability of a toilet is especially important—and reassuring—to patients undergoing barium studies of the colon, ultrasound studies of the abdomen, or other diagnostic procedures involving bowel or bladder discomfort.

Angiography Rooms

Digital angiography requires about twice the space usually allocated to the conventional radiographic/fluoroscopic room. The minimum area of the procedure room should be 400 square feet, with a control room adjacent to it. Ceilings need to be high enough to accommodate suspension of

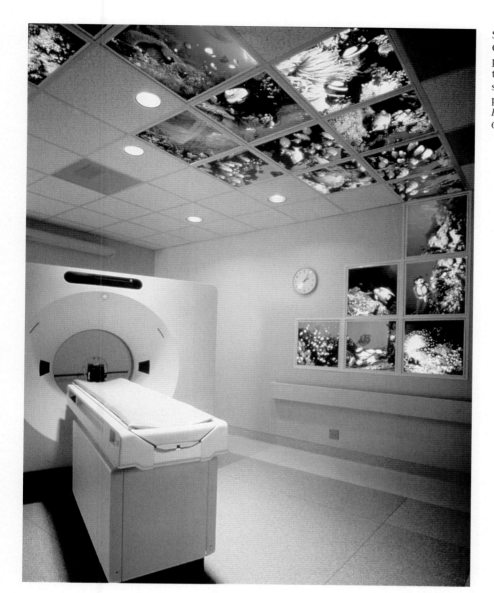

Scripps Memorial Hospital, La Jolla, California. In the windowless CT scan procedure room, cibachrome transparencies of soothing, underwater scenes provide a welcomed focus for patients who must remain immobile. *Photo by Steve McClelland Photography. Courtesy Jain Malkin, Inc.*

tubes, monitors, and other equipment by ceiling crane. Adequate provisions must be made for the extensive cabling required.

Since angiography is a real-time fluoroscopic procedure, the design of the room should facilitate viewing of the fluoroscope monitors and reduce operator and radiologist fatigue. Lighting is of great importance toward this end. A combination of fluorescent and incandescent lighting is appropriate, with background lighting provided by rheostat-controlled red floodlamps, which reduce eyestrain and enhance visualization of contrast-medium-filled blood vessels as viewed on the monitors. Monitors should be ceiling mounted and positioned ergonomically, so that operators do not have to crane their necks and rotate their heads for viewing.

The procedure room should include ample ready storage space, a photographic-grade sink, and a surgical scrub sink.

Support areas adjacent to the procedure room are the control area, component room, a sterile set-up room, and a soiled utility room. The control area and equipment room house X-ray generators, recording equipment, and other electronic gear, generally rack mounted as modules. A supplementary air conditioning system, designed to dissipate a minimum of 60,000 BTUs per hour, may also be housed here.

Cardiac Catheterization Rooms

Most of the design principles enumerated above for digital angiography apply as well to cardiac catheterization. Formerly, long-term storage of cine-films was a major consideration in designing the cardiac catheterization room. More recent technology uses videocassettes, and it is anticipated that digital imaging, with data recorded on tape or diskette, will play a greater and greater role in cardiac catheterization and angiographic procedures. Storage space will, therefore, likely become less critical. However, space for a dedicated computer workstation might be provided for on-site viewing, study, and enhancement of imaging data.

Both the digital imaging room and the cardiology catheterization room should have separate holding areas. Depending on the size of the imaging suite, these facilities might also warrant separate waiting rooms. Because of the invasive nature of the angiographic and catheterization procedures, segregation of inpatients and outpatients is critical. The possibility exists that cardiac catheterization patients will become surgical emergencies. Maintenance of sterile isolation is, therefore, of great importance. Sometimes patients are staged through the outpatient/same-day surgery area. In some settings, this is a mobile facility.

The CT Suite

The imaging room should be large enough to accommodate the formidable gantry and table assembly, ideally about 300 square feet or more in order to allow ample room for personnel to maneuver around the table. As discussed above, the designer can include many patient-centered elements to humanize the clinical nature of the space. Lighting should be variable, with bright fluorescent illumination available for setup and soft, rheostat-variable, background-level incandescent lighting designed for patient comfort during the actual imaging procedure.

Adjacent to the procedure room is a control area, which houses the operator's console, the radiologist's viewing desk, and, nearby, a laser camera. Until recently, a separate equipment room was required to house computer, transformer, and other necessary electronic components. Newer units incorporate the computer in the control or operations console and do not require a separate room. CT and other high-volume utility spaces require special detailing to hide cabling and computer wiring, which is not only an eyesore, but a physical—trip—nuisance.

It is desirable that the CT suite have its own holding area, large enough to accommodate two to four patients. Depending on the size of the imaging facility, the CT suite may also have its own dedicated waiting room.

Diagnostic X-ray Rooms

Conventional X-ray imaging requires a room of about 200 square feet, provided with a shielded alcove for the operator. Two special situations require additional design consideration.

Mammography, which may be available as part of the diagnostic imaging department/suite or which may be available separately in the OB/GYN department, ambulatory service, specialized women's ambulatory unit, or a free-standing facility, presents opportunities for market-driven design. Although physicians disagree about the scope of mammography as a routine screening procedure, it is likely that it will continue routinely to serve a significant number of women. The mammography unit should, therefore, be designed to appeal to women, and the emphasis should be on creating a patient-friendly and convenient environment. A 10 x 12 or 12 x 12 space is adequate to accommodate the required equipment, which makes few technical demands on design. Space must be larger if biopsies are also performed here. If windows are used in this room, they must be provided with blinds. For privacy, windows may be omitted entirely, but attractive wallcoverings and artwork are desirable.

Since mammography appeals to a particular and well-defined segment of the diagnostic marketplace, it is advisable to provide a dedicated waiting area for this service, including a gowning room adjacent to the mammography room—even when the mammography suite is part of a larger imaging department or freestanding facility. Again, the waiting area should be designed with women in mind and should suggest personal care values rather than create the aura of a clinic.

Depending on the size of the facility, mammography is often combined with ultrasound.

Ultrasound

Ultrasound is less costly than many other imaging systems. Many physicians own and operate such equipment in their offices, and ultrasound diagnosis services are offered in many freestanding facilities. Various hospital departments, including OB/GYN, emergency, and cardiovascular, are likely to have their own units. Unlike CT and MRI, ultrasound technology can be easily accommodated in a wide variety of settings.

Each procedure room for ultrasound examination requires as little as a 10 x 12-foot space, although 10 x 14 is preferable. No special control or storage rooms are required, and while many self-contained systems can print out an "instant photograph" of the ultrasound image, more detailed studies use film that requires processing, either in a dedicated (or shared) darkroom or in a daylight laser processing system.

In hospital diagnostic departments as well as in freestanding imaging facilities, ultrasound is heavily used. A cost-effective, non-invasive, and highly convenient modality, ultrasound has made inroads into the diagnostic territory of CT and MRI. Ultrasound can be used to study virtually any part of the body, except lungs, intestine, and skeleton, and, according to Mike Kamoroff of Diasonics, Inc., its applications are "limited only by the creativity of clinicians using it" (*Hospitals,* November 5, 1990). In most settings, then, designers will be asked to create facilities to accommodate a fairly high volume of patients, which means careful attention to the waiting area and to making each patient bay or procedure room pleasant, non-clinical, and non-threatening. Design and material resources are well devoted to patient amenities in this highly competitive area of diagnostic imaging.

MRI Imaging Suite

Magnetic Resonance Imaging generates powerful magnetic fields and powerful radio frequency transmissions. Both make very significant structural demands and impose rigorous architectural constraints. Various technical publications, including, first and foremost, those issued by the equipment manufacturers themselves, specify safety and other operating requirements. These vary depending on the type of MRI equipment installed, and researchers and manufacturers are continually evaluating optimal magnetic field strengths for various imaging applications. It is, therefore, impossible to promulgate any single standard to ensure safety as well as freedom from data artifacts, especially since the future will likely bring new equipment with new requirements. However, in general, planners, architects, and engineers must determine:

▲ The effects of metallic structures, vehicles, and electrical equipment on the MRI system; such elements can cause non-homogeneity of the magnetic field and result in imaging errors; this is a crucial design factor
▲ The effects of the magnetic field on personnel and equipment

Once these issues are addressed, planners, architects, and engineers must determine whether the MRI system can be retrofitted into an existing structure or whether a new facility must be built. (An interim solution may be provided by mobile and/or modular MRI units, which can be leased. Operation of such mobile units may help a hospital establish a need for the technology.)

If possible, the MRI suite should occupy a ground floor with no basement, thereby eliminating one dimension of the magnetic field's effect and the effect of structural, electrical, and R/F interference sources on the magnetic field. The weight of the magnet and, especially, the shielding many units require exercises tremendous load demands, which a ground-floor location makes much less costly to manage. The use of a freestanding magnet shielding dome reduces the structural shielding requirements, and new units may be totally self-shielded, requiring no additional structural shielding. Ground-floor locations also make it less costly to achieve the above-average floor-to-floor height MRI equipment generally requires.

Engineering studies are required to assess the effect of the magnetic field on personnel, operations, and structural members elsewhere in the building and in the vicinity of the building. A faulty installation can, of course, prove extremely costly as well as hazardous. R/F studies must also be conducted to determine the extent and nature of existing R&F fields, which can interfere with and distort imaging.

If the MRI facility is being installed into existing construction, wall openings and corridors must be of sufficient width to allow safe movement of the magnet during installation. The facility must also allow for total accessibility to the MRI equipment for maintenance and upgrading. If the magnet is of the superconductive type, it is important that replenishment of liquid nitrogen can be done conveniently and expeditiously.

The trend in MRI is toward smaller equipment, although some authorities believe that it pays to design for more space and shielding than may be required for the equipment that is to be initially installed. Although MRI may be getting smaller, it is very high technology, and, as such, it is subject to upgrading. More powerful equipment may demand more space. Renovation of highly shielded areas is extremely costly. It may be advisable to build—even over-build—these areas with an eye toward future expendability and upgrading to a more powerful magnet.

Support areas in an MRI suite include control rooms, equipment rooms (including separate storage of liquid nitrogen and helium dewars), and a computer room. The powerful magnetic field generated by the MRI device means that most of these rooms should be located at least twenty-three feet from the center of the magnet. A control room housing imaging recording devices must be at a distance of at least sixty-six feet from the center of the magnet.

Another important utility consideration is a dedicated cooling system capable of dissipating 400,000 BTUs per hour.

Given the degree of clinical crossover between the CT and MRI modalities, it is possible for these modalities to share such facilities as a patient-holding area and a darkroom. The darkroom must be outside the magnet's 10-gauss field.

A word of caution in sharing facilities. Entry into the fringe area of the magnetic field generated by the MRI must be strictly regulated and protected by a metal detector. No ferrous metal objects can be allowed near the magnet, since these might easily become deadly missiles. Patients with pacemakers or electronic dose-administering devices must also remain well distant from the fringe area. If any facilities are shared, the design must ensure that no unauthorized or unchecked staff members, patients, or others wander into the area of the magnetic field.

The MRI procedure room itself may range from a minimum of 325 square feet to 620 square feet, depending on the kind of equipment used and the strength of the magnet. The single biggest patient complaint about MRI examination is a feeling of claustrophobia and isolation. MRI is a physically painless procedure, but it can be a psychologically trying one. At minimum, the design must allow for adequate air conditioning, noise reduction, and ventilation, particularly of the cryogen that super-cools the magnet. As in other necessarily windowless environments, backlit photomurals or artificially illuminated stained glass artwork can do much to dispel any sense of claustrophobia. While circulation patterns should separate patients from technicians, the patient should be

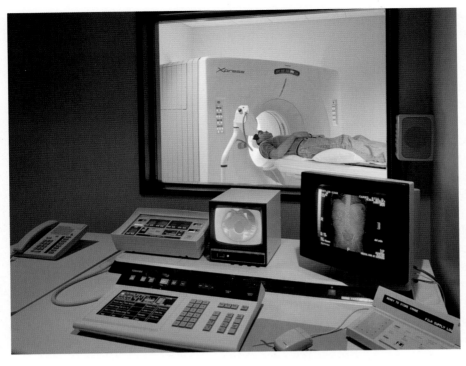

able to see the technician so that he does not feel that he has been shut in, alone, and abandoned. Another aspect of circulation is the inclusion of a quick, direct route out of the magnetic field fringe area. In the event of a medical or surgical emergency during or immediately after the MRI examination, it is critical to be able to move the patient quickly to an area where the magnetic field will not adversely affect such monitoring equipment as an EKG. However, much newer monitoring and anesthesia equipment is being designed with non-ferrous materials, which are not affected by the MRI magnetic field.

Covington Medical Park, Tacoma, Washington. Trends in the technology of diagnostics, in some cases, leads toward ever larger machines and components. The design for procedure rooms must certainly accommodate equipment of mammoth size and should counter the anxiety patients might feel in such spaces. *Photo by Gary Knight. Courtesy Earl Swensson Associates.*

Even MRI facilities that are part of a hospital campus are sometimes housed in their own building. A creative example of one such a facility is briefly analyzed in Jain Malkin's *Medical and Dental Space Planning for the 1990s* (New York: Van Nostrand Reinhold, 1990). Designed by Harvard, Jolly, Clees Toppe, the floorplan of the building is an oval, reflecting the pattern of the magnetic field. This is not merely symbolic, but makes shielding more efficient. The front portion of the oval is open, encompassing a landscaped reflecting pool that not only forms a pleasing and eminently humane entrance to the facility, but is a landscape buffer that keeps pedestrians and vehicles outside the critical fringe of the magnetic field. The reflecting pool and suggestion of a tropical garden that greet the visitor outside are picked up as decorative motifs inside the facility, which features photographs of gardens set against wall coverings and furnishings colored in a soft palette.

PET Imaging Suites

The cost versus benefits of Positron Emission Tomography (PET) continues to be hotly debated, and, at this point, only about 2 percent of American hospitals—about sixty facilities—operate PET facilities. In theory, the clinical promise of PET is great. Whereas state-of-the-art imaging technology offers an array of modalities for imaging organ structure and blood flow, they tell physicians little about chemical metabolic conditions. PET is a technology for imaging biochemical processes. While most scientists agree that PET is a valuable research tool, in practice, many clinicians question whether the information provided by PET is sufficiently valuable and sufficiently unique to justify the enormous capital expenditure required to install and operate a PET system. As mentioned earlier, the far less costly technology of Single Photon Emission Computed Tomography

(SPECT) may well provide much of the information that can be derived from PET.

Despite the questions and controversy, many nuclear medicine specialists are predicting what *Modern Healthcare* (November 30, 1992) calls a "burst of growth" in the use of PET. Much of this will depend on changes in reimbursement policies, since most insurance providers have not routinely reimbursed PET scans, and Medicare does not reimburse them at all. As of early 1994, however, more insurance providers were developing reimbursement policies for use of the technology. For the near future, PET is likely to be a regionally available diagnostic tool, maintained by certain large hospitals and in some freestanding PET imaging centers.

Like MRI, PET presents unique design requirements. The first step in planning is to select the equipment vendor, since PET equipment differs greatly in size and configuration. Planners and architects should also work with the chosen vendor from the start to plan the facility.

Space required varies from 1,500 to 2,000 square feet for installations in pre-existing nuclear medicine departments, to 3,500 to 4,500 square feet for new construction. Within this space areas must be allocated for the procedure room, a cyclotron to create the necessary isotopes, heat-exchange rooms, laboratory facilities, patient preparation rooms, a viewing area, and support facilities, such as a waiting room, offices, and a conference room.

As with MRI planning, load bearing is an important structural consideration for cyclotrons, heavy in themselves, that require heavy structural shielding. The floor plan must closely integrate the cyclotron with a "hot lab" and, in turn, the scanner, since many radioisotopes have extremely brief useful lives—a matter of minutes, in some cases—and transfer from the cyclotron, to the hot lab, to the scanner must be accomplished quickly and efficiently.

Aside from the design considerations to accommodate the technology, it must be recognized that a high percentage of any PET installation's patients will be outpatients. As with other sophisticated, high-ticket imaging services, patient-friendly waiting and reception facilities are essential. If the facility is freestanding—whether as part of a hospital campus or run as an independent service—provision should also be made for receiving non-ambulatory patients by ambulance. Given the expense of PET, it is likely that regional facilities will be called upon to receive critically ill patients from various hospitals.

Nuclear Medicine

While PET and some other, usually invasive, diagnostic imaging procedures may fall under the heading of nuclear medicine rather than diagnostics, and may be housed in a nuclear medicine department rather than an imaging suite, design for nuclear medicine will be treated in Chapter 10, "Ambulatory Care Design and Professional Offices."

Radiosurgery

Future trends are likely to include radiosurgery facilities within nuclear medicine departments, often on an outpatient basis. Current issues of radiology in surgery will be touched on in the next chapter, Chapter 7, "Surgery Facilities," while non-invasive radiosurgery and future directions in outpatient radiosurgery will be treated in Chapter 10, "Ambulatory Care Design and Professional Offices."

■ Patient-Centered Design in Hospital and Freestanding Imaging Facilities

Before we review examples of humane design for diagnostic facilities, we should take note of an aspect of the patient-centered or patient-focused approach that may have significant impact on design. Patient-centered treatment goes beyond providing a pleasant architectural environment for medical consumers. It is also a treatment philosophy based on the decentralization of caregiving. A prime tenet of this approach is that, whenever possible, service delivery should occur as close to the patient's bed as possible and should be administered not by a large group of specialists, but by a small cadre of caregivers, who, because they follow through with a particular patient throughout the course of treatment, provide the patient with great continuity of care.

In many hospitals, the patient-focused approach carries through to diagnostic imaging. Obviously, CT and MRI equipment cannot be trundled to the bedside. But some ultrasound equipment can, and so can equipment for bedside chest radiography—the single most frequently performed radiological examination. This has been made highly practical and efficient through digital storage of chest images, coupled with a PACS (Picture Archive and Storage System) and teleradiology capability. The digital storage of images and the ability to transmit those images virtually anywhere electronically is a trend of very great importance. Digital imaging makes it is not necessary to expose films, transport them to a central facility for processing, then transport them to the radiologist's desk for examination. Digital systems make processing unnecessary and transmit images to the radiologist as well as to whatever other physicians need to see them. If even this aspect of diagnostic imaging is performed at the bedside, the nature and design of the diagnostic imaging facility required will be affected. Space ordinarily devoted to routine conventional radiographic examination will be freed up for use with more advanced and space-hungry modalities. The use of bedside equipment also frees up more of the central diagnostic imaging facility for revenue-producing outpatient work.

Bedside diagnostic imaging is yet one more incentive for hospitals to develop strong ambulatory programs, which means that it is yet one more incentive for devoting funds and resources to marketing diagnostic imaging services through appealing, patient-centered design.

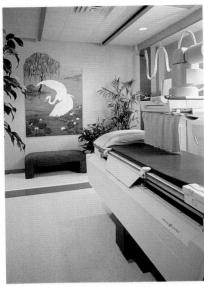

Morton Plant Hospital/Diagnostic Imaging Center, Clearwater, Florida. Interior Designer, Kathryn Stephens, A.S.I.D., makes imaginative use of furnishings and decoration in an imaging center for women. A room with pleasant colors and a residential feel serves to relax patients involved in what can be an emotional and stressful procedure. *Photo by George Cott/ Chroma, Inc. Courtesy Obrentz Design Group.*

DIAGNOSTIC IMAGING CENTER
Morton Plant Hospital
Clearwater, Florida

In 1988, Pauline Obrentz Interiors completed a renovation of the Health Services Diagnostic Imaging Center for the Morton Plant Hospital in Clearwater, Florida. In a story on the renovation published in *Contract* (vol. 31, no. 2, February 1989), Obrentz vice-president Kathryn Stephens observed that "we tried to make Morton Plant warm, inviting, unhospital-like—the kind of place you would want to live." The interior design uses motifs from the hospital's semi-tropical surroundings, with plants, a soft-colored palette, and plenty of cedar paneling. A woman's imaging center, which is a special department within the Diagnostic Imaging Center, is given an even softer appearance.

CENTER FOR NON-INVASIVE DIAGNOSIS
University of New Mexico
Albuquerque

Like the Morton Plant facility, the new Center for Non-Invasive Diagnosis at the University of New Mexico, Albuquerque, draws on locale for inspiration. This project, an MRI imaging and research facility, was new construction, designed by Westwork Architects and completed in 1986.

In an *Architecture* article on the project (Michael J. Crosbie, "Calming Setting for High-Tech Medicine," January 1987), Westwork's Glade Sperry, Jr., explained that his firm was faced with a decision whether to treat the building itself as a giant machine—which, in effect, it is—or to celebrate the architecture of the region. The design solution arrived at does a bit of the former while emphasizing the latter. The massive forms of the build-

Center for Non-Invasive Diagnosis/ University of New Mexico, Albuquerque, New Mexico. An effective use of the region's traditional architectural style hides the RF shielding required to operate the MRI equipment within and provides the necessary barrier to the magnetic field fringe. *Photo by Kirk Gittings. Courtesy Westwork Architects.*

ing echo the Southwest's adobe heritage but also serve as an aesthetically effective means of embodying the R&F shielding required by the MRI and enforcing the perimeter necessary to keep visitors and vehicles beyond the magnetic field fringe. The rear of the building consists of two semicircular walls, which not only complement the rectangular masses of the building, but, containing the magnet rooms, are shaped like the magnetic field created by the MRI and thereby provide efficient shielding and perimeter maintenance.

While the building makes use of large masses, it is domestic in scale and includes an entryway that echoes the courtyard of a local hacienda. An outdoor waiting area, in an alcove decorated with plantings, is well suited to the prevailing climate of the region and allows patients to maintain contact with the sun and the outdoors for as long as possible before undergoing the necessarily confining experience of the MRI examination.

Warm desert colors predominate on the exterior and in the interior, with a repeated contrast of high-tech polished chrome against natural materials. Sunlight in the reception area is plentiful. The principal idea here is to provide a reassuring, familiar entrance into what, for most people, is a most unfamiliar, even alien and frightening experience. The beauty of the Westwork design is that the natural, domestic, and regional elements are combined in a building that also celebrates the technology it houses.

MEDICAL IMAGING
SUMMIT MEDICAL CENTER
Hermitage, Tennessee

Summit Medical Center, completed in 1994, is a seven-and-a-half-story, 363,000-square-foot, 216-bed facility designed by Earl Swensson Associates with an emphasis on outpatient care. The hospital connects with a medical office building that rests on the first floor of the hospital. Because of the focus on outpatient care, inpatient diagnostics and outpatient diagnostics are separated, but overflow from one can be directed to the other as necessary. The layout of outpatient imaging is intended to keep the patient moving through the diagnostic area as quickly as possible, especially for such routine and heavily used procedures as fluoroscopy, chest X-ray, and mammography. The mammography suite has its own dedicated waiting room.

Adjacency is a major issue for patient-focused care and for work efficiency. The emergency department feeds into the inpatient imaging area; however, that department is also equipped with one X-ray machine for simple procedures. The catheterization lab is adjacent to surgery, and the entire imaging area is located near the pharmacy.

The outpatient waiting facility is totally separate from inpatient traffic, so that inpatient and outpatient traffic never cross. The primary waiting area feeds into a sub-waiting area, which feeds into the locker and dressing space. For added patient convenience, a pre-admission unit, located just inside the outpatient entrance, has its own chest X-ray room.

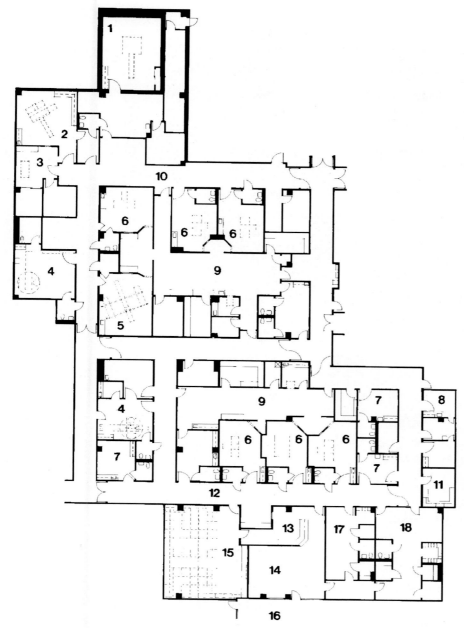

Summit Medical Center, Hermitage, Tennessee. In the plan for the center's Imaging Department, areas required for inpatient services are separated from outpatient facilities, but the overflow of one area can be easily directed to the other as necessary. *Courtesy Earl Swensson Associates.*

1 MRI
2 CT scan
3 Hot lab
4 Nuclear medicine
5 Special procedures
6 R/F (Radiography/fluoroscopy)
7 Ultrasound
8 Mammography
9 Work
10 Inpatient corridor
11 Resource library
12 Outpatient corridor
13 Registration
14 Waiting
15 Files
16 Main lobby
17 Men's locker
18 Women's locker

A chest X-ray is part of the preparatory procedure for most surgery, and the chest unit located in pre-admission means that most patients do not have to enter the hospital proper until the day of the surgery.

MEDICAL IMAGING

AUSTIN DIAGNOSTIC MEDICAL CENTER
Austin, Texas

The Morton Plant, University of New Mexico, and Summit facilities are associated with hospitals—although the New Mexico unit is highly specialized and physically separate from other hospital buildings—and Summit Medical Center is a good example of how even "mainstream" hospitals are transforming themselves to accommodate heavy outpatient

Austin Diagnostic Medical Center, Austin, Texas. A state-of-the-art multispecialty clinic features a strong emphasis on outpatient services as well as an inpatient component. The center has been designed to accommodate future expansion of outpatient services. The design includes convenient parking to the separate entrance for each specialty service. *Watercolor by Gerry Harvey. Courtesy Earl Swensson Associates/Gould Turner Group PC.*

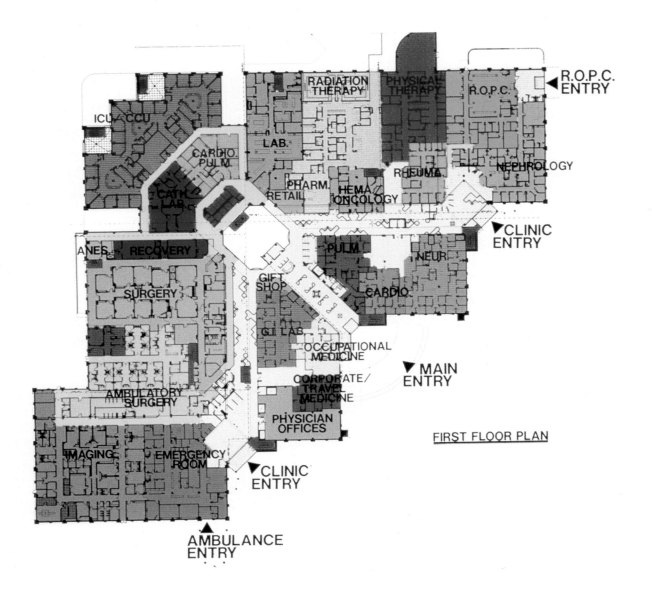

FIRST FLOOR PLAN

Austin Diagnostic Medical Center, Austin, Texas. Floor plan, first floor. *Courtesy Earl Swensson Associates/Gould Turner Group PC.*

loads. The Austin Diagnostic Medical Center, designed by Earl Swensson Associates in a joint venture with the Gould Turner Group of Nashville, and completed in 1995, is an example of another variation on the traditional hospital. It is a large multispecialty clinic, with 200 physicians, associated with a 150-bed hospital. The emphasis is on outpatient service, with all ancillary departments accessible from the outpatient mall as well as from inpatient areas, although the design separates inpatient and outpatient flow. Diagnostic imaging is integrated between inpatient and ambulatory services, but is also designed to limit cross traffic between the two. High-volume imaging services are clustered near the outpatient waiting area, which is subdivided according to type of imaging required. The imaging department is contiguous with the emergency room, and trauma and orthopedics have access to nuclear medicine, CT scan, and MRI in a seamless flow. Where it makes most sense for efficiency, some imaging is decentralized; for example, each nursing floor has its own chest X-ray and phlebotomy.

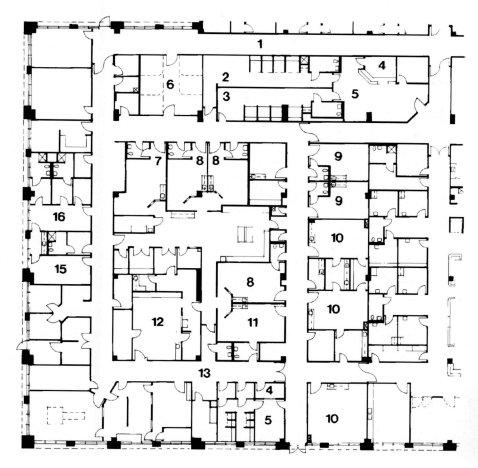

Austin Diagnostic Medical Center, Austin, Texas. Floor plan, Imaging Department. *Courtesy Earl Swensson Associates/Gould Turner Group PC.*

1 Inpatient corridor
2 Women's locker
3 Men's locker
4 Reception
5 Waiting
6 Holding
7 R/T (Radiography/tomography)
8 R/F (Radiography/fluoroscopy)
9 Ultrasound
10 Nuclear medicine
11 Radiology
12 Angiography exam
13 Outpatient corridor
14 MRI
15 Conference
16 Staff lounge

Modesto Imaging Center, Modesto, California. For this freestanding center, the architects found inspiration in the art deco style to construct a facility that is clearly non-institutional in feel and appeal. *Photo by Scot Zimmerman. Courtesy Anthony C. Pings and Associates.*

Modesto Imaging Center, Modesto, California. The traditional furnishings of the center counter the high-tech nature of the facility. Plantings and artworks further soften the environment. *Photo by Scot Zimmerman. Courtesy Anthony C. Pings and Associates.*

The design of the central imaging department at Austin Diagnostic Medical Center is accessible and appealing to outpatients, yet is also efficient for inpatient use, requiring a minimum of movement from one location to another. The unit is also flexible; as may be necessary, inpatient areas can take the overflow from outpatient areas and vice versa.

MODESTO IMAGING CENTER

Modesto, California

Hybrid clinic-diagnostic-hospital facilities, like the Austin Diagnostic Medical Center, as well as so-called hospitals without beds are becoming common features of the healthcare landscape. Completely freestanding imaging centers are also making their presence felt in increasing numbers, including centers that operate high-end technologies such as CT and MRI. In their design for the Modesto (California) Imaging Center, Anthony C. Pings and Associates created an art-deco-inspired look that reflects the high-tech nature of the building's function while introducing an elegant and sophisticated decorative element based on a familiar and popular style. As in the New Mexico facility, the result is a celebration of high technology that also emphasizes comfort and the reassurance of a familiar "fun" style from the recent past.

Color schemes are predominantly warm neutrals set off by a number of brightly colored, vivid artworks. Seating in the waiting area is on a large, curved sectional sofa, which imparts a domestic touch. Within the

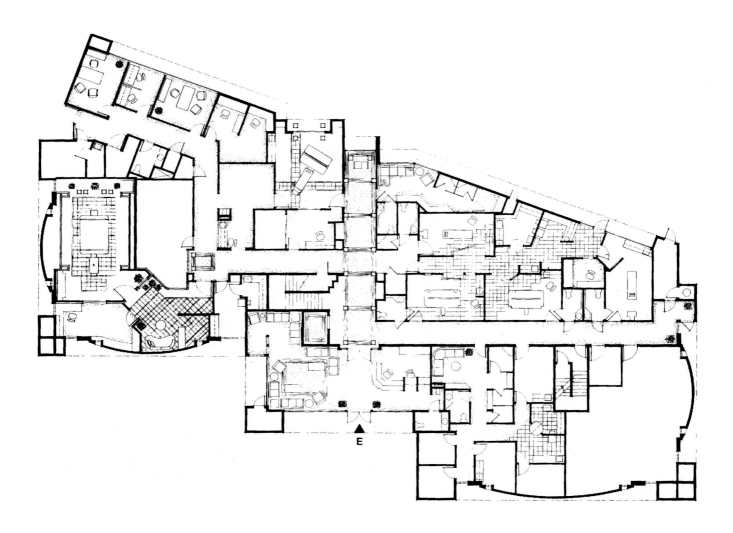

E

Modesto Imaging Center, Modesto, California. Floor plan, first floor. *Courtesy Anthony C. Pings and Associates.*

CT-scan procedure room, glass block in one section of the wall alleviates the feeling of claustrophobia and admits a modicum of natural light.

All design examples demonstrate the trend toward softening the alienating impact of high-tech diagnostics by means of local and even domestic metaphors. The new construction projects, in New Mexico and California, further demonstrate that these metaphors need not compromise the sense of the building's function, especially if that function is fully thought through, so that the building emerges not as a structure in celebration of technology, but as a celebration of technology in the service of human beings.

BAPTIST OUTPATIENT CENTER
BAPTIST MEDICAL CENTER
Jacksonville, Florida

Baptist Medical Center is a large urban facility, which saw the need for an imaging facility as well as cancer treatment center, eye surgery, and laser surgery center. Rather than revamp the inpatient center within the main hospital, Baptist commissioned Earl Swensson Associates and The Haskell Company to design a new outpatient building, completed in 1991, on property near the main hospital campus. This was the best solution for

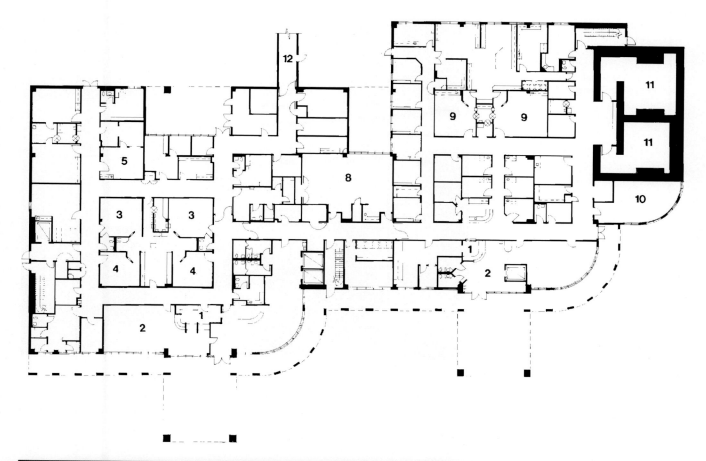

Baptist Outpatient Center, Jacksonville, Florida. Floor plan. *Courtesy Earl Swensson Associates.*

1   Reception
2   Waiting
3   R/F (Radiography/fluoroscopy)
4   R/T (Radiography/tomography)
5   CT scan
6   Patient holding
7   Ultrasound
8   Conference
9   Simulator
10   Subwaiting
11   MRI
12   Connector to hospital

Baptist Outpatient Center, Jacksonville, Florida. To accommodate an increase in outpatient services, the Baptist Medical Center built a freestanding outpatient facility close enough to the main building to share supply facilities. The covered walk at the front of the building leads patients to separate entrances for the cancer center, the eye center, and the diagnostic center. A connector at the rear of the building joins the outpatient center to the hospital building. *Photo by Dennis O'Kain. Courtesy The Haskell Company.*

outpatient accessibility, including ease of access and parking. While freestanding, the facility is close enough to the main hospital to share supply facilities with it, thereby eliminating expensive duplication of inventory and support services.

Imaging is on the first floor and includes two radiography and fluoroscopy rooms and two radiographic tomography rooms; these four areas

Baptist Outpatient Center, Jacksonville, Florida. In the waiting room of the cancer center, wicker furniture and terra cotta flooring reflect style traditions of the region. *Photo by Dennis O'Kain. Courtesy The Haskell Company.*

are supported by the same central work core. The imaging department also includes CT scan, nuclear medicine, and an ultrasound/women's imaging unit with a dedicated waiting area. MRI is available in an adjacent mobile unit. The entire imaging operation is proximate to the cancer treatment unit, which makes extensive demands on imaging facilities.

The facility was designed with flexibility as a principal goal. In times of low volume, one person can staff support, reception, and information stations. The design of the facility is readily expandable to accommodate future technologies and projected increases in patient volume.

7

Surgery Facilities

■ Planning to Meet Needs

Critical care centers almost always perform four general classes of surgery: major invasive procedures, universally invasive rigid endoscopy, surgical intervention that treats patients without extensive invasion (for example, balloon angioplasty, lithotripsy, laser procedures, and so on), and ambulatory, outpatient procedures. Too often, the design of traditional hospitals fails to differentiate among these adequately and efficiently. This chapter considers design strategies for accommodating all four classes of surgery, as well as an additional, intermediate class, short-stay surgery.

It is critically important for hospital planners to assess surgery needs before design—of new construction or renovation—begins. Today, in many hospitals, outpatient surgery makes up 75 to 80 percent of the surgery load. This means that designers must devote careful consideration to outpatient waiting and reception areas, staging and holding areas, and recovery needs. Waiting and recovery areas should also take into consideration the presence of companions and family members. In addition, even for surgical inpatients, it is desirable to provide separate staging and recovery areas for trauma versus non-trauma cases. Hospitals must also determine where such procedures as balloon angioplasty, certain types of laser surgery, and lithotripsy will be carried out. Many of these kinds of procedures can be performed in ambulatory facilities entirely separate from the surgical department, including in the physician's office.

Planning the number and type of surgical facilities depends on at least eleven factors:

1. Number of surgical procedures performed (based on a total of all patient beds and a study of the preceding five years in an existing facility, or, for new facility construction, based on projections extrapolated from comparable existing facilities)
2. Type of surgery performed (based on the above studies/projections)

Scripps Memorial Hospital, La Jolla, California. For the Surgical Family waiting area, interior designer Jain Malkin used warm woods, colors, plantings, and comfortable furniture to create an attractive environment for the sometimes anxious families of patients. The Stichler Design Group served as architect to the project. *Photo by Steve McClelland. Courtesy Jain Malkin, Inc.*

3. Average length of surgical procedures (based on the above studies/projections)
4. Number of inpatient versus outpatient surgeries (based on the above studies/projections)
5. Number of emergency surgeries performed (based on the above studies/projections)
6. Planned hours of availability of surgical facilities for scheduled procedures
7. Number of critical-care beds available for surgical patients (note that fewer than 20 percent require such beds)
8. Surgical needs of the community
9. Use rate of existing operating rooms (based on the above studies/projections)
10. Physician population (for example, is it heavy in orthopedic surgery, urology, etc.?)
11. Effect of emerging technologies on surgery: Laser and other minimally invasive surgery (MIS) techniques are already having a great impact on surgery. The trend toward MIS will continue and intensify, changing the design definitions of "operating room."

Throughout this book, we have reiterated the prevailing trend toward the removal of barriers that have traditionally set the hospital environment apart from the "rest of the world." Indeed, the trend toward ambulatory and short-stay surgery is part of the movement toward integrating the hospital and healthcare facility with the surrounding community and environment. However, even in the most progressive hospitals, the general-purpose surgical suite is one function area that still requires something like the traditional barriers. The surgical suite must provide a safe environment for the patient undergoing surgical intervention.

Toward this end, four conditions must be achieved:

1. The surgical suite must be relatively isolated within the hospital in order to exclude unauthorized persons.
2. The surgical suite, and, in particular, the operating rooms themselves, must be bacteriologically isolated from the rest of the hospital.
3. The surgical suite must provide instant access to all of the equipment, supplies, and instruments required for procedures without the necessity of leaving the protected area.
4. The surgical suite serves to centralize requisite staff, a condition that has become more vital than ever as the surgical staff has evolved into a coordinated team of highly trained specialists.

The surgical suite consists of:

1. Operating or procedure rooms
2. Sterile and non-sterile storage areas
3. Sterile and non-sterile corridors, to facilitate traffic flow
4. Support areas, including—
   a. Preoperative holding areas (of increasing importance as more facilities offer ambulatory and short-stay surgery, in which the patient is not admitted to an overnight bed)
   b. Recovery room (again, of increasing concern to designers, since ambulatory patients are released directly from this area)
   c. Satellite pathology laboratory facilities

There are four generally accepted surgical suite layouts, each designed to maintain a "three-zone concept," consisting of an unrestricted area, semirestricted area, and a restricted area.

The unrestricted area is the entrance and exit from the suite and often includes the holding or preoperative area, the postoperative area or recovery room, and dressing rooms, lounges, offices, and receiving or storage areas. The semirestricted area is a transitional zone into the operating room proper. It contains storage areas for clean and sterile supplies, sterilization, processing, and distribution area for instruments and equipment. The restricted area consists of the procedure—or operating—room itself as well as adjacent substerile areas, where scrub sinks and autoclaves are located. Storage areas for supplies that may be needed during procedures are also located here.

The four basic layouts that maintain this spectrum of isolation are: central (single) corridor plan, double corridor plan, peripheral corridor plan with sterile core, and cluster, pod, or modular plan.

The central corridor plan is the simplest of the four, but also the least flexible and least isolating. It is practical only for small surgical suites of two to four procedure rooms. All facilities are accessed from a single, central corridor.

The double corridor plan is usually a U- or T-shaped configuration suitable for five to fifteen procedure rooms along the periphery of the corridors, with the central area between the corridors providing rooms for sterile supply, instrument sterilization, processing, and distribution, and

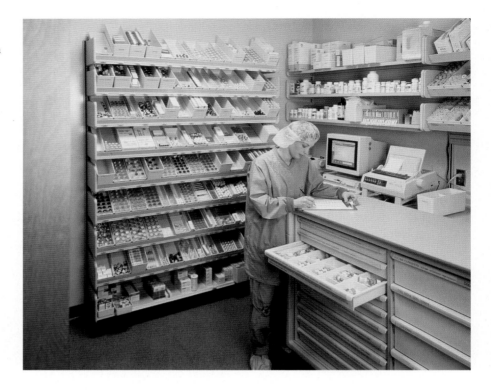

Milcare Satellite Pharmacy. Placing frequently needed supplies within a cluster, pod, or modular configuration of procedure rooms allows for the sterile distribution of materials in a manner that saves time and transport requirements. *Photo by Roger Hill. Courtesy Milcare, Division of Herman Miller.*

other ancillary functions. This configuration furnishes greater isolation than the simple single corridor design, and it is an economical means of sharing support facilities among a number of procedure rooms. However, it does not offer flexibility for later expansion, and it does not facilitate ease of communication (for supply and transport of patients) with other areas in the hospital. It also does little to minimize the risks of cross-contamination from one procedure room to another.

The plan that provides the most stringent isolation of procedure rooms from the rest of the hospital and from one another is the peripheral corridor design. This design divides the surgical suite into a non-sterile outer core and a sterile inner-core, the outer-core corridor ringing the procedure rooms, which, in turn, surround an inner core corridor that provides communication between the procedure rooms and a central sterile storage area. While this plan ensures a high degree of sterile isolation, it is very space-consuming and demands strict regulation of a somewhat complex traffic-flow pattern, thereby tending to increase the shunting of patients.

What is perhaps the most practical and flexible layout is also the newest. The cluster, pod, or modular design consists of a small number of procedure rooms clustered around a central core area, which allows for sterile distribution of supplies among the four procedure rooms via pass-through doors or windows. Each surgical suite might contain three, four, or five pods, and the suite is accessed by a peripheral corridor surrounding the entire suite. Not only does this design provide for excellent isolation, it is also highly flexible, offering maximum potential for future expansion. The pod or cluster plan is inherently elegant and economical and lends itself to a virtually infinite variety of floorplan configurations and overall building footprints.

■ The Procedure Room

General Considerations

Many shapes have been tried for the procedure room itself, but there is little practical reason to vary from the basic rectangle or square. Insofar as there is a recommended minimum size for the operating room, it is about 450 square feet. This has proved suitable for general procedures, although the trend is toward larger spaces of about 500 square feet. "Minor" surgery, cystoscopy, endoscopy, and most outpatient surgery requires less space—a minimum of 200 square feet, though 300-plus is preferable. Technology- and equipment-intensive surgical procedures, such as cardiac and neurosurgery, require 550 square feet of floor space. After careful study of the hospital's surgical requirements, procedure rooms of varying space configurations should be planned. The trend toward performing more rigid endoscopic procedures requires large procedure rooms to accommodate equipment.

Finishes for the procedure room should be as non-porous as possible, since rough or porous surfaces readily harbor bacteria. Floor and wall

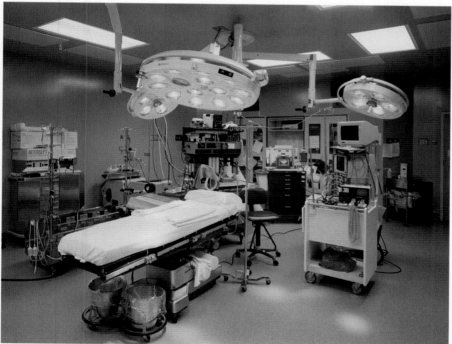

Scripps Clinic of Green Hospital, La Jolla, California. Modern surgical procedures quickly fill up even a large operating room with high tech equipment. Pictured here is the range and variety of equipment needed. Note the built-in casework and the sloping corners that facilitate clean up. *Photo by K. D. Lawson. Courtesy Earl Swensson Associates.*

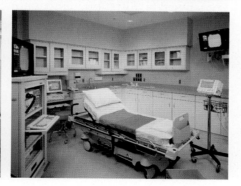

Bottom left: Millstein Hospital Building, Columbia Presbyterian Hospital. Another example of the space requirements for operating room equipment. *Photo by Robert Miller. Courtesy of the photographer.*

Bottom right: Mt. Sinai Integrated Medical Campus, MOB, Beechwood, Ohio. An endoscopic procedure room of the Mt. Sinai facility shows that the design requirements of a room for this kind of surgery—the use of which is increasing—are quite different from that needed for invasive surgery. *Photo by Gary Knight. Courtesy Earl Swensson Associates.*

materials should be applied as seamlessly as possible. The material must be able to withstand repeated washings with harsh germicidal cleaners. The most-favored materials at present are laminated polyester with an epoxy finish, hard vinyl flooring that can be heat sealed seamlessly, and ceramic glass panels that can be seamlessly sealed. Floor-wall junctions should be curved to facilitate cleaning. The top surfaces of any casework that is not built in should be sloped for ease of cleaning.

Color

Color in the procedure room has recently become a matter subject to some discussion. The green that is universally used in surgical gowns, towels, and sheets, is often used in a lighter hue as the dominant color in the operating rooms themselves. The green was introduced in 1914 by San Francisco surgeon Harry Sherman, who complained about the glare caused by the traditional white operating room appointments. He argued that green not only reduced glare and was relaxing—psychologically "cool"—it also contrasted vividly with blood and predominantly pink tissue, helping to keep the surgeon's eyes acute to these vitally important hues.

While many procedure rooms are still designed with green or other cool pastels, many others now feature warmer tones, including beige and pale gold in addition to aqua. Peach and rose tones have also been used, but such colors may inhibit quick detection of gross contamination and are, therefore, not ideal choices. According to numerous recent interior designers, operating-room green is perceived as sickly and depressing. Another trend is the use of more than one dominant color, a design element introduced to relieve the visual fatigue and lapses in concentration that may be caused by exposure to an expanse of a single color.

Color, of course, is a key issue in market-conscious, patient-friendly design. Therefore, the use of color in the procedure room should be considered not only from the point of view of improving staff performance by reducing fatigue and enhancing concentration, but also from the point of view of the patient, whose well-being (and sense of well-being) may be enhanced by alternatives to the sickly "OR green."

Ventilation and Cleanroom Technology

The current standards for the operating room environment address air-exchange rate, filtration, temperature, humidity, and the maintenance of positive pressure.

Current generally accepted standards call for a ventilation system that provides for 20 to 25 air changes per hour. U.S. Department of Health and Human Services specifies 15 changes, of which at least 3 must consist of fresh outside air. Local codes vary, some requiring 100 percent outside air, others allowing up to 80 percent filtered recirculated air.

Prevailing standards call for air filtration systems that achieve 90 percent efficiency in accordance with ASHRAE Standard 52-76.

Prevailing standards for temperatures are 65 degrees to 75 degrees Fahrenheit, with a relative humidity of between 50 and 55 percent. The humidity standard, which was established during an era of flammable anesthetics, is subject to reevaluation in light of the general adoption of non-flammable anesthetics. A lower relative humidity is less conducive to bacterial growth.

Finally, the OR should have a positive pressure of about .0005 inches of H_2O relative to the surrounding area. This is to ensure that only filtered air, not ambient air, enters the operating room.

In general, most authorities agree that the current prevailing environmental standards are acceptable for general surgery, producing a clean wound infection rate of less than 1 to 2 percent. However, designers of some recent operating rooms intended for high-risk interventions, including transplantation surgery and other procedures involving the introduction of immunosuppressive drugs, and surgery on elderly or infirm persons highly susceptible to infection, have advocated the use of "cleanroom technology," which borrows some of the techniques developed by high-tech industries (for example, manufacturers of micro-processor chips) that require extraordinarily contaminant-free environments.

Cleanroom operating room design may become increasingly common. In addition to more sophisticated filtration and pressurization equipment, it is likely that these rooms will use laminar airflow clean air systems rather than the conventional plenum air-handling systems. Plenum systems are essentially very efficient and highly filtered air conditioning and ventilation systems, whereas laminar airflow may involve vertical ceiling-to-floor or horizontal, ceiling-borne, wall-to-wall systems or yet other configurations. In general, these have a major impact on the interior design of the operating room, and the cost and benefits of laminar airflow versus plenum systems is currently a hotly debated topic. The use of sidewall delivery or high induction-rate ceiling diffusers pose the potential for contamination of the surgical zone. Panel systems with laminar flow avoid this potential. Low-return registers are also required by most regulatory agencies. Two per room, on opposite walls or corners, is the usually accepted minimum.

Lighting

Lighting in the operating room is obviously of crucial importance. Two types of illumination are required, general (ambient) room lighting and task lighting. These two sources must be coordinated to provide maximum visibility over the wound, yet provide a restful field of vision away from the wound, while still providing sufficient, glare-free illumination for the other members of the surgical team. Moreover, care must be taken to ensure that the task lighting does not unduly raise the temperature of the surgical field.

Experts agree that, while the architect or lighting engineer is chiefly responsible for specifying the ambient lighting in the procedure room, the surgeons who will use that room should be consulted on the type of task illumination to be made available.

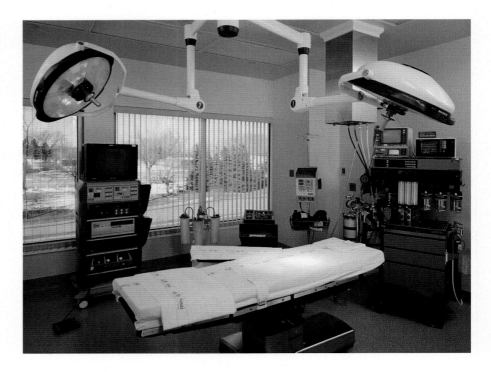

Mt. Sinai Integrated Medical Campus, MOB, Beechwood, Ohio. Windows to the outside world—covered by closed slats when necessary—provide variations in light in a procedure room. *Photo by Gary Knight. Courtesy Earl Swensson Associates.*

Relatively recent innovations in fiber optics continue to influence choices in task lighting, and needs and preferences vary depending on the procedure and the individual surgeon.

Finally, the color of the light is a significant consideration, since it is critical for the surgeon to be able to assess the state of the tissues accurately and without distortion. In a 1969 letter written to *Plastic and Reconstructive Surgery* (vol. 44, no. 5), plastic surgeon Dr. Hugh A. Johnson noted that he preferred to examine patients by natural north light—the kind of light long favored by artists for its absolute trueness to color. While it is unlikely that operating rooms will be constructed with northern exposure in mind, Earl Swensson Associates and other architectural firms have been encouraging the use of windows in operating rooms wherever appropriate and possible. It is often desirable to design operating rooms so that the windowed wall faces an enclosed courtyard. In any event, designers of lighting of operating rooms need to be aware of the importance of achieving a color temperature mix that closely approximates natural light. Recently, lighting has been developed that so closely simulates daylight, it is often used in mock windows. Operating rooms in which eye surgery is performed should not have windows, or, if windows are present, an internal slat system should be available to block out the light.

■ The Impact of New Technologies

While such advances as cleanroom technology make high-risk and ever-more "heroic" major procedures possible, the principal effect of emerging technologies has been to decrease the number of traditional inpatient surgical procedures. The implications for hospitals are obvious: either restructure significantly for ambulatory surgical care or give up that growing market to freestanding ambulatory surgery centers and private physicians who perform office surgery.

The major issues involved in designing freestanding ambulatory surgery facilities as well as hospital-associated ambulatory surgery facilities will be discussed in Chapter 10, "Ambulatory Care Design and Professional Offices." However, we will briefly review the relevant technologies here for their impact on the market and design of inpatient surgical facilities.

Endoscopic Surgery

One of the surgical technologies that is now prompting hospitals to reshape their surgical service strategies is endoscopic surgery. According to *Hospitals* (May 5, 1992), by 1995, endoscopic surgery will be used in 90 percent of cholecystectomies, prostate cancer stagings, and certain lung procedures. It will be used in 80 percent of kidney removals, and in 70 percent of appendectomies, hysterectomies, and hernia repairs. Endoscopic surgery is already playing a significant role in such procedures as vagotomy and bowel and colon resections. Over the past five years, 40 percent of bowel procedures use the endoscope. Some endoscopic surgery procedures can be performed on an ambulatory basis, while others —for example, hernia repair—are conducive to short stays, a much smaller surgical wound, and less intensive anesthesia. While most surgeons are enthusiastic about the potential of endoscopic surgery, a significant number caution both patients and practitioners to beware of uncritical acceptance of the technique in all situations. However, even the most skeptical surgeons compare the magnitude of the continuing impact of endoscopic surgery to the impact of anesthesia, introduced a century ago.

Gynecologists were among the first to make widespread use of laparoscopes, chiefly to perform tubal ligations and to diagnose pelvic pain and fertility problems. As fiber optics and surgical instruments were developed to use in conjunction with the laparoscope, surgical procedures began to take their place beside the diagnostic uses. Coupled with surgical laser technology, endoscopic surgery continues to expand further.

Several hospitals across the nation have already opened endoscopic surgery facilities, and many more will be following. In 1991, for example, Nashville's Baptist Hospital opened an 8,000-square-foot laparoscopic and laser facility with four operating rooms (and two more planned for expansion), recovery rooms, and support facilities that include conference and observation rooms for teaching purposes. It is expected that, eventually, 95 percent of Baptist Hospital's gynecological surgery will be performed at the facility, and 80 to 90 percent of the surgery there will be done on an outpatient basis.

Arthroscopy

Arthroscopy uses a technology similar to the laparoscope to permit small-incision, ambulatory or short-stay surgery on joints. The nature of the surgery is such that it might be offered not only in hospital ambulatory surgery facilities and freestanding facilities, but in dedicated sports medicine departments or freestanding sports medicine clinics.

Laser Surgery

Numerous laser procedures can be performed outside of an operating room, in a physician's office, or in a special procedure room that is much smaller than a conventional operating room. However, various major invasive procedures employing lasers do require a more-or-less conventional operating room specially modified for laser use. The modifications consist mainly in designing or adapting the ceiling for mounting microscopes and video monitoring equipment. ORs intended for cystoscopy and other minor procedures can be as small as 14 by 14 feet. Many other procedures can be accommodated in the more or less standard 18-by-18-foot procedure room, although 20 by 20 feet is required for CO_2 lasers, which are equipped with a smoke evacuator.

Certain laser types, such as the endoscopic Nd:Yag laser, have special power requirements, which need to be addressed in the M/E facilities of the procedure room.

Finally, special consideration must be given to finishes in laser procedure rooms and to minimizing vibration. Walls in laser rooms cannot be reflective; therefore, high-gloss epoxy-base paints must be avoided, and tile or vinyl work should have a buff finish in medium tones rather than light colors. The walls must be free from glass or windows, which could reflect and bounce the laser beam. The laser procedure room, especially when the laser is used in eye surgery, must not be subject to vibration. This is an issue that must be addressed in terms of materials and adjacencies.

Non-Invasive Radiosurgery

Nuclear medicine departments perform non-invasive radiosurgery procedures primarily on malignancies of the brain. These include "gamma knife" surgery, in which cobalt radiation is carefully directed at the malignancy, and a newer technology, stereotactic radiosurgery, in which radiation is directed at the tumor by means of a special skull-positioning headset that focuses the radiation directly and exclusively on the malignancy. The gamma knife procedure requires a linear accelerator and radioactive cobalt isotope fuel, as well as the various support and shielding measures that go along with this. Some stereotactic devices use microwave-generated energy, which requires no fuel and, therefore, no accelerator.

Design of non-invasive radiosurgery facilities is discussed under Oncology Facilities in Chapter 10, "Ambulatory Care Design and Professional Offices."

Lithotripsy

Lithotripsy is an alternative to surgery for the treatment of kidney stones. In hospitals, this treatment modality is generally assigned to the radiology department. It can even be adapted as a mobile technology. However, a recovery room should be adjacent or nearby.

■ Restructuring the Surgical Department for Ambulatory or Short-Stay Procedures

In Chapter 10, "Ambulatory Care Design and Professional Offices, we will explore design alternatives for hospital-associated dedicated ambulatory surgery facilities and freestanding ambulatory surgery facilities. However, many hospitals are choosing to "mainstream" inpatients and outpatients, adapting their traditional inpatient surgical services to serve both inpatient and ambulatory patients.

Usually, this entails an enlargement and upgrading of preoperative (holding) and postoperative (recovery) facilities to create a more patient-friendly environment. The chief complaint among outpatients in the mainstream arrangement is a perception that the recovery-room nursing staff devotes more time to the inpatients than outpatients. This perception is almost certainly accurate, because the outpatients have generally been subjected to less anesthesia and are more conscious and alert and, therefore, require less attention and monitoring than the inpatients.

Mainstreaming can be a workable interim alternative in hospitals that, for various reasons, are unable to create dedicated outpatient surgery facilities. In smaller hospitals and in hospitals located in medically underserved areas, integrating the outpatient and inpatient surgical services may also be an economical means of adapting to the changing surgery marketplace. However, in larger hospitals and more highly competitive markets, the establishment of a discrete ambulatory surgery facility is the prevailing trend and, in many cases, is probably crucial to remaining competitive or even financially viable.

The Holding Room

Before the 1980s, it was common either to transport patients directly from their rooms—or the ward—to surgery, often holding them for a time, on a gurney, out in a hallway. During the 1980s, dedicated preoperative "holding rooms" began to become accepted practice as a more humane alternative to the hallway and as a way of ensuring preoperative continuity of care under members of the perioperative nursing staff. With the increase in ambulatory and short-stay surgery, these holding areas have become increasingly important, since many patients are admitted directly to them. In most cases, a formal staging area makes it unnecessary to admit surgical patients the day before the scheduled procedure.

An even more recent trend is the transformation of the "holding room" into a "preoperative testing center" or a "preoperative care unit."

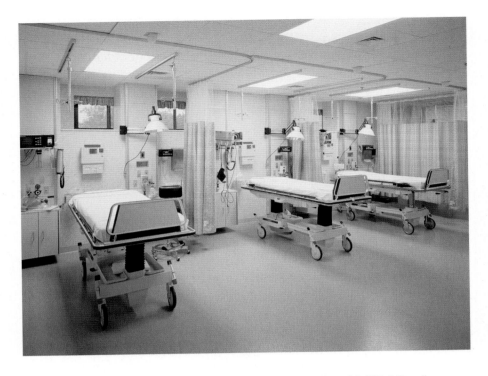

Lynchburg General Hospital, Lynchburg, Virginia. Recovery room facilities need to accommodate patients' after-effects of anesthesia. Bold colors and harsh light make recovery unpleasant. The Lynchburg hospital room provides natural light which aids caregivers in assessing patient recovery. *Photo by Jonathan Hillyer. Courtesy Earl Swensson Associates.*

The change in terminology is significant in and of itself. "Holding" implies a passive form of workflow management, and many patients might well question if there is any real difference between the concept of a holding room and, say, a corral. In contrast, a preoperative testing center or care unit implies active steps toward preparation for surgery. Such units, where preoperative evaluation is performed, can do much to address the gap in care that might result when a patient is admitted to surgery on the day of the procedure rather than on the day before.

Recovery Room (Post-Anesthesia Care Unit)

The patient leaves the OR and then undergoes the early stages of recovery in a single-bed cubicle. Light levels should be relatively low, and soothing indirect light is best. Somber color schemes should be avoided, but designers need to be aware that patients recovering from anesthesia often suffer headache and nausea rather like a bad hangover. Irritating lights or bold color patterns can aggravate this unpleasant condition. Designers also need to be careful about specifying fluorescent lighting in recovery areas. It is important that the lighting approximate natural light as much as possible, since caregivers can tell a great deal about the patient's condition from his skin tone.

An alternative to curtained recovery cubicles are small rooms with sliding glass doors. Closed, the doors provide quiet and a sense of privacy, yet they also permit the nursing staff to monitor recovery unobtrusively and efficiently.

After the patient is sufficiently alert and stabilized, he is either transported to his room, if he is an inpatient, or to a second-stage recovery area, variously called the discharge holding area or discharge lounge.

Discharge Holding Area/Lounge

Ambulatory surgery patients can generally be discharged directly from the recovery room, but many short-stay surgical patients and even certain same-day surgical patients cannot be safely discharged directly from recovery. Depending on the occupancy rate at the hospital in question, it may well be practically or financially unfeasible to transfer these patients to a surgical bed. A recent answer to this dilemma is the discharge holding area or discharge lounge. This is a comfortable area, pleasingly decorated and equipped with such amenities as recliner-style chairs, television, and reading matter, as well as provision for meals and the administration of any required medication. Patients in the lounge are monitored by licensed practical nursing staff and patient care assistants. The discharge holding area or lounge can also serve as the site of post-operative patient education—a relaxed place for a caregiver to review with the patient any necessary postoperative self-care steps. Of course, the discharge holding area can also be used by ambulatory patients who, for one reason or another, are not quite ready to go home, but have sufficiently recovered no longer to warrant occupying valuable recovery room space and recovery staff resources. Thus the discharge holding area provides a considerable measure of flexibility in a surgery unit that serves a mix of inpatient, same-day, short-stay, and ambulatory patients.

In 1988, New York's Lenox Hill Hospital introduced a combined early morning admission/late discharge/transfusion facility. The 2,000-square-foot space receives surgical patients as early as 6:30 in the morning, a time when surgical beds are in short supply, because patients scheduled for discharge have not yet left. The area makes it unnecessary for early-admission patients to be admitted the night before. The area also serves as a discharge lounge.

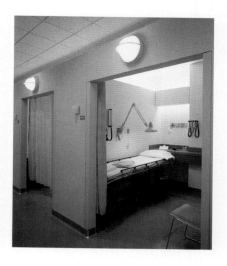

Lenox Hill Hospital, New York, New York. The hospital's combined early morning admission/late discharge/transfusion facility places surgical patients who arrive as early as 6:30 A.M. in private cubicles for presurgery preparation that can also serve as outpatient transfusion procedure rooms. *Photo by Norman McGrath. Courtesy Norman Rosenfeld Architects.*

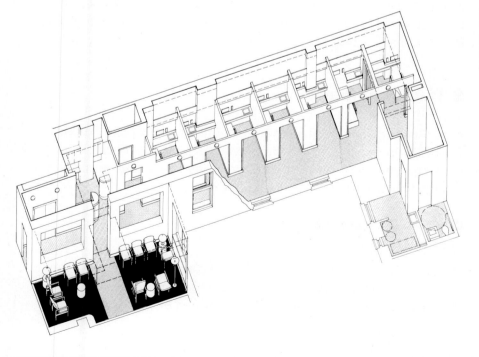

Lenox Hill Hospital, New York, New York. An axonometric view of the hospital's early morning admission/late discharge unit. *Courtesy Norman Rosenfeld Architects.*

Fresno Surgery Center, Fresno, California. This freestanding ambulatory and short-stay surgery center provides the luxury setting of a first-class hotel at a savings in costs for a comparable hospital stay. *Photo by Josef Kasparowitz/Kasparowitz Architectural Photography. Courtesy Fresno Surgery Center.*

Hospital planners reasoned that, as an early admission and late discharge facility, the area would furnish first and last impressions of Lenox Hill Hospital. As such, they commissioned Norman Rosenfeld Architects to create an extremely comfortable waiting area, elegantly furnished to resemble a large living room and featuring a wood parquet floor, wood counters, incandescent downlights, and fresh-cut flowers. Seating is comfortable and includes some recliners for newly discharged patients, a small television set in one corner, and table lamp illumination. Presurgical admission includes private cubicles for presurgery preparation. Similar cubicles also serve patients requiring transfusion, and, indeed, the presurgical prep cubicles can double as transfusion cubicles during slack periods in surgical admission and discharge.

■ Recovery/Discharge Trends

A number of hospitals have addressed discharge from same-day and short-stay surgical procedures by either contracting with nearby hotels or entering into joint ventures with hotel developers. The hotel stay is also an alternative to an extended hospital stay for patients who require more care and supervision than they can be given in the home setting, but do not require the more intensive care a hospital setting provides.

Another recovery/discharge trend is exemplified in the physician-owned Fresno Recovery Care Center, a 24,000-square-foot freestanding ambulatory and short-stay surgery center that provides recovery care for patients who require up to 72 hours of postoperative care, but who do not need the intensive care a full hospital setting can provide. The attraction, besides savings over hospital-room rates, is a hotel-like atmosphere and level of service. The rooms are beautifully appointed, with ample and comfortable seating provided in addition to the bed. Wood paneling and architectural details ensure that no "institutional" note intrudes. The Fresno Recovery Care Center is a bold introduction of hospitality design into a hospital setting and likely heralds an increasingly visible trend.

■ Two Examples

We close the chapter with an overview of two contemporary surgical departments, one in a large metropolitan hospital, the other a specialized hand and microsurgery facility. Design examples for surgery facilities in an ambulatory setting will be found in Chapter 10.

CENTENNIAL MEDICAL CENTER
Nashville, Tennessee

Designed by Earl Swensson Associates and completed in 1994, Centennial is a large urban medical center containing a surgery department that encompasses fifteen operating rooms supported by seventeen recovery

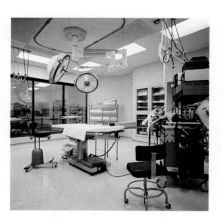

The Atrium at Centennial Medical Center, Nashville, Tennessee. In some instances, windows in an operating room are feasible. Note that to facilitate room cleaning, corners are sloped and casework is built in. *Photo by Gary Knight. Courtesy Earl Swensson Associates.*

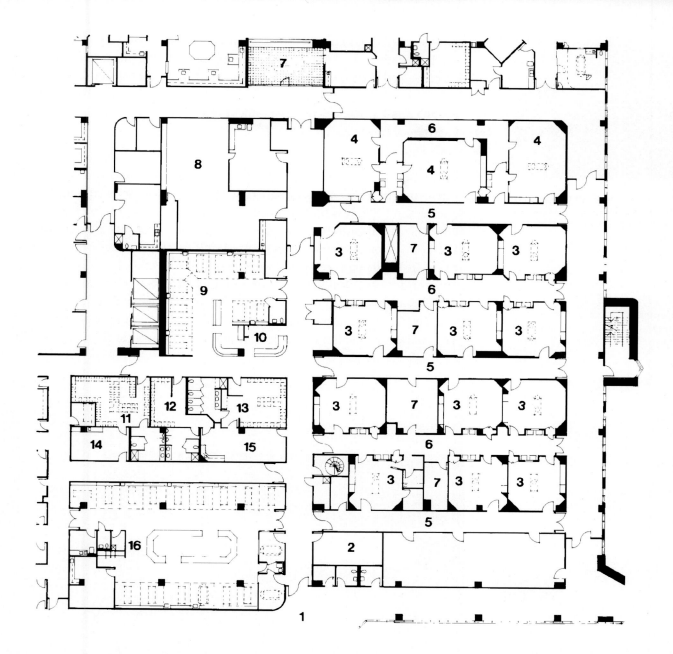

beds. Immediately adjacent to the surgery facilities is a cardiac Special Intensive Care Unit (SICU) with ten beds.

The ORs, located on the second floor, are set up so that specific surgery disciplines may work a group of ORs. The procedure rooms are clustered around staff core areas in groups of three. Patient access to the rooms is dedicated, and the department itself is accessible to an outer service support corridor, which facilitates housekeeping, materials delivery, pharmacy, and other support services without violating sterile areas. Similarly, staff lounges and change facilities are also located at the periphery of the department. The public, vendors, patient families, and other individuals can be met at the periphery without penetrating patient areas.

Patient holding is set up at the nucleus of the department as a control center that is back-to-back with a control desk for holding and scheduling. This nucleus area receives outpatients from the first floor and

Centennial Medical Center, Nashville, Tennessee. Floor plan. *Courtesy Earl Swensson Associates.*

1 Family waiting
2 Pharmacy
3 Operating room
4 Heart operating room
5 Patient corridor
6 Staff corridor
7 Clean storage
8 Work
9 Patient holding
10 Nurses' station
11 Men's/physicians' lockers
12 Male staff lockers
13 Female staff lockers
14 Physicians' lounge
15 Staff lounge
16 Recovery

Centennial Medical Center, Nashville, Tennessee. *Computer rending by Kerry Foth. Courtesy Earl Swensson Associates.*

Centennial Medical Center, Nashville, Tennessee. Floor plan, second floor. *Courtesy Earl Swensson Associates.*

inpatients from the floors above. To increase efficiency, sterile services are located adjacent to surgery. These are supplied from central sterile support, located above, via a clean-and-soiled dumbwaiter system.

HAND AND MICROSURGERY SERVICES

COLUMBIA DOCTORS HOSPITAL

Little Rock, Arkansas

Columbia Doctors Hospital's new surgery facility for hand and microsurgery services was designed by Earl Swensson Associates and completed 1992. It is built around a central core concept to increase efficiency, control traffic, and provide higher levels of infection control. Each of the four ORs in this specialized unit have two doors—an entrance from the sterile core and one from the non-sterile main hallway. Patients enter and leave through the "contaminated" doorway. Contaminated supplies are also removed through it. The sterile entrance off the core is reserved for sterile supplies (case carts) and scrubbed-and-gowned staff. The sterile core facilitates traffic flow and OR turnaround time. Because of

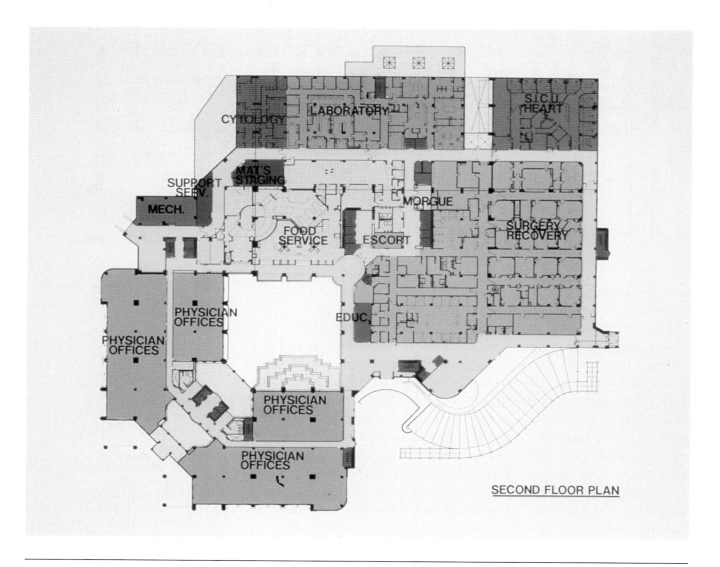

SECOND FLOOR PLAN

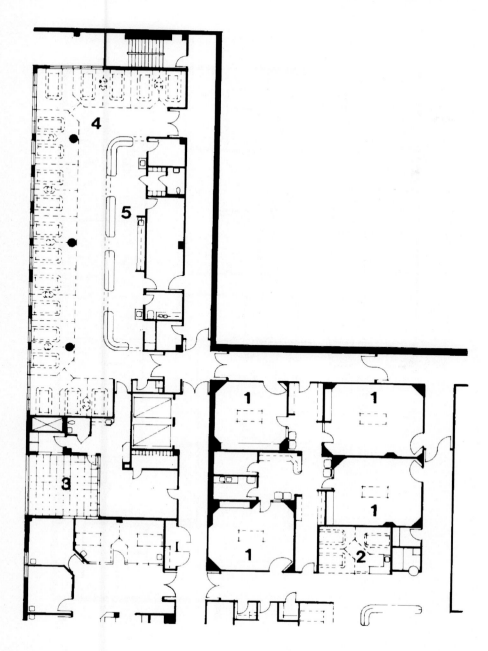

Columbia Doctors Hospital, Little
Rock, Arkansas. Floor plan, Hand and
Microsurgery Services, second floor.
Courtesy Earl Swensson Associates.

1   Operating room
2   Anesthesia work
3   Roof terrace
4   Recovery
5   Nurses' station

the specialized equipment used in hand and microsurgery, sterilization of
fragile instruments is carried out within the suite.

An elevator leads directly from the first floor registration and admit-
testing area to the pre-op holding area on the second floor of the hospital.
The first floor area is divided into three separate areas: hand and
microsurgery, pediatric surgery, and outpatient surgery. The division
reflects the needs of the nursing staff. However, all three areas share
support services, and, when patient census is high in one area, the overflow can be directed to another.

Recovery, located adjacent to surgery, consists of eighteen beds—
sufficient to accommodate the caseload of a facility designated as the
region's center for hand and microsurgery. To fit all of these beds comfortably and adequately, the recovery space was designed with maximum
observation in mind. Structural columns impinge very little on layout.

Surgery Facilities

Columbia Doctors Hospital, Little
Rock, Arkansas. Floor plan, Hand and
Microsurgery Services, first floor.
Courtesy Earl Swensson Associates.

1 Entrance
2 Outpatient waiting
3 Hand center waiting
4 Admitting
5 Hand center staging
6 Pediatric staging
7 Nurses' station
8 Outpatient staging

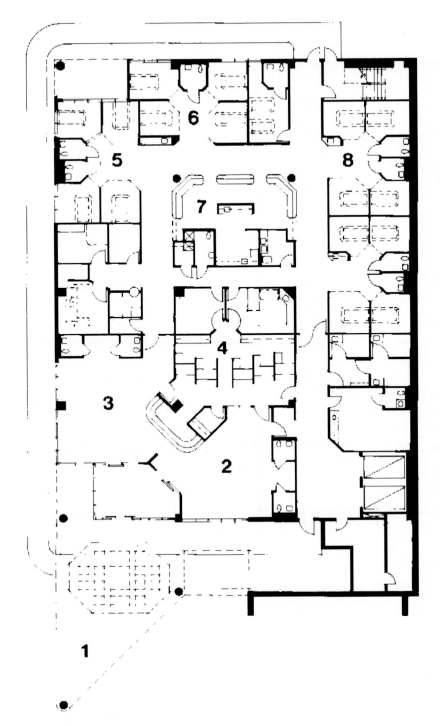

Power columns—one for every two patients—were used in preference to
headwalls in order to achieve greater efficiency. The use of power columns
also allow for the inclusion of more windows, so the recovery area is
bathed in an abundance of natural light.

The nurses' station is designed for maximum flexibility. No walls
separate one end of the station from the other. In times of high patient
census, the station can be staffed by more nurses than in times of low
census. During low census periods, a single nurse, positioned in the center
of the station, can adequately monitor the recovery area. No observation
control is sacrificed.

8

Critical Care

■ Condition Critical

Many people—caregivers, architectural and design professionals, and patients—regard critical care facilities as the heart of the hospital. The definition of the critical care unit developed by the Joint Commission on Accreditation for Hospitals in 1981 supports this common perception by calling critical care "an appropriately equipped area of the hospital where there is a concentration of nurses, physicians, and others. . . ." Here a seriously ill patient can expect the maximum of care: the very best the hospital has to offer in terms of personnel and technology.

For this reason, it is particularly alarming to review the substantial literature that now exists devoted to how the environment of the critical care unit (especially the intensive care unit [ICU] and the coronary care unit [CCU]) can adversely affect patient health while simultaneously increasing stress and fatigue among the physicians, nurses, and others who work in these areas. The fact is that many ICUs and CCUs are—literally —sickening.

If, for better or worse, the critical care unit is a powerful distillation of what the modern hospital has become, it concentrates in particular the *technology* of modern medicine, bringing to bear on each patient a panoply of machinery, monitors, and invasive, movement-restricting tubes and electrical leads. In most ICUs, the focus is not so much on the patient as it is upon a disease or disorder, as if the procedures necessary for sustaining life in the physical sense were somehow incompatible with simultaneously sustaining emotional well-being. The assumption seems to be that the ICU patient is either unconscious and unaware of his surroundings or too sick to care about them. The problem is that emotional health cannot be neatly isolated from physical health. What is stressful or depressing has an adverse effect on the patient's physical state.

This is no mere matter of designing a critical care unit with clever little touches intended to "cheer up" the patients. The problems in many existing units are far more serious. The machinery makes many patients feel invaded and powerless. The sense of claustrophobia created by packing monitoring equipment, respirators, and IV delivery equipment into a small space can dramatically increase anxiety levels. Windowed walls are always at a premium in designing any large building, and because it is frequently assumed that ICU patients are unconscious or at a low level of consciousness, windows are too often absent from critical care design. Not only does this heighten the sense of claustrophobia inherent in these technology-packed areas, but a number of studies have demonstrated that patients in windowless rooms are subject to temporal dislocation (they have, for example, an inaccurate memory of the length of their stay in ICU) and even subject to what has been called the "ICU syndrome" or "ICU psychosis," which is characterized by delirium, hallucinations, and delusions. According to one study (Larkin M. Wilson, M.D., "Intensive Care Delirium," published in the *Archives of Internal Medicine,* vol. 130, August 1972), patients in intensive care units without windows were more than twice as likely to develop delirium than those who occupied windowed rooms. In patients with abnormal hemoglobin or blood urea nitrogen levels, the incidence of delirium was almost three times greater in windowless units.

The disorienting effects of windowlessness are often aggravated by harsh lighting, especially from fluorescent fixtures, and by lighting that is not cyclically dimmed to correspond to the body's circadian rhythms. The most obvious effect of this, which resembles the kind of "brainwashing" tortures to which American POWs were subjected during the Korean War, is sleep deprivation. Sleeplessness is a common problem in critical care units, and it is not only due to lighting, but to the remarkably high level of noise that prevails in many of these units. Many studies of ICU and CCU noise levels exist. The startling fact is that these levels commonly range from 45 to more than 90 decibels over a twenty-four-hour period. In the average domestic bedroom, most individuals would find noise levels exceeding 30 decibels incompatible with sleep.

Excessive noise is particularly stressful for cardiac patients, who exhibit increased cardiac workloads and arrhythmias in noisy environments. In addition, pain perception seems to be heightened by the presence of excessive noise. The types of noise that occur in many critical care units are also of a particularly stressful sort: alarms, the sounds of electronic monitors, a babble of television sets, radios, and staff conversation. Interestingly, most patients find the human noises more objectionable than the machine-generated noise.

These are the most frequently noted and most intensively studied problems in critical care environments, and they are all problems that in large part can be solved through design. In addition, there are somewhat more diffuse negative responses reported by patients, including a sense that they could not "escape" their environment; a general and anxiety-provoking sense of unrelenting urgency in the environment; sensory deprivation; crowding; and loss of privacy. Many related feelings also affect those who work in the critical care unit, leading them to depersonalize patients. All of these responses can be at least mitigated through design solutions.

■ Historical Perspective

To appreciate most fully the present state of the art of critical care and to evaluate trends, it is useful to understand the historical evolution of these units. As early as 1863, Florence Nightingale noted the existence of a "recess or small room leading from the operating theatre" in many "small country hospitals," which was the origin of the surgical recovery room. During the two world wars, the recovery room continued to evolve to cope with patients who required extensive postoperative care and to consolidate them in order to make most efficient use of a limited number of nurses.

In the meantime, in 1930, the first intensive care unit appeared in a German hospital. Drawing on the consolidation and intensive monitoring concept inherent in the recovery room, the German plan also called for assembling teams of the most highly skilled nurses and an experienced physician to provide a heightened degree of care for critically ill patients. In the United States, it was the polio epidemic of the late 1940s and 1950s that spurred development of specialized units devoted to treating patients with polio-induced respiratory ailments, and in 1952, in Denmark, the first formal respiratory intensive care unit was established. When the "iron lung" was replaced by the mechanical ventilator in the late 1950s, it became logistically desirable to centralize this technology rather than distribute it throughout the hospital. In this way, technology drove the creation of the intensive care unit. The experience with polio victims suggested that patients afflicted with critical conditions could be concentrated in designated areas so that fewer nurses could provide special—intensive—care to more than one patient at a time.

During the 1960s, design for critical care diverged in two directions. Intensive care units located adjacent to surgical facilities and intended to care for and monitor patients who had undergone serious and complex surgical procedures were designed as open wards, the beds separated by cubicle curtains, whereas medical or coronary care units were designed as individual rooms or cubicles.

■ Planning

In all areas of hospital and healthcare facility design, the trend is toward formally including users of the facility in the design process. This is particularly important in the potentially high-stress environment of the critical care unit, where designing for maximum efficiency depends, in no small part, on listening to the professional staff. Architects and hospital administrators should convene a task force of representatives from the medical staff specialties, administration, planning, marketing, nursing, engineering, pharmacy, respiratory therapy, biomedical, infection control, and support services (including materials management and housekeeping). In consultation with the task force, the architect must develop a strong programming statement that defines the purpose and nature of the critical care facility or facilities, including the role of specialized critical care and step-down care, which are explained below.

■ The Range of Critical Care

In programming the critical care facility, planners, architects, and administrators are confronted with a broad range of critical care options, which are products of a combination of the evolution of medical technology, the development of managed care and cost containment, and the individual hospital's size and definition of mission. Insofar as critical care is perceived—by patients as well as staff—as a concentration of the best a hospital has to offer, there is incentive and a trend toward developing excellence in this area and offering a high degree of specialization. We shall discuss some aspects of these specialized critical care facilities later in the chapter. However, intensive care is resource intensive. It is one of the costliest of hospital services, and, particularly in the emerging climate of managed care and cost containment, hospitals are looking for alternatives to critical care—even as they continue to acquire and develop critical care technologies and facilities.

In 1988, the Task Force on Guidelines of the Society of Critical Care Medicine defined three levels of critical care (designated as Level Ia, Level Ic, and Level II) hospitals might offer, depending on their size and definition of mission.

Critical care units of the first level offer delivery of care to the "desperately ill patient with complicated needs requiring the continuous availability of sophisticated equipment, specialized nurses, and physicians trained in the care of the critically ill." Within this category is a Level Ic, which provides these essential services, and a Level Ia, which adds a teaching and research component to these services.

Level II units are appropriate to hospitals with more limited resources. According to the Task Force, the Level II unit should be capable of delivering high-quality care to patients with single-organ failure, but, in cases of complicated need or multisystem failure, transfer to a facility offering Level I care should be made.

Even Level II critical care is expensive and increasingly subject to rationing. The trend is now toward developing intermediate care units—frequently called "step-down" units—in cases where high-risk patients require close monitoring but not intensive intervention. The step-down unit is often used for patients suffering from chronic ventilatory failure who do not, however, require intensive respiratory monitoring or therapy.

Another step-down development is the Special Care Unit (SCU), which is designed for the chronically critically ill patient. One such facility, at the University Hospitals of Cleveland and Case Western Reserve University, is an eight-bed unit consisting entirely of private rooms, which open from a central hallway and have a view to the outside. Each room is large enough to accommodate family members overnight, and an ample family lounge is located nearby as part of the unit. Physiologic monitoring is limited to EKG and periodic arterial pressure monitoring. The primary technologic support system in evidence is a ventilator. Whereas most critical care units exclude the family or accommodate family members provisionally (if not grudgingly), the SCU encourages both the family and the patient to play active roles in making decisions about care.

It is likely that intermediate care and such Special Care Units will figure with increasing prominence in critical care design.

Because the principal focus of critical care is so often respiratory, many hospitals have introduced specifically designated respiratory intensive care units (R-ICU) or pulmonary ICUs (P-ICU). Other specialized critical care units include:

▲ *Neurological Intensive Care*
▲ *Wound Intensive Care (often associated with a special Burn Unit)*
▲ *Surgical ICU*
▲ *Medical ICU*
▲ *Geriatric Intensive Care*
▲ *Pediatric ICU (PICU)*
▲ *Neonatal ICU and high-risk OB*

In addition, hospitals increasingly allocate critical care space to ICUs that offer a high degree of isolation—an issue that will be discussed later in this chapter.

■ Technology and Humanity: Design Priorities

If there is one thing that creative hospital and healthcare facility design consistently demonstrates, it is that high technology need not be incompatible with humane, comfortable, patient-centered design. Effective and humane critical care design need not hide technology, but it should aim at integrating high technology into an essentially familiar—rather than alien and alienating—environment.

Location and Size

The location of the critical care unit depends on such factors as the focus of the unit (surgical, medical, specialized) and its size. The ICU may be strategically located near the ED and surgical service for efficiency of patient transfer, when necessary, and for economy of sharing support services. It may also be advantageous to have the surgical recovery facilities located near the ICU to facilitate sharing of staff and common support services, such as clinical lab facilities and radiology. Specialty ICUs are often most logically located adjacent to the surgical/medical beds devoted to that specialty.

Whatever its location and adjacencies, the critical care unit must exclude through-traffic. Some of the corridor strategies discussed in "Chapter 7, Surgery Facilities" may be applied to the critical care unit to achieve the balance of access and isolation these areas demand.

As traditionally conceived, each surgical ICU has between six and twelve beds. Twelve beds is seen as the upper limit of what an ICU nurs-

Lynchburg General Hospital, Lynchburg, Virginia. Floor plan, ICU pod. *Courtesy Earl Swensson Associates.*

1 Nurses' station
2 Clean work
3 Nourishment
4 Dictation
5 ICU room
6 Nursing office
7 Corridor to elevator

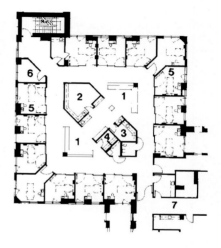

Lynchburg General Hospital, Lynchburg, Virginia. The design of the Surgical Intensive Care Unit (SICU) allows the nursing staff to observe the patients in their care without leaving the workstation. *Photo by Jonathan Hillyer. Courtesy Earl Swensson Associates.*

ing staff and station can adequately monitor. This guideline will become decreasingly significant as ICUs incorporate bedside computers that enable "paperless charting" and direct recording of vital signs through monitoring devices. Such technology will encourage "decentralized nursing," which will allow nursing staff to spend less time at a central nursing station and more time in patient rooms and at mini-work stations in designated alcoves directly adjacent to these rooms. In many localities, decentralized nursing requires either a change in building codes or a variance from existing codes, which often require the equivalent of traditional nursing stations.

As to the rooms themselves, the AHA minimum is 150 square feet per room. This may be adequate for non-critical patients, but it is too small for patients on life-support and monitoring equipment. The Task Force on Guidelines of the Society of Critical Care Medicine recommends 150 to 200 square feet per bed in open units, while private patient rooms should contain 225 to 250 square feet. Many other authorities suggest 300 square feet to accommodate multiple life-support equipment while allowing sufficient room for access to all four sides of the patient's bed. The ICU patient room should be planned to facilitate operation in the event of a crisis.

Lynchburg General Hospital, Lynchburg, Virginia. Patient rooms in the SICU minimize the institutional feel of a necessarily heavily equipped, high-tech room. The room is filled with natural light from the windows, and chairs invite visitors to give companionship to the patient. *Photo by Jonathan Hillyer. Courtesy Earl Swensson Associates.*

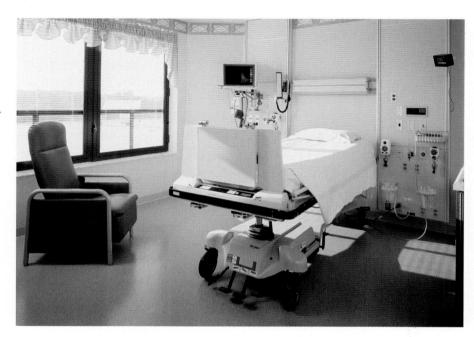

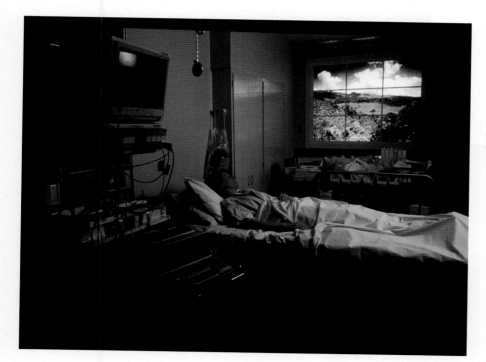

Windows

Of all lighting, the most comforting and familiar is natural illumination. Windows must be a part of all effective ICU and CCU design, and, ideally, the patient should have a view that encompasses both ground and sky. The height of the window should be kept low enough to allow an optimum view. The idea is to admit a maximum of natural light and to maintain maximum contact and orientation with the world outside the room.

Ceilings

The designer must bear in mind an obvious fact: the intensive care patient is usually flat on his back and, therefore, spends considerable time looking at the ceiling. Ceiling material should be chosen with care to reduce glare and to provide an interesting texture that promotes a sense of orientation in the supine occupant of the room.

Other Essentials for Reality Orientation

While a view to the outside world and a thoughtful ceiling treatment are essential to maintaining reality orientation, other simple elements should not be neglected.

The ICU patient room should include a clock. Special "stat clocks" are available, which normally function as standard clocks, but automatically become digital elapsed-time counters in a code blue (cardiac arrest) situation. Note that some state codes mandate the inclusion of a clock in the room.

The room should also include a clearly visible calendar, a radio, and a television set, equipped with remote control.

PineLake Medical Center, Mayfield, Kentucky. From the nursing station, staff has a clear view of the patients in the ICU. In spite of the necessary equipment, furnishings minimize the institutional feel of the room. *Photo by Gary Knight. Courtesy Earl Swensson Associates.*

cy and Visibility

contact with the outside is important, most patients put a high
on privacy. Design should allow for adequate privacy without,
er, isolating the patient. The design challenge here is that the
t must be visible to staff, and access to the room must be un-
cted, yet a sense of privacy must also be created.

Since the critical care unit is located apart from through-traffic areas, it is possible to use sliding glass doors or folding glass doors, which effectively seal out noise while allowing nursing staff to observe patients. Sliding doors should be detailed without bottom tracks, so that nothing will impede crash carts and other rolled equipment. Folding doors should entirely "break away," allowing fullest access to the patient room in "crash" or emergency situations. The design also eliminates the bump— annoying to the patient—created by a floor track. The technology also exists to create an "observation wall" made of Varilite panels, which can change from clear to water white at the touch of a button, thereby giving the patient a significant measure of control over his privacy while still allowing for observation.

Visibility of Technology

Another sight-line issue is the visibility of technology. Most life-support and monitoring devices should be kept out of the patient's range of vision. Wall-mounting and column-mounting equipment helps with this.

Lighting

Where possible, general illumination should be indirect incandescent, which conveys greater warmth and familiarity than direct fluorescent light. The cooler color temperature of fluorescent lighting is more sugges- tive of commercial or institutional spaces than it is of a welcoming "residential" environment. While procedure (examination) lights should be placed directly over the patient so that staff are not working in their own shadows, the sources of general illumination should be located away from the patient's prevailing line of sight in order to reduce fatigue and stress. Too often, even general illumination in the ICU uses over-bed light fixtures, which are in themselves "institutional" and alienating. Table lamps are welcome touches of familiarity, and soffits and cornices also soften the institutional effect.

It is vitally important that the patient, even the critically ill patient, have easy access to control of the general illumination in his room. A switch or, better yet, rheostat should be within easy reach. This seemingly small measure of control over his immediate environment significantly enhances the patient's overall sense of control—a sense that is under heavy assault during illness and, particularly, during a period of relative immobility.

General lighting levels should be kept as low as is compatible with staff efficiency. Lowering light levels tends to lower staff noise levels as well. Consider putting corridor lighting on a timed cycle to mesh with circadian rhythms. Thoughtful corridor lighting design might incorporate focused task lighting, so that the general lighting in traffic areas can be kept at low levels during the night.

Oak Park Hospital, Oak Park, Illinois. The waiting area in the ICU/CCU and Telemetry Unit provides attractive surroundings and comfortable furnishings for patients' families. Photo by Hedrich Blessing. Courtesy O'Donnell Wicklund Pigozzi & Peterson.

Color and Furnishings

Color is a frequent subject of discussion in general medical-surgical patient rooms. It should also become an important consideration in the ICU/CCU. In too many existing critical care units, the most colorful furnishings are the items of medical equipment. It would be better to manufacture medical equipment in the same neutral shades used for office machines, especially personal computers, and provide color in critical care unit through the use of well-chosen artwork, comfortable chairs, and elegant, well-made casework.

Noise

As discussed above, noise levels in critical care areas are often excessive. The use of acoustic insulation, draperies, and carpeting (in corridors, not patient rooms) significantly reduces noise levels. Laying out the critical care suite to reduce corridor traffic is another positive step. Employing low general lighting levels during the night and evenings not only mimics circadian rhythms, it tends to signal to personnel and others that they should speak quietly. Finally, equipment alarms should be kept at the minimum number and volume consistent with safety.

Odors

Ask most people to enumerate what they find objectionable—or anxiety-provoking—about hospitals, and the "hospital smell" will be high on the list. Control of odors is not often thought of as a design issue; however, technologies now exist not only to circulate air and exhaust air efficiently, but to neutralize odors and even to manipulate odors through "aroma therapy," the injection of scents through the HVAC system.

Visitor Accommodation

As in the emergency department, visitor accommodations are often neglected in the critical care unit, and family and friends are sometimes actively discouraged from visiting patients in intensive care. Generally, accommodation for family and other visitors is both a humane consideration for the family and positively beneficial to the patient. At minimum, an adequate waiting area should be made available, and the intensive care patient room should include a comfortable chair or two for a companion. In Oak Park Hospital's ICU/CCU (Oak Park, Illinois) designed by O'Donnell Wicklund Pigozzi & Peterson Architects of Deerfield, Illinois, family accommodations were designed to create an apartmentlike setting, including a family room, kitchen, and living room, all directly adjacent to the critical care units.

Oak Park Hospital, Oak Park, Illinois. The view into a patient room of the ICU/CCU and Telemetry Unit shows the decorative glass and wood trim reminiscent of the work of Frank Lloyd Wright. Humanizing touches in the ICU room include chairs for visitors, artworks on the walls, and attractive window treatments. *Photo by Hedrich Blessing. Courtesy O'Donnell Wicklund Pigozzi & Peterson.*

The hospital wanted to merge ICU/CCU with the Telemetry Unit, a unit for patients requiring a less acute level of care. The existing ICU/CCU, built in the 1950s, functioned poorly in combination with the demands of current high technology, and the outmoded facility also presented an image problem. The entire ICU, CCU, and Telemetry Unit was renovated by OWP&P in the Prairie Style closely identified with Frank Lloyd Wright, much of whose residential work is found in the Chicago suburb. The Prairie Style motif allows for close integration of furnishings and artwork (most notably, Wright-esque art glass) with the elegantly residential look of the interior architecture. Warm colors and strong horizontal lines, hallmarks of the Prairie Style, predominate. The ICU/CCU, Telemetry Unit, and the family accommodation space they share between them are united in design, but also retain unique identity through the use of four autumnal colors. Cool greens and blues, in combination with warm white, is used in the ICU to convey tranquility as well as a sense of the renewal of life. Rich reds were added to the these colors in the Telemetry Unit and in the public areas. Oak trim is used extensively throughout, for warmth and for the Prairie Style horizontal accent.

While accommodation for family members has been seen as increasingly important in the hospital setting, especially where critically ill patients are concerned, neither should visitation be forced upon ICU/CCU patients, some of whom express a preference for being left alone. One recent study reported mixed benefits of allowing children to visit patients in intensive care.

Staff Accommodation

Intensive care of patients demands intensive effort from the professional staff. They are subject to bombardment of the senses and many emotional

Oak Park Hospital, Oak Park, Illinois. Floor plan, ICU/CCU and Telemetry Unit. *Courtesy O'Donnell Wicklund Pigozzi & Peterson.*

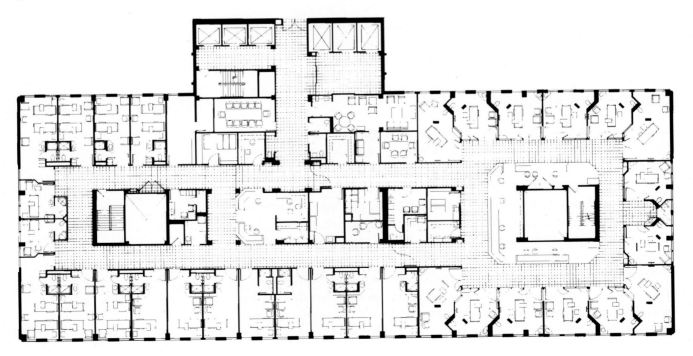

stresses. In general, the same design measures that reduce patient anxiety and increase patient comfort do the same for staff. This includes, especially, designing for the minimization of noise, careful attention to lighting (with generally low levels—at least at night—in corridors punctuated by task lighting at work stations), and the relegation of technology to the visual background while non-institutional architectural details, furnishings, and artwork are featured in the foreground.

An adequate lounge area adjacent to the critical care area is essential. Depending on the size of the unit, a formally designated conference/consultation/education room may or may not be required as part of the unit, but thoughtful design will incorporate adequate space for professional conversation sufficiently isolated from the patient rooms so that it will not intrude upon patient privacy. Alcoves, niches, or pockets worked into corridors not only provide visual interest in these spaces, they offer inviting areas for consultation.

Staff members, particularly those who work long shifts, are subject to some of the same sense of isolation and disorientation that may afflict patients. If possible, windows should be available in staff areas and even in corridors. Of course, the reality is that window space is often at a premium in ICU/CCU areas. Skylights may be used in corridors and other staff areas, while clerestory designs allow for "borrowed" daylight in corridors, and the Japanese have begun to employ devices that collect sunlight and transmit it through fiber optics to living and work areas that lack direct exposure to the outside.

Achieving a Balance

In emphasizing the "human" aspects of ICU/CCU design, we do not mean to denigrate technology. Not only does medical machinery save

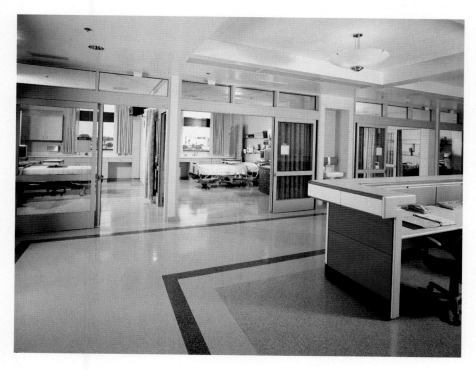

Thornton Hospital, University of California, San Diego, San Diego, California. Facilities feature a modular nursing station highlighted by special lighting and ceiling treatment. Patient rooms with clerestory light up the corridors even when curtains in the patient rooms are drawn. *Photo by David Hewitt/Anne Garrison. Courtesy Stone Marraccini Patterson.*

Morton Plant Hospital, Clearwater, Florida. TRO-The Ritchie Organzation located stations outside each ICU room to allow nursing staff to monitor patients closely. Designers for the project were Kathryn Stephens, ASID, and Kathy McCullough, ASID, for Obrentz Design Group. *Photo by George Cott/Chroma, Inc. Courtesy Obrentz Design Group.*

lives, it has the potential of actually humanizing the relation of caregiver to patient. For example, the critical care information system in use at Tampa General Hospital allows for the automatic recording of vital-sign data, saving each nurse an average of 11.86 minutes per shift and resulting in a 63 percent decrease in the amount of nursing time spent collecting vital-sign data. Concomitant with this has come a 40 percent increase in the time nurses spend communicating with and treating patients. At Latter Day Saints Hospital in Salt Lake City, bedside terminals increased the amount of data recorded on patients' charts by 40 to 50 percent. A 1989 Peat Marwick Main study of three hospitals reported an average reduction of twenty-six minutes of overtime for each nurse shift and a 34 percent decrease in medication errors. (Dan Soule, "Information Systems in Critical Care," *Hospital Management International 1990.)* In 1992, Lutheran Hospital-La Crosse (La Crosse, Wisconsin) reported that the use of bedside computers resulted in a 100 percent increase in time that could be devoted to traditional "hands on" patient care, while manual charting activities decreased by 21.8 percent and general paperwork time fell 15.8 percent. (David Allen and Margaret Davis, "A Computerized CIS Enhances Bedside Intensive Care," *Nursing Management,* July 1992.) The development of "bedside laboratory" technology can be employed to assess blood gases, electrolytes, glucose, and hemacrit using a very small blood sample—0.5 ml—in less than ninety seconds.

Despite all of this promise, patient care suffers if the machinery becomes the focus of the designer's and the practitioner's attention. Edwina A. McConnell reported some critical care nurses' complaints that they spend more time with machines than they do with patients ("The Impact of Machines on the Work of Critical Care Nurses," *Critical Care Nursing Quarterly,* March 1990), and, as has been observed above, patients express anxiety over being "tied down" to machines.

Good design can do much to accommodate the machinery while keeping it out of the way. Particular attention should be devoted to the headwall, which, especially in the critical care environment, bristles with connections for medical gases, suction, electrical power, and terminal hookups. Consideration must be given as to whether the hookups should fan out from the patient to the headwall, whether they will converge at a power column, or run to an overhead rail system. In general medical-surgical patient rooms—and even in some critical care facilities—attractive casework can be used to hide all or some of the hookups in the headwall.

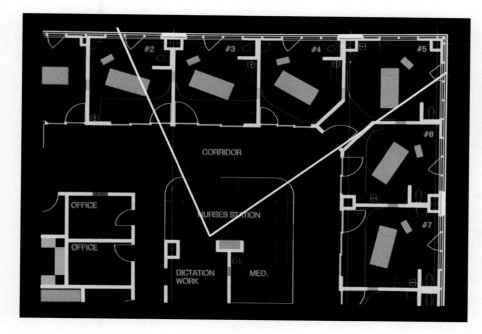

Left: Centennial Medical Center, Nashville, Tennessee. For the center's ICU unit on the fourth floor, the architects used a computer simulation to lay out the unit. The white lines from the nursing station indicate lines of sight to each patient's head. *Courtesy Earl Swensson Associates.*

Centennial Medical Center, Nashville, Tennessee. This computer rendering of the ICU shows staff positioned at the nursing station and her line of vision into each patient room. *Courtesy Earl Swensson Associates.*

The choice of headwall, power column, or rail system is in large part determined by the layout of the room (especially the orientation of the bed), which, in turn, is a function of overall unit design and the need to balance the demands of technology, accessibility, and privacy. The starting point for the layout of the room is the orientation of the bed. From the point of view of the nurse, the bed should be situated to allow ready observation of the entire body, especially the head. Tradition dictates that the head of the bed be against a wall, and, certainly, headwalls accommodate readily to this approach. However, in a crisis, it is often essential to have access to the patient from all four sides. Certainly, the bed can be pulled quickly out from the wall, but tubes and monitor leads may continue to inhibit access or may even present a trip hazard. Some architects have proposed a partial solution to this in non-square rooms or rooms with one angled wall, meant to increase clearance around the bed (and to give the room greater sensory interest for the patient). However, a simpler approach is to treat the bed as an island. An example of this is the critical care unit at Centennial Medical Center in Nashville, designed by Earl Swensson Associates. The rooms are square, but the beds are placed *diagonally* in the middle of the room adjacent to a power column. This allows 360-degree access to the patient.

Metropolitan Hospital, New York, New York. Floor plan, Medical ICU. The beds of the unit have been angled to provide more work space around the bed. *Courtesy Larsen Associates.*

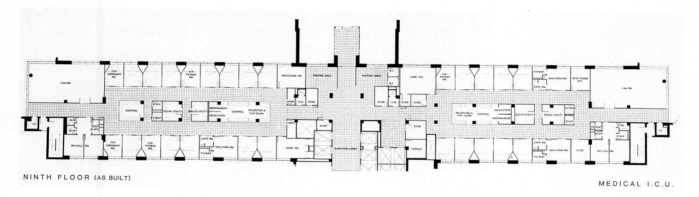

NINTH FLOOR (AS BUILT)

MEDICAL I.C.U.

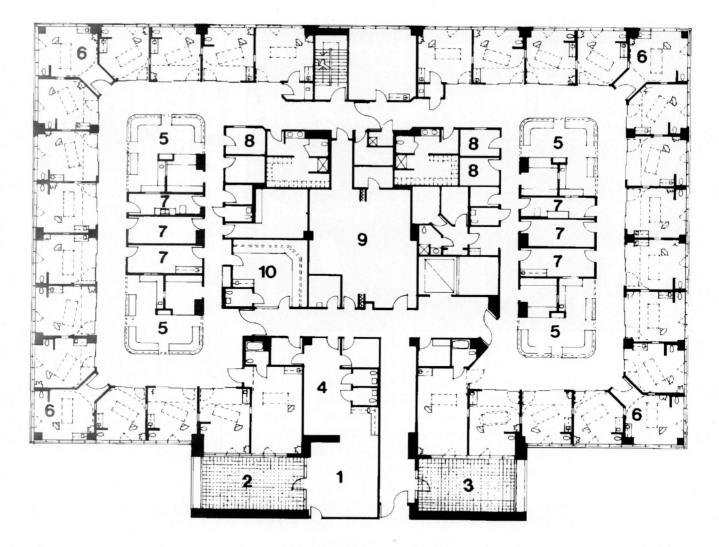

Centennial Medical Center, Nashville, Tennessee. Floor plan, fourth floor ICU. *Courtesy Earl Swensson Associates.*

1   Waiting
2   Terrace
3   Staff terrace
4   Lounge/vending
5   Nurses' station
6   ICU rooms
7   Support
8   Office
9   Clinical education
10 Monitor room

■ Contemporary ICU Designs

CENTENNIAL MEDICAL CENTER
Nashville, Tennessee

In this Earl Swensson Associates project, completed in 1994, two sixteen-bed units (with the possibility to expand to an additional sixteen beds) surround a core of shared support facilities. Each sixteen-bed unit also surrounds its own core of support facilities, and each unit is further divided into eight-bed units clustered around a nursing station, so that one such station serves every eight beds. In addition, a pneumatic tube station also serves every eight beds, making it possible to send records, drugs, specimens, and blood immediately.

A three-dimensional computer model was used to determine sight lines and bed locations, and the head of each bed is located ideally for nurse visibility. Each room is accessed by a triple sliding glass door system, which can stack as one door and can break away for better access in an emergency. The power column is located in the center of each room to allow staff accessibility at all points around the bed. The placement also permits a great degree of flexibility in room arrangement. Bedside diagnostic services are available.

Each ICU room includes patient-focused amenities such as access to natural light and a bedside lounge chair for a family member. Additional family amenities in the ICU area include a waiting area, a vending and lounge area, and a kitchenette. Two consultation rooms are directly accessible to the waiting rooms.

There is also an outdoor covered patio area for family members, including smokers, who are not permitted to smoke inside the building.

PARKRIDGE MEDICAL CENTER

Chattanooga, Tennessee

Completed in 1992, the sixteen-bed Parkridge ICU/CCU is designed to be monitored from a single nursing station. Supplies, charts, and dictation are located within the nursing station, while soiled and clean utility is located in hardwall areas outside of the nursing unit so that sight lines remain unobstructed. Breakaway doors allow unobstructed access to each room.

Parkridge Hospital, Chattanooga, Tennessee. Floor plan, ICU. *Courtesy Earl Swensson Associates.*

1 Nurses' station
2 Soiled utility
3 Med. room
4 ICU room

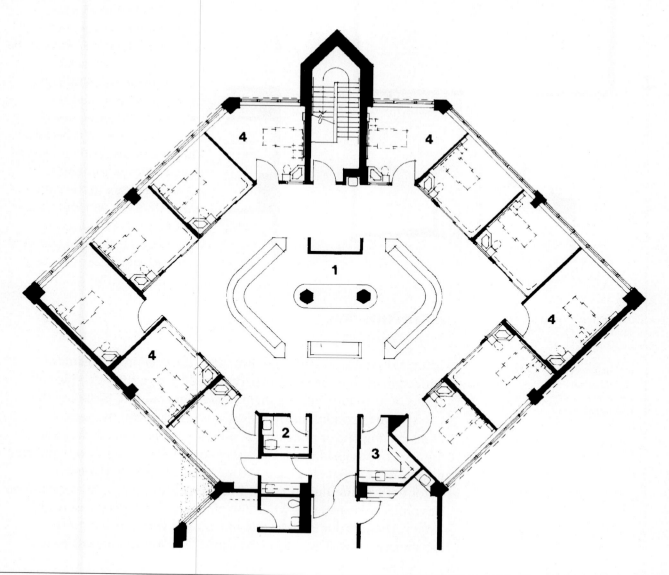

LONGVIEW REGIONAL HOSPITAL

Longview, Texas

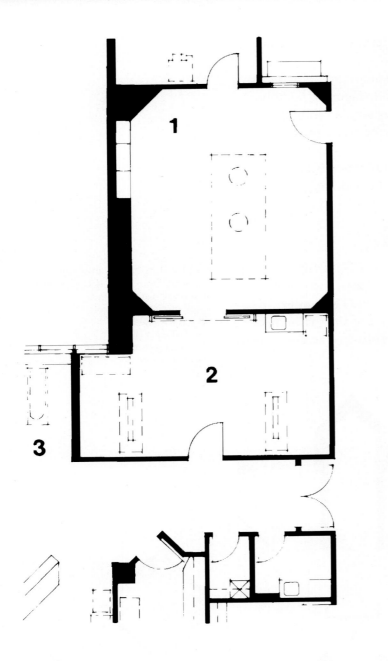

Earl Swensson Associates designed a two-bed cardiac recovery unit, completed in 1992, for the expanded heart surgery program at Longview Regional. The post-cardiac surgery solution ESa created here is unique. The CCU/recovery room is directly adjacent to the surgery room itself, separated only by sliding glass doors, which preserve sterile conditions. The patient is operated on and then moved into the adjacent cardiac recovery room. Once stabilized, she may be moved to general surgical intensive care or to other units. However, should the patient suffer a setback or cardiac arrest, the sliding glass doors break away, and the patient can be immediately returned to surgery, if necessary. This innovative, patient-focused design solution (bringing appropriate care to the patient, rather than the patient to the site of care) required special cooperation from state and local code agencies.

Longview Regional Hospital, Longview, Texas. Floor plan, CCU. *Courtesy Earl Swensson Associates.*

1 Cardiac operating room
2 Cardiac recovery
3 General recovery
4 Operating room

GRIFFIN HOSPITAL

Derby, Connecticut

Griffin Hospital is an affiliate of Planetree, the non-profit organization founded in 1978 to promote patient-focused care. Griffin designed all aspects of its facility with a patient-focused orientation, including the ICU. Unlike the traditional ICU, which is laid out with the patient rooms ringing one or more central nurses' stations, while family and visitors are consigned to a relatively remote (and, often, not very private) waiting area located off a chaotic corridor, the Griffin ICU removes visitor traffic from the central work area by means of a perimeter corridor. This protects the patients, while also affording families a measure of privacy. The corridor includes waiting lounges with kitchen, toilet, and showers, as well as outdoor balconies. The lounges are adjacent

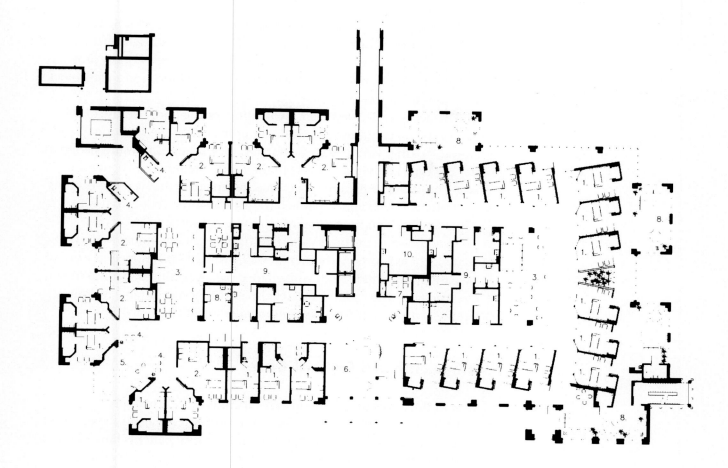

to the patient rooms. The rooms themselves are angled to maximize sightlines from the nurses' station.

■ Intensive Care Unit (ICU) Initiative

If there is one thing that administrators, medical professionals, designers, and architects agree on it is that the critical care unit is a kind of hospital within a hospital and, therefore, a "monumentally difficult" (the phrase is used by a number of writers) design challenge, which is not reducible to a set of cut-and-dried rules. One new approach to the challenge follows.

In 1990, the journal *Interiors* and the National Symposium on Health Care Interior Design co-sponsored an ICU Initiative at the Third Symposium on Health Care Interior Design. As part of the initiative, Orlando Diaz-Azcuy of Orlando Diaz-Azcuy Designs collaborated with Anshen & Allen Architects to create an innovative ICU patient room aimed at balancing the demands of high-tech medicine with high-touch humanity. The room measures 16 by 13 feet and includes a bed positioned parallel to an "observation wall" made of Varilite panels, which can be transformed from transparent to water-white translucent at the discretion of the patient. The head of the bed is positioned against a "technology wall," which contains the life-support and monitoring equipment. This apparatus is hidden in office-style cabinets built into the wall.

Griffin Hospital, Griffin, Connecticut. Floor plan, ICU. A design of patient-focused care features a circulation pattern that separates visitors from staff. *Courtesy Stecker LaBau Arneill McManus.*

1   Single patient room
2   Semi-private room
3   Central nurses' station
4   Satellite nurses' station
5   Patient waiting
6   Resource room
7   Conference/library
8   Family and care partner space
9   Support space
10 Treatment

Lighting comes from multiple sources: soffitted recessed lighting on a patient-controlled dimmer, asymmetrical wall lighting, Lightolier reading lights positioned over the bed, and an exam light. The window provides daylight, in addition to contact with the outside world, and a glass-block wall illuminates the toilet area.

The designer decided against carpeting for the floor because of the odor of the materials used to clean it, but instead of the traditional (and clinical-looking) vinyl, he chose terrazzo tiles arranged in warm patterns that not only add visual interest to the room, but provide orientation cues. The ceiling is textured blue, creating an effect that is both soothing and visually interesting. A painted frieze defines the ceiling and wall planes and adds another dimension of visual interest to the room.

In addition to the observation, technology, and window walls, Diaz-Azcuy included an "environmental wall," which is positioned in front of the patient bed and is faced with stained oak. A writing desk drops down from the wall. The room is also furnished with a comfortable reclining/rocking chair, which could accommodate the patient or a visitor.

■ Specialized Critical Care

Most of the issues that figure in general critical care also apply to specialized critical care units. Indeed, some authorities argue against specialized critical care units on the grounds that most critical patients have common needs and that critical care specialization is an arbitrary function of departmental organization rather than patient need. This view, however, does not take into account the possible cost-containment benefits of certain specialized alternatives to traditional intensive care. If specialized critical care is opted for, planners and architects will want to make some special considerations for the following.

Coronary Care Unit

After the surgical-medical ICU, the Coronary Care Unit (CCU) is the most commonly found critical care unit in the hospital. The central design issue in the CCU is finding a strategy to promote tranquility and even relative visual and acoustical isolation. So-called "ICU psychosis" is a shocking enough symptom of poor critical care design. In the case of the CCU, noise and visual clutter have a readily demonstrable adverse effect on heart rates, arrhythmias, and blood pressure.

Respiratory Care and Step-Down Units

The respiratory care unit has developed as an alternative to the traditional ICU in response to the constraints of managed care and cost containment. A 1987 study by R. J. Henning et al (*Critical Care Medicine* 15, 1987) demonstrated that 40 percent of medical intensive care patients and 30 percent of surgical intensive care patients were admitted to these costly units strictly for the purposes of monitoring and did not require any active intervention. The patients were not suffering from any immediately life-threatening processes. The study suggested a rationale for providing more cost-effective intermediate care units for those patients in need chiefly of close monitoring rather than aggressive intervention.

Cost savings are achieved in part through reduction in the amount and nature of required equipment and, in even larger part, through reduced staffing needs. Whereas the nurse to patient ratio in the ICU may be 1:2 or even 1:1, in the respiratory or step-down unit the ratio can safely be set at 1:3 or 1:4.

Critical Care of the Elderly

Until very recently, most buildings were standardized on the model of a thirty-year-old healthy male user or occupant. Increasingly, however, architects and planners are designing for a seventy-year-old woman who is in less than optimum health. While no radical steps need to be taken to design special critical care facilities to accommodate older patients, certain design features can be incorporated into general ICUs to make them more friendly to the aged.

Gerontologists speak of an "environmental docility hypothesis," which holds that as competence decreases, the probability that behavior will be influenced by environmental factors increases. We know that critically ill patients often feel at the mercy of their environment. This seems to be even more compelling among the critically ill elderly.

Some of the design areas discussed earlier, especially noise control, light, and color, are particularly important in designing with the elderly in mind. Noise reduction should be a high design priority. Because of diminished visual acuity in the elderly, lighting should be planned to avoid glare. This also means keeping highly reflective surfaces to a minimum. Color discrimination also deteriorates with age. Differentiating among dark shades and among pastels is a particular problem. Thoughtful use of contrast to emphasize planes and corners aids orientation. However, the elderly person should not feel dominated by the colors in his environment.

Neurological Intensive Care

An array of neurological conditions may require intensive care. These include postoperative neurosurgical cases; stroke; subarachnoid hemorrhage; head injury; cerebral hemorrhage; Guillain-Barré syndrome with respiratory failure; medical complications of neurological disease; brain tumor; acute spinal cord trauma; status epilepticus; encephalitis-meningitis; myasthenia gravis with respiratory failure; and global brain ischemia. Many of these conditions can be treated appropriately in the general surgical or medical ICU, but the monitoring and treatment of intracranial pressure (ICP) in particular has been cited by many authorities as ample rationale for creating specialized neurological critical care units.

Probably the best model for the neurological ICU is the coronary care unit (CCU), which focuses on continuous and sophisticated monitoring

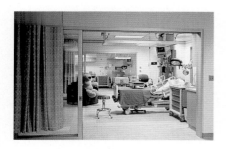

Shriners Hospital for Crippled Children/Galveston Burns Institute, Galveston, Texas. In this ICU for children, designers used muted colors and placed windows where possible. The radiant heat panels above the beds are linked to sensors on the patient—who because of the nature of the injuries lacks an insulating epidermal layer. The heating system compensates precisely for any heat loss. The hard finishing materials are easy to clean and thus minimize the possibility of bacterial infection. *Photo by James Wilson. Courtesy HDR, Inc.*

in order to achieve early detection of developing problems. Increasingly sophisticated monitoring devices will have to be accommodated in neurological critical care, and these must be added to a full array of respiratory and ventilation equipment.

Perhaps the single greatest design impact of the neurological ICU is the issue of adjacency. It is desirable to locate this unit near such diagnostic facilities as MRI and CT.

Burn Unit

Another specialized critical care facility found in larger, often regionally designated hospitals is the burn unit. Some hospitals, most notably the network run by the Shrine of North America (Shriners), are devoted entirely to the treatment and rehabilitation of burn victims.

For design, the single most important clinical factor in treating burns is creating structures that minimize the risk of infection. Burn unit critical care patient rooms should be private, rather than open ward, to minimize the risk of cross-infection. The ICU at Shriner's Hospital Galveston Burns Institute (HDR, Inc.) features patient rooms that are fully enclosed with glass to allow maximum visibility while providing for isolation. Interior finish materials were chosen for ease of cleaning and resistance to bacteria growth. This meant the use of terrazzo and vinyl for floors, and ceramic tile and glazed coatings for walls. Some wood accents were employed, however, especially in casework, to soften the clinical appearance of these materials. The HVAC system was designed to surgical operating room standards, and positive air pressure as well as HEPA filtering promotes surgical suite air quality.

The Galveston ICU patient rooms also include radiant heat systems above each bed. These are linked to thermal sensors mounted on patients who lack an insulating epidermal layer, and, in this way, any heat loss is precisely compensated for by the radiant panels. Environmental control extends to maintenance of high relative humidity as needed to help prevent damaged skin from drying out.

In addition to meeting the demanding clinical conditions required by the advanced treatment of severe burns, the burn unit ICU should project as much of a non-institutional sense of well-being as possible. Severe burn injury is not only physically painful, but is especially depressing and anxiety provoking. Patients suffering from disfiguring injury benefit from maintenance of contact with the outside world. Tragically, it is also the case that a great proportion of burn victims are children. The focus of the Shrine-sponsored institutions is, of course, pediatric. But all advanced burn units should be designed with the younger patient in mind.

A 1989 study by David J. Barillo, M.D., et al ("Utilization of the Burn Unit for Nonburn Patients: The 'Wound Intensive Care Unit,'" *Annual of Plastic Surgery* 23, 1989) showed that while burn treatment facilities were expanding, the incidence of thermal injury was decreasing. Barillo predicted that decreased incidence of burn injuries, coupled with increasingly stringent DRG (diagnosis-related group) reimbursement policies would likely decrease use of burn units. Barillo pointed out that the burn unit could easily be adapted to the treatment of nonburn patients as a "wound intensive area." Such flexible use may prompt even more hospitals to include burn facilities despite stabilized or decreasing demand for treatment of burn patients.

■ Isolation Issues

In discussing the burn ICU we have touched upon the issue of isolation to prevent infection. Patients admitted to ICU have a higher risk of nosocomial infection than other hospitalized patients. According to a 1982 study (Leigh G. Donowitz, M.D., et al, "High Risk of Hospital-Acquired Infection in the ICU Patient," *Critical Care Medicine* 10, no. 6, 1989), general medical/surgical patients had a 6 percent risk of acquiring infection, whereas ICU patients had an 18 percent risk.

Most authorities believe that design for isolation is primarily a matter of ventilation, filtering, and maintaining positive air pressure in the patient room. It is assumed that nursing the patient in a one-patient room with the door closed is the best safeguard against infection in intensive care. As the trend in all other parts of the hospital has for some time been toward exclusively private patient rooms, so the open-ward ICU will likely disappear. However, it is sobering to temper assumptions about the effect of architectural design on nosocomial infections by considering the results of a study by J. Huebner et al ("Influence of Architectural Design on Nosocomial Infections in Intensive Care Units—a Prospective 2-Year Analysis," *Intensive Care Medicine* 15, 1989), which concluded that the difference between the incidence of infection in an old intensive care ward built in 1924 and a new one constructed in 1986 was slight: 34.2 percent versus 31.9 percent.

■ The Neonatal Intensive Care Unit

The location and design of the neonatal intensive care unit (NICU) are sufficiently unique to warrant special treatment here. Pediatric critical care medicine became a recognized discipline by about 1960. Its origins are traceable to Pierre Budin, a Parisian pediatrician who created a "department for weaklings," primarily to care for and study premature neonates, and James Wilson, a pediatrician who established a four-bed negative-pressure ventilator ("iron lung") for pediatric patients at Boston's Children's Hospital in 1932.

Generally, funding for critical care may be threatened by cost containment efforts and rationing as policymakers strive to claim more medical dollars for preventive care and fewer for critical care. However, neonatal and pediatric intensive care may well be exempt from such fund reallocation, at least in the short term, if for no other reason than that few policymakers want to be seen as depriving children of care. Certainly, however, neonatologists and others will be increasingly confronted with care-giving decisions balancing survival, cost, and the quality of life.

General Design Issues

The modern neonatal critical care facility is the product of two factors:

▲ The development of an understanding that the pathophysiologic phenomena associated with the newborn are so distinctive that they require an appropriate setting where the critically ill infant can be effectively managed, and

▲ Convergent advances in electronics and biochemistry, which made such a setting feasible.

These advances include:

▲ Methods for continuous evaluation of numerous parameters of neonatal (and fetal) illness.

▲ Methods of continuous monitoring of cardiorespiratory function.

▲ Microtechniques for the rapid biochemical determinations from minute blood samples.

▲ Servo-controlled radiant-heat incubators.

These advances, coupled with improved methods for controlling infection, prompted the development of the NICU: a common area where all medically and surgically ill infants are treated, premature and full term, infected and non-infected.

Even though treating all critically ill neonates in a single area allows for the cost-effective concentration of resources, neonatal intensive care is expensive and is, therefore, subject to the kind of regionalization that governs the scope and extent of emergency departments and trauma centers. Three levels are recognized.

▲ Level I facilities have as their primary goal the management of normal pregnancy, labor, and delivery as well as the early identification of high-risk situations and the provision of emergency care in the event of unanticipated complications.

▲ Level II facilities include Level I services, with the addition of a neonatal critical care unit capable of managing most neonatal complications.

▲ Level III facilities encompass the services of levels I and II, while also offering the most advanced critical care. These are designated regional centers for neonatal intensive care.

Level II and III NICUs perform the following functions:

▲ Observe critical infants

▲ Monitor critical infants electronically and biomedically

▲ Carry out advanced therapeutic procedures

▲ Promote maternal-child contact to the fullest extent possible.

The last function reflects a growing realization that maternal handling as well as sensory stimulation (but not overstimulation or inappropriate stimulation) are crucial in the neonate's earliest hours and days—even if the infant is critically ill. Thus planners and designers of NICU facilities are faced with a set of requirements that are, in many points, contradic-

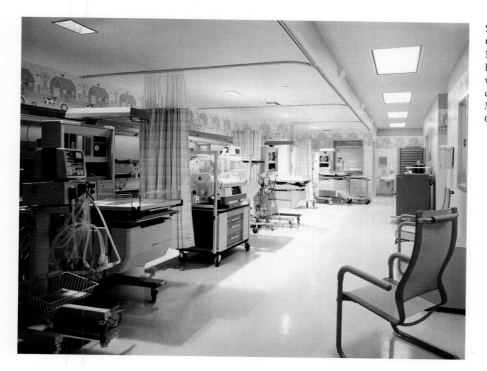

Sharp Chula Vista Medical Center, Chula Vista, California. In the Level II Nursery, designers added touches of a home environment in the use of color, wallpaper borders, and comfortable chairs for mothers. *Photo by Steve McClelland. Courtesy Stichler Design Group.*

tory. On the one hand, there is a call for a common technically sophisticated space, while, on the other, there is a call for a humane environment that facilitates maternal contact.

A number of recent studies have suggested that humanizing the NICU may be more of a clinically urgent matter than merely a desirable goal. Some authorities have suggested that continual exposure to bright lights may contribute to retinopathy of prematurity (ROP), a leading cause of blindness in premature infants. Another effect of continual high-level illumination is disruption of diurnal patterns at this earliest stage of development. Parents of premature infants that have been exposed to unvarying illumination twenty-four hours a day report disturbances in the infant's sleep pattern for weeks, even months after they return home with the child. Monitoring of cardiorespiratory function demonstrates that these vital signs tend to be more stable when infants are exposed to cycled lighting that mimics diurnal patterns.

Overstimulation of cardiorespiratory function may not be solely the result of continual exposure to bright lighting. When light levels are high, noise levels are commensurately high. When light levels are dimmed, noise level also decline. Indeed, noise in traditional NICUs is often at a distressingly high level. Alarms and incubators are the biggest mechanical noise producers. These not only elevate levels of arousal, there is evidence that protracted exposure to incubator noise levels in excess of 70 decibels may contribute to actual cochlear damage and subsequent hearing loss. (*See* Fred H. Bass, Ph.D., et al, "Further Observations on Noise Levels in Infant Incubators," *Pediatrics* 63, no. 1 [January 1979] and Stanley N. Graven, M.D., et al, "The High-Risk Infant Environment, Part I, *Journal of Perinatology* 12, no. 2 [1992].) Since at least the early 1980s, studies have appeared warning that the NICU truly is a "high-risk environment" (*see* Susan Blackburn, "The Neonatal ICU: A High-Risk Environment," *Ameri-*

can Journal of Nursing, November 1982). As in the adult ICU, sensory overload is also a threat of professional staff. In a more recent development, undertaken in part to minimize the ill effects of the traditional NICU unit, architects have moved away from the warehouse-style NICU, designing instead smaller units of four to six bassinets.

The only humanizing architectural element that most authorities argue *against* including in the design of the NICU is windows, primarily due to their thermal effects, which can cause potentially harmful dips or spikes in ambient temperature. In settings where fully enclosed incubators are used, it is even possible that too much sunlight can cause excessive warming due to a greenhouse effect. The NICU at McKennan Hospital, designed by Earl Swensson Associates in Sioux Falls, South Dakota, does include windows, which admit a diffuse north light. Radiant heaters located at the windows prevent cold air infiltration.

The McKennan NICU also incorporates muted colors, since babies, especially under stress, do not respond well to bright colors. The room is further defined by black-and-white wallpaper borders. Lighting at this NICU is a mixture of true-color fluorescent and indirect cove lighting. To maximize work efficiency, the lab and work room are adjacent to the NICU to enable nurses to monitor the unit more closely. Casework, which was custom designed by the architects, also aims at maximum efficiency, with rounded forms and recessed panels for vacuum bottles and flow meters to provide greater mobility and access for nurses.

The McKennan unit makes a parent room available to accommodate well parents who want to be close to their babies. A nourishment area vends soft drinks, coffee, and so on. There is also a "hold nursery" provision, a place for well babies, who would normally be cared for in a Level I nursery on the third floor, whose mothers require a longer-than-normal hospital stay. The fourth-floor "holding nursery" allows the infant to remain closer to his mother during the day. At night, he is moved back to the well-baby nursery on the third floor.

The 1991 NICU at Centennial: The Women's Hospital, Nashville, Tennessee, was designed by Earl Swensson Associates. A state-of-the-art facility, it is designed to provide intensive care for special needs while maintaining contact between the family (mother, father, siblings) and the infant. Twenty beds (bassinets) are licensed, of which twelve are designated for intensive care and eight for intermediate. The facility is laid out for maximum visibility and a close connection between the nurses' work room and the NICU proper. The space is designed to bring as much of the nurses' work into the NICU itself so that the staff can remain close to the infants. While visibility is a key feature in this design, the usual clinical-institutional pitfalls are avoided. Lighting levels are automatically cycled to promote the babies' regular sleep schedule, and finishes throughout the facility are more traditional than institutional. As far as possible, the NICU maintains the homelike setting that predominates throughout the Family Birth Unit.

The Patient Care Unit

Anyone who talks with medical professionals and hospital planners or who reads the current literature devoted to the future of the hospital is tempted to conclude that hospitals have given up on their traditional principal constituent, the inpatient. Such a conclusion is unwarranted.

It is true that the inpatient market continues to shrink. It is also true that a substantial number of futurists—including staff members of Earl Swensson Associates—foresee a time, probably within the next century, when the hospital will, indeed, cease to exist, at least in any form familiar to us now. Genetic engineering will radically alter the incidence and treatment of disease, and various forms of community, step-down, and home care will radically alter the management of disease. However, for the nearer term—that portion of the future for which we are building today—inpatient care will continue to be a significant hospital role.

With the possible exception of hospital lobby areas, nowhere is the trend toward "patient-focused" care more visibly evident than in the design and decoration of patient rooms. Patient-focused room design was given its single greatest burst of momentum by the Planetree movement, which had its origin in 1978. That was the year a healthcare consumer named Angelica Thieriot was hospitalized and experienced, firsthand, how traditional hospital design (and procedures) heightened discomfort, diminished dignity, increased anxiety, and generally exacerbated illness. As a result of her nightmarish experience, Thieriot founded a nonprofit organization to provide health and medical information aimed at improving the human quality of patient care. Called Planetree, after the plane tree under which Hippocrates sat while he taught, the organization sponsored a Health Resource Center, and it developed a model hospital unit in San Francisco's Pacific Presbyterian Medical Center in 1985. Soon, other institutions were designing patient units on the Planetree model. Such units are characterized by self-responsibility and humane care. Traditional hospital rules and regulations are relaxed, and the feel of the Planetree-inspired units is generally more residential than institutional, with kitchenettes where visitors and patients can prepare their own food; indirect, full-spectrum lighting; a predominance of wood finishes rather

Mid-Columbia Medical Center, The Dalles, Oregon. The nursing station is open to patients and family. The medical center, designed by Marc Schweitzer, has adopted the Planetree concept of patient care. *Photo by Bruce Beaton. Courtesy Mid-Columbia Medical Center.*

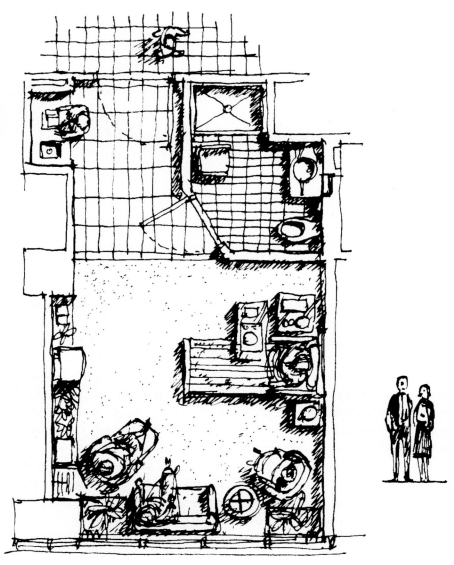

A room dedicated to patient-focused care might include a nurses' work area, plenty of seating for visitors, casework for TV/VCR and personal possessions, and handicapped-accessible bath facilities. *Sketch by Earl S. Swensson.*

than plastic or metal; artwork of genuine merit on loan from museums; rooms decorated with some of the patient's own belongings; a patient-visitor lounge, equipped with a VCR and cassette library; and, throughout, the maintenance of a generally "high-touch" environment.

While all of this may seem a far cry from what is now the often-maligned concept of the so-called "Nightingale ward"—the patient care paradigm established by Florence Nightingale in the mid nineteenth century—patient-focused design may actually be seen as having originated in the reforms of the Lady with the Lamp. Elsewhere we have briefly outlined the development of the modern hospital. No less than Theriot's Planetree efforts, Nightingale's reforms were aimed at humanizing inhumane hospital conditions. The conditions Nightingale faced—filth, disorder, and a nursing "profession" held in vile repute—were the result of the *absence* of an efficient institution rather than overbearing institutionalism. Her reforms, therefore, were directed at bringing order to chaos, replacing dirt with cleanliness, and creating an environment in which nurses could perform efficiently and effectively as valued medical professionals.

There was little question of housing patients in private rooms. To begin with, in the medical care system of Nightingale's day, this would have been economically unfeasible. Well-to-do patients were treated at home. Only the working poor and the indigent submitted themselves to hospitals. Medical economics dictated treatment in wards rather than rooms, and Nightingale turned this economic necessity into a patient-management asset. The design of the Nightingale ward was intended to facilitate nursing care, allowing fewer nurses to minister effectively to larger numbers of patients. Moreover, the public nature of the ward lent moral credibility to the nurse's role by eliminating the potential intimacies of care in a private room. It might be argued that Nightingale's reforms were not focused on the patient, but, rather, had as their objective the convenience of the institution and the moral and professional rehabilitation of the nursing profession. But this view fails to take into account the historical context of her reforms. They enabled the creation of an institution in place of disorder and (at best) benign neglect. And who could deny that, by transforming nursing into a true profession, Nightingale did not vastly improve—humanize—patient care?

The reforms of Florence Nightingale were monumental steps toward patient-focused care. But, as we have learned most dramatically during the last decade or so, the paradigms that shape healthcare are hardly immutable and immune to change. In large part due to Nightingale's reforms, and in part due to the technical advancement of medicine, by the close of the nineteenth century, consignment to a hospital was no longer the equivalent of a death sentence. Hospitals began to emerge as places where people actually got well. With the amelioration of the hospital's image, wealthier patients began to seek hospital care, creating a demand for private rooms. While some medical authorities touted the private room as a means of reducing the potential for cross-infection of patients, the motivation for the introduction of the private room was socio-economic rather than strictly medical. Certainly, private rooms did not make the nurse's job easier. Quite the contrary, for many years, far into the twentieth century, the open ward was looked upon as the more efficient environment for providing patient care.

At a superficial glance, the on-going trend toward patient units with exclusively private rooms may seem nothing more than an extension of a response to a marketplace that began at the end of the nineteenth century. But it is not only the marketplace that has evolved. The fact is that the medical approach to patient care has also developed. No longer is the nurse a mere observer and practical caretaker who has charge of the patient in the doctor's absence. He or she is now part of a patient-care team, a team whose work is increasingly facilitated by bedside diagnostic, monitoring, and medication-dispensing equipment. The team approach and technological developments have made the open ward essentially obsolete. Not since the late nineteenth century has it been the most comfortable patient environment. Now it is also no longer the most efficient means of monitoring and managing patients.

■ From Patient Focus to Clinical Integration

The headline of the "Publisher's Page" of the March/April 1993 *Healthcare Forum Journal* reads: "Integrate or Disintegrate." Executive publisher Kathryn E. Johnson declared: "By now it is no secret that survival in the 1990s and beyond is going to require new linkages and systems that are user-friendly to both patients and providers; only those organizations that are part of the best integrated packages will get paid. The emerging imperative is to integrate—or disintegrate."

In an effort to adapt to the demands of managed care and cost containment, hospitals are attempting to evolve into organic components of "organized delivery systems," networks of organizations that provide a coordinated continuum of services to a defined population. The "ODS," intimately linked to an insurance product, assumes fiscal and clinical responsibility for the health status of a defined population. Instead of focusing on an "illness" paradigm—stressing acute care, provider dominance, and individual patients—the ODS is structured according to a "wellness" paradigm and emphasizes health status prediction and management, provider-patient partnerships, and a collective population-based focus.

Through the principle of "vertical integration," the ODS owns, manages, and coordinates such diverse health services as home healthcare agencies, hospices, group practices, rehabilitative services, acute inpatient care, and so on. If vertical integration structures the "macro" aspects of the ODS, "clinical integration" informs the "micro" aspects. Clinical integration is the coordination of patient care across the functions and operating units of an organized delivery system. In a clinically integrated facility, the care of each patient may be managed from admission to discharge by a designated nurse. Care is delivered by a team of personnel supervised by the nurse. The nurse also coordinates patient care with

St. Michael Hospital, Texarkana, Texas. Model. Completed in 1994, the facility consists of a replacement hospital, two MOBs, and a rehabilitation hospital. Many design features of the replacement hospital promote increased care giving and greater efficiency: triangular nursing units will increase in size from 30-bed to 36-bed units; patient room size will increase 34 percent to allow more room for family; yet, the average walking distance from the nursing station to a patient room will decrease by 25 percent. The facility has been described in the *Healing Health* newsletter as "one of the outstanding healthcare facilities under construction. . . . It will become a model for the future." *Photo by Ed Stewart Photographers. Courtesy Walkins Carter Hamilton.*

physicians and other healthcare consultants. Even support functions, such as dietary assistance and housekeeping, are unit based.

Clinical integration depends on "work redesign" to create a four-level patient-care team.

1. A professional RN patient care manager works with physicians and others to assess the appropriate use of resources in order to facilitate treatment. The RN brings patients, physicians and others together to determine and create a plan to achieve desired outcomes. He or she manages staff, including hiring, scheduling, and skill-developing, for his or her group of patients. Finally, the RN manages the financial and material resources required for achieving desired goals.

2. The patient care nurse administers tests and medication.

3. The patient care technician provides such care as hygiene, certain technical procedures (for example, EKG), routine wound care, and so on.

4. The unit assistant provides housecleaning in the patient room, delivers supplies, and so on.

Vertical integration, with its attendant trend toward clinical integration and work redesign, makes the patient room the most intensive focus of inpatient care. Wherever possible, the team comes to the patient, instead of the patient being transported to various professionals.

■ Convergence and Conflict

As in many other areas of the hospital, "technology" and "humanity" often present conflicting demands in the design of the patient room and the entire patient unit. Most authorities, physicians, nurses, planners, administrators, architects, and patients agree that the patient room, as the new locus of treatment, should be a human and humane environment. Yet, while the overall goal may be agreed on, there are still many competing needs to be considered.

Eric Meub, writing in *Ekriture* (issue #3, July 1993), suggests that the redefinition of the hospital's *internal* messages—a sense of security, of community, comprehension of the surrounding order, freedom of choice—may sometimes conflict with what *external* architectural form conveys.

> . . . the urban hospital, with its emphasis on nurture, protection and inward focus, may present a conflicting expression to the street.
>
> Gently rounded forms may seem to convey centrality and enclosure, yet their compactness pushes vital exterior spaces to the perimeter. An orthogonal approach, however, while leaving room for a central, upper story garden court, pushes the mass aggressively to the edge of the site. In the end, it is the internal message that must be most clear. The edifice can speak to the site, the public, even the press, but it is the room which must console the spirit.

Four hospital nursing floors. *Sketches by Earl S. Swensson.*

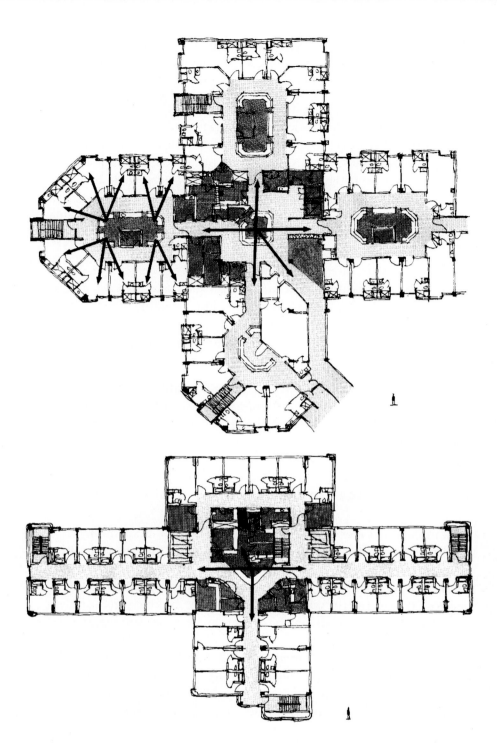

These "spiritual" imperatives include (to borrow from AHA Technical Document 055301, September 1991, "The Quest for the Perfect Patient Unit Design"):

▲ *Privacy*
▲ *Dignity*
▲ *Peace and quiet*
▲ *Sense of being observed in case help is needed*
▲ *Cleanliness*
▲ *Security*

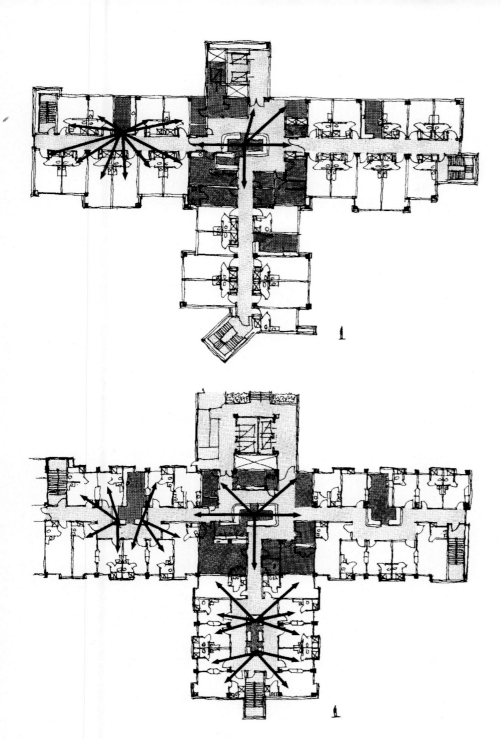

▲ *Diversion and entertainment*

▲ *Isolation from other patients, when required*

▲ *Company of other patients, when appropriate*

▲ *Interesting area for ambulation*

▲ *Tangible goal outside the patient room, to encourage ambulation*

▲ *Access to bathroom and shower*

▲ *Easy access to lighting, bed, and television controls*

▲ *Easy access to phone*

▲ *Easy access to nurses' call signal*

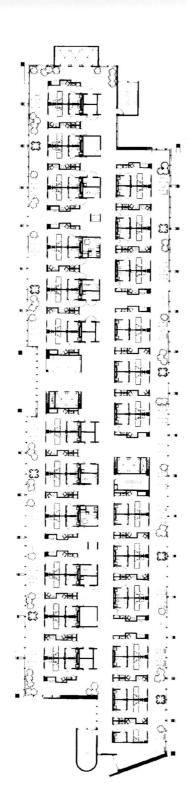

St. Luke's Medical Center, Milwaukee, Wisconsin. Floor plan, Cardiac Patient Tower. The perimeter of the unit features a solarium for visitors and peripheral stations for nursing staff. Support services are located in the center of the unit. Clerestory windows in the patient rooms add natural light. *Courtesy Bobrow/Thomas and Associates.*

▲ *Accessible place for personal belongings*
▲ *Accommodation for visitor*
▲ *Good, glare-free light*
▲ *View to the outside*
▲ *Aesthetic, pleasing environment*

Visitors' needs generally do not conflict with those of the patient, except that a high volume of visitation may be disturbing to some patients, especially if the rooms open onto busy principal corridors. The patient unit should address the following visitor needs:

▲ *Easy access and way-finding*
▲ *Access to information*
▲ *Waiting lounge*
▲ *Privacy for conversation with staff and physicians*
▲ *Privacy for conversation with patient*
▲ *Telephone*
▲ *Designated restrooms*
▲ *Dining facility*
▲ *Accommodation for overnight stay with critical patients*

Increasingly, hospitals are designing to accommodate family members as "care partners." Larger patient rooms permit a family member to sleep in the room.

The needs of nursing staff may, in some places, conflict with patient needs:

▲ *Easy access to patients*
▲ *Ability to see patients*
▲ *Minimized walking distances*
▲ *Sense of "knowing what's going on" in unit*
▲ *Ability to move beds, equipment, and supplies in and out of room*

The foregoing may well conflict with the patient's need for privacy, freedom of choice, and peace and quiet. The rest of the nursing staff's needs should pose no conflicts:

▲ *Ability to accommodate differing approaches to staffing (team vs. primary)*
▲ *Ability to deal with shift in severity index (step-down)*
▲ *Ability to work effectively, day shift, night shift*
▲ *Access to information retrieval and input*
▲ *Access to high-urgency/frequency use items*
▲ *Access to supplies and disposal*
▲ *Access to equipment storage in designated spaces*
▲ *Access to medication*
▲ *Ability of all care providers to confer in privacy*
▲ *Access to office and conference space*
▲ *Staff lounge facility*
▲ *Security—personal and property*

Well-designed provisions for security should be welcomed by patients as well as staff. However, there is the potential for conflict with a patient's sense of freedom and choice.

Physicians' needs generally do not conflict with those of the patient, so far as design is concerned. AHA Technical Document 055301 notes:

▲ *Bed availability*
▲ *Accommodation for all types of payers*
▲ *Accommodation for any specialty or subspecialty*
▲ *Cutting-edge care setting*
▲ *Caregiver easy to find*
▲ *Patient easy to find*
▲ *Chart easy to find*
▲ *Ability for all care providers to confer in privacy*
▲ *Quiet place for dictation or direct data entry, data retrieval, reference*
▲ *Access to properly equipped procedure room*
▲ *Access to clerical support*
▲ *Competitive unit with attractive image*
▲ *Abillity to move beds, equipment, and supplies in and out of room.*

The academic physician has additional needs that patients may find intrusive, but good design can minimize these feelings:

▲ *Unit large enough to accommodate medical teaching team*
▲ *Space for teaching without getting in the way of other functions*
▲ *Co-locate specialty beds for ease of rounds*
▲ *Confer with students on unit in privacy*
▲ *Access to charts/X-rays/texts/computer terminal/printer*
▲ *On-call facility*
▲ *Locker facility*
▲ *Resident office*
▲ *Resident workroom*
▲ *Classroom nearby*

In addition, the patient unit must accommodate clerical staff, other caregivers (physical therapists, inhalation therapists, etc.), and support services (dietary, pharmacy, materials management, etc.).

The clerical staff needs the ability to:

▲ *Observe unit to control flow of visitors and ancillary support staff and keep track of patient movement*
▲ *Communicate with patients*
▲ *Communicate with staff*
▲ *Access data for retrieval and input*
▲ *Communicate with other departments*
▲ *Accommodate pick-up and drop off of patient*

Physical therapists, inhalation therapists, I.V. therapists, radiology technicians, and other care givers require:

▲ *Office space*
▲ *On-floor storage space for supplies*

▲ *Dedicated space for patient care*
▲ *Communication with home department*
▲ *Equipment storage*
▲ *Remote monitoring capabilities*

Finally, support services requires:

▲ *Access to service elevators*
▲ *Access to patient care unit without impinging on patient space*
▲ *Floor space for supply and dietary carts, etc.*
▲ *Satellite facilities: pharmacy, lab, reheat pantry*
▲ *Transport system for lab specimens*
▲ *Decentralized housekeeping centers*
▲ *Low-maintenance engineering system, with good access to frequent maintenance points*

Maintenance operations should not impinge on patient or staff space or activities.

Patient-focused, clinically integrated design attempts as fully as possible to accommodate and reconcile these potentially conflicting needs.

■ Design for Patient-Focused, Clinically Integrated Facilities

In September 1992, Wanda J. Jones and Milton Bullard published the findings of a research project they undertook sponsored by Ratcliff Architects (Emeryville, California) and The H.O.M. Group (San Francisco). They set out to answer a single question: "What would a totally Patient-Focused Hospital *operate like* and *look like* if we applied all the ideas arising from the various demonstration projects and extended them to their logical limits?" The conclusions Jones and Bullard reached suggest some general design trends for patient rooms and nursing floors. Many of these features are already being incorporated in advanced patient room design.

The ward and semi-private room will have no place in patient-focused facilities. Instead, these hospitals will feature large single-patient rooms. If the standard room today is about 180 net square feet, the patient-focused room will be 250. The greater space is required for effective treatment by the care team, including the use of portable equipment brought to the patient and the performance of certain procedures in the room. This flexibility reduces the necessity of transporting the patient from specialist to specialist and procedure to procedure. Moreover, the larger room allows for more comfortable conferencing and counseling, and it can accommodate family members, either as visitors or as care partners. (One design possibility incorporates a large window seat that can be converted into a bed for such a "care partner.")

Jones and Bullard observe that the larger patient room can perform many of the functions of an ICU, provided that the proper equipment is brought in, thereby making it unnecessary to move the patient in an out of a separate ICU. Indeed, it may be possible to convert any number of the larger rooms to dedicated ICUs as required without major new construction. Since, under managed care, inpatients will, by definition, be sicker patients (those who are less ill will be treated on an ambulatory or very short-term-stay basis), the potential for ready conversion to ICU function is very important.

Finally, planning facilities with larger rooms makes long-term economic sense. To be sure, initial capital costs are greater, but the gain in flexibility and future adaptability can represent a substantial savings. Larger rooms are more easily adapted to such "down-program" uses as hospice, rehabilitation, elderly housing, and the like.

Another step toward enhancing flexibility is the inclusion of disabled-accessible bathrooms for all rooms. This will render all rooms accessible to all patients at all times, regardless of age, sex, or handicapped status. It will never be necessary for Admitting to scramble in order to accommodate a disabled patient.

While so-called "inboard" bathrooms—that is, bathrooms next to the corridor—are industry standard, Jones and Bullard believe that the bathrooms should be located on the outside wall. These "outboard" bathrooms allow the entire room space to be made available for use according to the state's code analysis; it keeps the interior wall free, which could readily be converted to glass, if the room were transformed into an ICU. Advocates of the inboard bathroom point out, however, that such placement provides additional privacy for patients, is a good location for hand washing and utility use by staff, creates a vestibule that accommodates the door swing, is logical from a construction cost standpoint, and makes the patient room more closely resemble a hotel room, providing space for an expansive exterior window.

Jones and Bullard recommend the design of what they call the "care suite," a cluster of beds smaller than the conventional nursing unit, which can be readily supervised by a care team—or "care pair" (a cross-trained pair of nurses supported by technicians). These care suites are further developments of two trends prevalent in recent hospital design, both alternatives to the traditional "racetrack" nursing unit: the triangle and the pod. As triangle and pod plans represented a major step toward modularization from the racetrack plan, so the care suite is a further modular departure from the triangle and pod.

The care suites could be designed such that the individual patient rooms do not open onto a busy corridor. These clusters are also more easily managed to accommodate fluctuating patient census. It is easier to close a six-bed cluster than a 34-bed standard nursing unit. It would also be relatively easy to assign different suites to specific types of patients, allowing programs to grow or shrink in manageable increments. Finally, rooms located at the ends of each suite could readily be transformed into isolation rooms. Each care suite could include a lounge, library, kitchenette, and conference facilities, in all making for a more human scale, a sense of community, security, and serenity.

Thornton Hospital, University of California, San Diego, California. Floor plan, second floor. Note the triangular design of the nursing unit. *Courtesy Stone Marraccini Patterson.*

1 Public elevator lobby
2 Service elevator lobby
3 Mechanical service bays
4 Atrium
5 Lounge
6 Courtyard below
7 Patient care unit (27 beds)
8 Surgical suite
9 Cardiac catherization lab
10 Special procedures suite
11 Intensive care unit (12 beds)

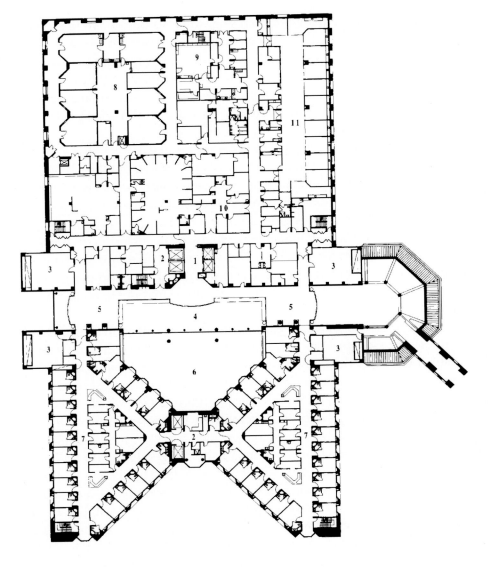

Patient focusing depends in large measure on implementation of emerging "bedside information systems," or clinical computing. Clinical computing links all care activity in real time, handling guidelines and protocols as well as results obtained from tests and procedures. The most advanced systems can accept input from patient monitoring devices (such as blood pressure, temperature, EKG, and so on). Clinical computing allows for more detailed and frequently updated charting, while it requires less time than manual charting. The technology also allows for the generation of check-off lists and quality assurance evaluations, which are crucial aspects of "total quality management" (TQM) systems. Such paperwork would be time-consuming and cumbersome in the absence of bedside computing. Studies indicate that clinical computing also significantly reduces charting and medication errors. Most significantly for design, bedside technologies allow for the kind of decentralized care that really makes care suites and "care pairs" feasible. With clinical computing all patient data can be shared—in real time—by all members of the care team. With advanced data communications, data can also be shared with consultants off-site, across the street or halfway around the world.

Jones and Bullard pose the question, "Does Patient-Focusing depend on clinical computing?" They reply: "The short answer is yes," but "it is possible to adopt clinical computing incrementally." Indeed, in the near term, there may be no other viable choice than to phase the technology in gradually, since, to date, there is no one comprehensive application available. A 1990 story in *Modern Healthcare* (July 16, 1990) reported that hospital planners and administrators were talking a great deal about bedside computers, but very few were actually plugging in. High-function systems still tend to be costly, while the lower-end equipment does satisfy some traditional nursing needs, but does not contribute much to the hospital's efficient use of data overall. Even at a time when one is accustomed to expect everything from computers, the requirements for bedside technology are especially demanding:

▲ *Customers want systems that will add minimally to per-bed capital costs.*
▲ *The system must be simple to use.*
▲ *The system must be thoroughly networked, able to share data completely and immediately with all other hospital computers.*
▲ *Displays must be sharp and graphics capable.*
▲ *The equipment must be durable. In a hospital environment, the equipment will be subject to jostling, dropping, bumping, and spillage. In some settings, particularly urban hospitals, vandalism may well be a significant problem.*
▲ *The equipment must be small and unobtrusive. At its most advanced, of course, the bedside computer will replace in-room monitoring equipment and so will actually save space.*
▲ *The software must be flexible and readily capable of being customized.*
▲ *Processors must be high powered and fast.*

One technology that may address many of the issues listed above is the handheld computer, familiar to anyone who has ever done business with couriers such as UPS and Federal Express. Pen-based handheld units—where data is entered with a penlike stylus rather than by keyboard—are naturals for many charting applications. Handheld units would make expensive, space-consuming, and damage-prone bedside terminals unnecessary. The handheld units could be "docked" as necessary with a headwall-mounted port to interface with the hospital network. It would also be possible to install a CRT (computer monitor) for each bed, complete with a port to accept output from the handheld computer. Alternatively, liquid crystal-type displays, such as those found on laptop or notebook computers, are currently available, in monochrome as well as color. Such a display could be part of the handheld unit, making the unit entirely independent of the room.

Another technology, this one even farther out along the cutting edge, may also contribute to decentralized patient care. Robotics has just begun experimentally to enter some hospitals as an alternative method of transporting supplies and laboratory specimens from one location to another. These are usually modified industrial robots that can be programmed to follow painted lines on floors and are "smart" enough to avoid bumping into obstacles, including people.

Bedside robotics is in its infancy. In Japan, a robot called Mekong has been under research and development for lifting, moving, and carrying patients. Nursing is a highly strenuous activity, and, as Pamela J. Rogers observes in "Bedside Revolution in Robotics" (*Hospital Management International 1991*, pp. 318-21), the "housewife has more equipment for saving her time and energy in performing basic tasks than is generally available to the bedside nurse." Nursing tasks, Rogers continues, are more closely related "to heavy industrial work involving loads than to the domestic duties of the sickroom," and she sites a 1979 University of Surrey study, which indicated that 40,000 of the 430,000 nurses then working in the (British) National Health Service were afflicted with back pain. As a result, 764,000 working days were lost. "In most cases, the pain could be related to patient handling."

Two trends are clear: Patient management, from admission to discharge and even follow-up, will devolve increasingly upon a nurse or nursing teams. An increasing proportion of patients admitted to in-hospital care will be the sickest individuals, who will make more demands on the nurses' skill—and on his or her physical strength. In view of these convergent trends, it seems likely that bedside robotics will continue to develop and eventually figure as an element of patient care design.

■ Patient Unit and Room Designs

CARDIAC PATIENT TOWER
ST. LUKE'S MEDICAL CENTER
Milwaukee, Wisconsin

In 1992, Bobrow/Thomas & Associates of Los Angeles designed two 48-patient units for the Cardiac Patient Tower of this medical center, which are intended to embody the new technological trends that have enabled decentralized nursing: computer workstations, paperless charting, cross-training of nursing care teams, bedside diagnostics. Portable—or movable—diagnostic equipment is banked on each floor of the facility, so that the necessity of transporting patients for diagnostic procedures is minimized. Instead of bedside computer terminals, workstations are deployed on desks that flank the single-patient rooms. Because there is no central nurse's station, staff travel time and corridor activity are minimized, despite the linear design. Moreover, the linear design is readily expandable as hospital needs change.

PINELAKE MEDICAL CENTER
Mayfield, Kentucky

In 1993, Earl Swensson Associates, Nashville, replaced a forty-year-old hospital with the 107-bed, 170,000-square-foot PineLake Medical Center and an integrated 50,000-square foot medical office building. The challenge was to combine state-of-the-art healthcare delivery with a highly humanized, comfortable environment incorporating convenient way-finding for all patients and minimizing conflict between inpatient and

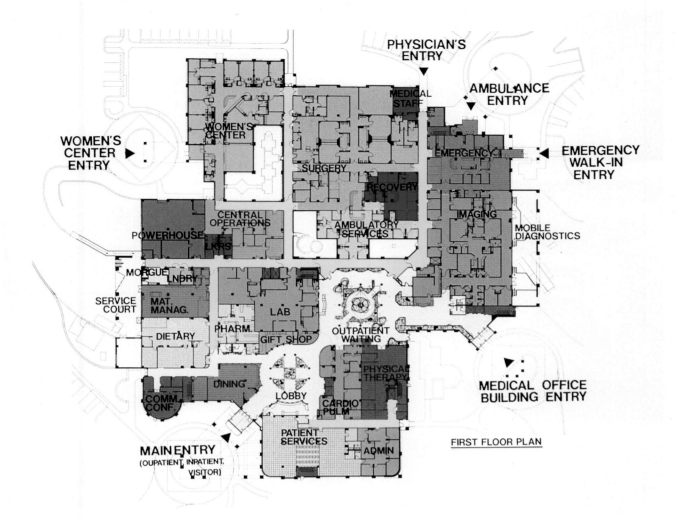

PineLake Medical Center, Mayfield, Kentucky. Floor plan, first floor. *Courtesy Earl Swensson Associates.*

outpatient traffic. The goal was not only to "please" patients, but to provide a facility that would attract excellent physicians to this rural area. Finally, PineLake was designed to facilitate cross-training through decentralization of traditional hospital departments into three basic components: patient care, patient administration, and operations support. The design team developed the interior layout around three areas of interrelated activities; for example, inpatient and outpatient registration and waiting functions are grouped into a central area, including such patient administration functions as the business and medical records offices. By computer linking this area to the patient care pods and adjoining medical office building, about half the staff formerly based in administrative areas has been moved to the patient floors. With patient wings designed as a cross-shaped tower, the intersection, or hub, is used as a business and reception station. "Ward" secretaries, stationed at these locations, perform such functions as chart management, concurrent coding, and even registration.

Each wing contains eight patient rooms, which are oversized to accommodate family members. A love seat and lounge chair are included in each room. The rooms are furnished in a residential style, including an

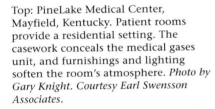

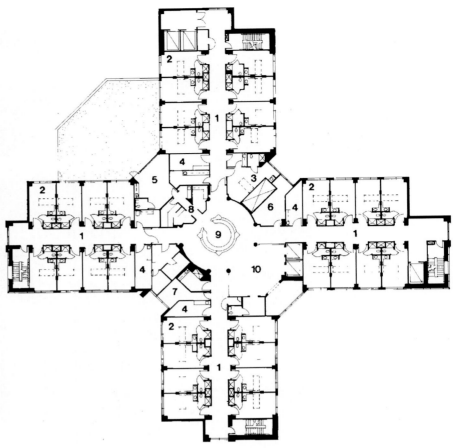

Top: PineLake Medical Center, Mayfield, Kentucky. Patient rooms provide a residential setting. The casework conceals the medical gases unit, and furnishings and lighting soften the room's atmosphere. *Photo by Gary Knight. Courtesy Earl Swensson Associates.*

Bottom: PineLake Medical Center, Mayfield, Kentucky. A flip-down charting space at each patient room allows nursing staff to work outside the room itself. The nursing station appears in the background. *Photo by Gary Knight. Courtesy Earl Swensson Associates.*

Right: PineLake Medical Center, Mayfield, Kentucky. Floor plan, fourth floor. *Courtesy Earl Swensson Associates.*

1 Corridor
2 Patient room
3 Rec/dining
4 Nurses' sub-station
5 Lounge
6 Conference
7 Office
8 Work
9 Nurses' station/clerk
10 Waiting

armoire, which contains the television and provides storage for personal clothing as well as supplies. To achieve a residential look, three of the walls are painted, while the patient headwall has a durable covering, and medical gases are enclosed and concealed into cabinet areas that are part of the vanity. A wallpaper border on the ceiling ties the residential design together. Room lighting is also residential, but it is instantly convertible to exam lighting when necessary. An inboard toilet provides maximum privacy. The rooms are wired for eventual installation of bedside computers.

ESa chose interior finishes to create a natural environment for healing, using warm, natural-hue colors. In public areas, planters were used to create "meandering" paths, and intimate groups of seating were deployed in the reception/waiting area. With each wing—or pod—limited to eight beds, a decentralized nursing station, located no more than fifty feet from any room, provides patient-focused care. Locating supplies close to the rooms reduces travel time and corridor activity. The more traditional central nurses' stations are used for business functions, such as coders and unit secretaries, during the day. At night or during periods of low census, the installation is used as a nurses' station.

The Patient Care Unit

SENTARA NORFOLK GENERAL HOSPITAL RIVER PAVILION
Norfolk, Virginia

HDR, Inc., designed a 215,000 square-foot, six-story, 72-bed hospital addition completed in 1993. Floors 5 and 6 of the addition, a cardiac care unit and a multi-use unit, were specifically designed for patient-focused care. Charting is done on computer terminals in the patient's room, and zones on each floor are devoted to staff support (conference room, lounge, lockers, supply), stat lab, and diagnostic support. The object is for cross-trained nurses to perform as many charting and diagnostic procedures on site as possible. The fifth-floor cardiac unit, unlike the sixth-floor multi-purpose unit, does not have a stat lab, since many tests in this area require more specialized expertise than even a cross-trained nurse can provide. However, the floor is equipped with a room for telemetry monitoring.

Sentara Norfolk General Hospital, Norfolk, Virginia. Floor plan. *Courtesy HDR, Inc.*

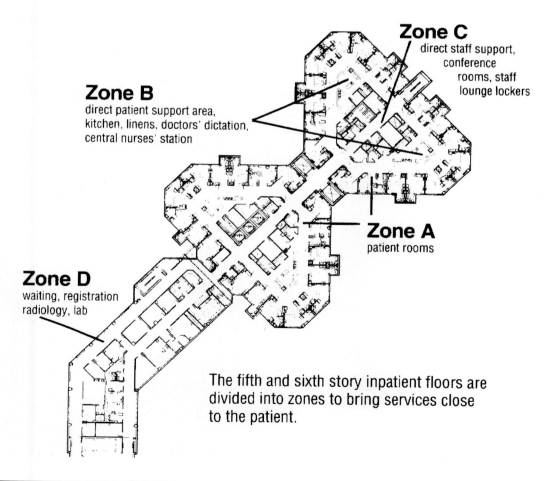

Zone C
direct staff support, conference rooms, staff lounge lockers

Zone B
direct patient support area, kitchen, linens, doctors' dictation, central nurses' station

Zone A
patient rooms

Zone D
waiting, registration radiology, lab

The fifth and sixth story inpatient floors are divided into zones to bring services close to the patient.

Room size is large—14 x 14 feet—not only to enhance patient comfort, but to allow for immediate conversion to ICU function. Charting desks in each room are wired for computer terminals, and the space under the desk stows an exchange cart, which can be accessed from outside the room, so that supplies can be replenished without disturbing the patient.

■ A New Patient Accommodation Trend: The VIP Suite

If the general medical-surgical patient room is now borrowing much from the hospitality industry, a number of hospitals are taking the analogy a step further by introducing "VIP suites," which correspond to the "concierge floor" or "executive level" of many up-market hotels. The VIP suite is a fully self-contained environment designed to provide a high level of creature comforts. VIP facilities characteristically include a separate kitchen that serves 24 hours a day; a separate, private waiting lobby for visitors; private consultation rooms for family and patients; lounges and reading areas; game rooms; and even dining rooms (although present experience suggests that these are under-utilized; most patients prefer to dine in their suites). Decor tends to be traditional, since the assumption is that (at least for the near term) the clientele who occupy the VIP suites will be older patients, whose tastes lean toward the traditional.

The Camellia Pavilion, designed by Hellmuth, Obata & Kassabaum for the University of Alabama at Birmingham Hospital, was profiled in a 1991 issue of *Journal of Health Care Interior Design*. Rooms in the Georgian-styled pavilion offer a minimum of 390 to 400 square feet—and that is just bedroom space. True suites, which include a sitting room, double the square footage. As in a hotel, such amenities as televisions and VCRs are

Camellia Pavilion at University of Alabama Hospital, Birmingham, Alabama. The sitting room of the patient suite has been furnished with hardwood floors and traditional furniture. The room provides additional space for families and visitors. *Photo by Alise O'Brien. Courtesy Hellmuth, Obata, & Kassabaum, Inc.*

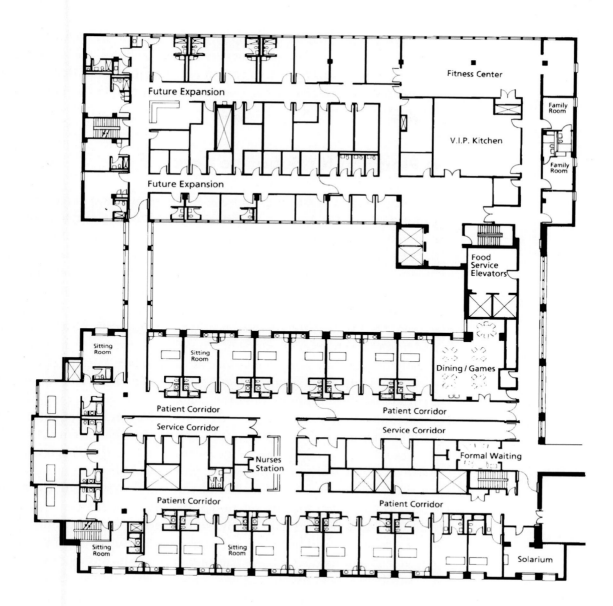

Camellia Pavilion at University of Alabama Hospital, Birmingham, Alabama. Floor plan, VIP suites. The design of the facility separates corridors for patients and visitors from corridors for support services. *Courtesy Hellmuth, Obata, & Kassabaum, Inc.*

concealed in armoires rather than suspended, hospital-fashion, from the ceiling. Desks feature data ports for the patient's personal computer, and there is a full bath with a tub and a shower. The larger suites have *two* full baths, the second one meant to accommodate the assistants or security people who might be part of a VIP's entourage. Also included in the bathroom is a refrigerator and juice bar.

Entry to the Camellia Pavilion's VIP suites is separate from, but close to, the main hospital entrance. The pavilion entrance opens into a private room that functions as a small lobby, from which visitors can take elevators to the VIP suite. Cart and service traffic is separated from visitor and patient traffic in order to reduce corridor bustle and noise. The Camellia Pavilion shares a fitness center with other parts of the hospital. Although physical therapy is performed in the fitness center, the facility is also open to staff and visitors for their use. This in itself minimizes the clinical feel of the rehabilitation facility.

Hospitals that offer VIP suites report a very high rate of occupancy, on average 10 percent higher than the rate for standard rooms, and it is likely that an increasing number of hospitals will design for the inclusion of such facilities. Architects and designers face the technical and aesthetic challenges of making high-tech equipment work in settings that, as in the Georgian-inspired Camellia Pavilion, are not only traditional, but even historical in inspiration.

■ Planning for Subacute Care

Advancements in medicine promise us healthier lives and longer lives. Unfortunately, "healthier" and "longer" tend, at some point, to become mutually exclusive goals. Medicine has learned to cure many diseases once thought incurable, and, even more, it is learning to manage those illnesses it cannot cure. Some chronically ill patients can be cared for on an outpatient basis or through homecare programs. This is a trend most students of the medical marketplace see as growing. Yet, as medicine extends the lives of patients who are critically chronically ill, ambulatory and homecare are often insufficient. Therefore, a growing segment of inpatient healthcare is so-called subacute care. In fact, Michael Boroch, a partner in Loudon and Company of Nashville, Tennessee, and consultant to healthcare organizations, observes: "Subacute care is a very important trend in the healthcare field, not a flash in the pan. At present, it is a $6 to $9 million industry and is growing at a rate of 35 to 40 percent per year."

Traditionally—that is, before the ascendancy of DRGs (Diagnosis-Related Groups)—chronic care was the province of freestanding skilled-nursing facilities (SNFs), while subacute care was the responsibility of the acute hospital. After the introduction of the DRG model, freestanding skilled-nursing facilities have continued to operate, but, increasingly, acute hospitals are admitting only genuinely acute patients. While the chronic patient requires, on average, one to two years of supportive care, the subacute patient usually requires some fifteen to twenty days of restorative and rehabilitative care. In many areas, this patient's needs are being served inadequately. It is possible for freestanding SNFs and even longer-term chronic-care facilities to design in order to capture this market, but the more active current trend is toward hospital-based SNFs, including the conversion of medical/surgical beds to this function.

The fastest-growing market for SNF care is among elderly patients. Oftentimes, community nursing homes are not equipped to treat patients requiring tube feedings, those with new colostomies (and associated complications), serious decubitus ulcers (bed sores), ventilator-dependent patients, stroke-related disabilities, chronic pulmonary complications, the complications of joint and hip procedures, and other disorders. Depending on the course of the AIDS epidemic, these patients, too, are likely to present a market for subacute care, particularly as various therapies extend survival without, however, curing the underlying disease. Finally, advances in the treatment of neonates with severe disorders mean that more patients who, in the past, would have died in infancy, now survive for longer periods, albeit—frequently—with disabilities that require either long-term care or more-or-less protracted episodes of skilled-nursing care.

What all of these groups have in common is a requirement for eight to nine hours of nursing per day, compared to four to six hours in an acute setting and twelve to twenty-four hours in ICU.

The literature devoted to long-term care environments, especially for the aged and those afflicted with Alzheimer's disease and other forms of dementia, is both vast and relatively recent. This in itself is a significant indicator of changing demographics and the healthcare community's recognition of these changes.

In eldercare, the traditional distinctions between long-term and subacute care will increasingly blur as the emphasis in all levels of care shifts from maintenance to rehabilitation. The term "nursing home" will be heard less and less as SNFs increasingly stress *living* over *nursing*. This emphasis applies generally to all emerging skilled-nursing, rehabilitation, and psychiatric/neurological facilities, regardless of the age group served. Perhaps the single overriding concept that informs emerging trends in SNF and long-term facility design is best expressed in the title of a recent book on planning environments for people with dementia: *Holding on to Home.*

Superficially, "holding on to home" may mean creating non-institutional, homelike environments. Indeed, this is often deemed desirable, as are environments fashioned after the hospitality model. On a deeper level, however, designs that facilitate "holding on to home" are designs that enable optimum functioning.

The challenge to the architect and designer is to change focus from creating merely aesthetically satisfying structures to creating aesthetically satisfying structures that are barrier-free and that make way-finding crystal clear by facilitating cognitive mapping. Nowhere is the paradigm shift from design standardized on a healthy thirty-year-old male to design standardized on a frail seventy-year-old woman more apparent than in effective layout and detailing for the skilled-nursing facility. For example:

▲ Architects customarily conceal functional items, especially toilets. In an extended-care facility, such items must be clearly indicated and marked. Alzheimer's patients and others have difficulty remembering the location of architectural features they cannot physically see. The homely example of the clearly indicated toilet is a demonstration of a way in which thoughtful design can promote health, a sense of well-being and independence, and facilitate holding on to home. If a patient cannot readily find the toilet, the likelihood of incontinence is increased and, with that, the patient's sense of dignity and independence is diminished. Furthermore, since the average incontinent patient generates a quite literally staggering seventy pounds of laundry per day, careful design for way-finding saves patient time and money and staff costs, not to mention stress on the environment. Many such homely elements contribute to advanced SNF design.

▲ Architects and designers must be sensitive to balancing the perceptions and expectations of a patient's family on the one hand with building features that benefit the patient on the other. For example, glare is a particular problem for aging eyes. Not only should lighting be designed to minimize glare, but shiny surfaces, which produce glare, should be avoided. This means that unwaxed, matte-finished flooring is best for patients—even though their families may equate "shiny" with "elegant," "new," and "clean." Again, glare-free design actively encourages patient mobility, while a family-pleasing shiny floor may well discourage it.

▲ The kind of color palette that appeals to most designers for a residential, hospitality, or even acute hospital environment may be inappropriate for long-term care facilities. As eyes age, the ability to distinguish violets, blues, and greens diminishes, while colors at the other end of the spectrum, red, orange, and yellow, tend to remain much more distinct. Common sense suggests that these latter colors will *not* contribute to a pleasing, serene interior environment—and this common sense view is perfectly true, *if* design is standardized on the healthy thirty-year-old. For a frail seventy-year-old, however, such "loud" colors create an environment that encourages mobility, facilitates way-finding, and, therefore, promotes well-being.

PEACHWOOD INN
Rochester Hills, Michigan

Along with barrier-free design and design aimed at compensating for loss of sensory acuity, there is the issue of creating an environment that suggests home and maintains contact with the outside world. One of the most innovative examples of such design is Peachwood Inn, in Rochester Hills, Michigan, which was designed in accordance with the "Caretel" concept developed by Horace D'Angelo, Jr., and profiled in *The Journal of Health Care Interior Design* (1990). "By and large, people in the nursing home industry are wonderful, caring people who want to provide the elderly with care," D'Angelo said, in explaining his concept.

> This is not an easy job. I realized that the public probably appreciated the work involved in running a long-term care facility, and I understood the role their own guilt played in their perceived negative image of nursing homes. I decided the reason the public perceived long-term care as negative was its presentation, and that a positive presentation was necessary for all of the development elements to fall into place.
>
> That is when I decided to rethink the elements involved in building a long-term care facility and define a new conceptual model. The model I wanted to create was a hybrid between an excellent nursing home and a European residential hotel. The facility would bear a name similar to that of a hotel—the Peachwood Inn rather than the Peachwood Nursing Care Center. The units would bear names traditionally given to English country manors—Devon, Auburn, or Picadilly.
>
> I also rethought the presentation of long-term care. No longer would the ill and the elderly be housed in a clinical setting where only their clinical needs are met. The facility would also meet their social and aesthetic needs. . . . I wanted . . . to create a long-term-care facility that was different, that was "a place to live."

Peachwood Inn, Inc., Rochester Hills, Michigan. A resident's room in a facility designed to "meet social and aesthetic needs" of the elderly who live there. The furnishings of home used in this facility are especially important for the elderly. *Photo by Beth Singer. Courtesy Peachwood Inn, Inc.*

Peachwood Inn, Inc., Rochester Hills, Michigan. Conceived as a cross between a nursing home and a European residential hotel, the facility, designed by Hobbs & Black Associates, features three dining rooms. *Photo by Beth Singer. Courtesy Peachwood Inn, Inc.*

The building was layed out in an X-shaped plan, which incorporates a series of pleasant courtyards comprising four sixty-bed "neighborhoods." Dining facilities, all-too-often oppressively institutional in SNFs, are, in Peachwood, homelike facilities shared between "neighborhoods." Residents have a choice of dining rooms, from small, intimate facilities to larger dining areas, which also afford assistance for those who have difficulty feeding themselves. A "Tavern on the Green" is available for a before-dinner drink, and residents are encouraged to entertain their family members here.

While virtually any SNF can promote a non-institutional feeling of individuality by encouraging residents or patients to decorate their rooms with their own belongings and treasures, design can build in a certain amount of individuality from the start. Peachwood Inn's rooms come in nine distinct varieties and feature residential-style wallcoverings and furniture, as well as built-in window seats, suitable for sitting or for display of personal items. Some rooms feature bay windows, and all have wide closet doors designed so that wheelchair-bound residents can open their own closets.

In corridor areas, careful attention is devoted to way-finding, lighting, and acoustics—as well as to minimizing design features that smack of an institution. Corridors are carpeted, and different colors of carpeting are used to help distinguish among various areas. The corridor handrails are finished to a richly stained natural wood appearance and are positioned like a wainscot separating the lower corridor color from the upper. Lighting is indirect and glare-free.

Key to promoting independence and general well-being in long-term care is providing tangible goals for ambulation. Peachwood Inn draws on a cross between "neighborhood" and "shopping mall" concepts in such public areas as Picadilly Lane, which offers residents Aunt Peach's Ice Cream Parlor, a gift shop, Shearlock's Home Beauty Shop, and Bogie's, a movie theater. The Bugatti Bar and Bistro, at the end of Picadilly Lane, features a vintage Bugatti parked at the entrance.

CORRINE DOLAN ALZHEIMER CENTER AT HEATHER HILL
Chardon, Ohio

Designed by Stephen Nemtim of Taliesin Associated Architects of the Frank Lloyd Wright Foundation, and completed in 1989, the Corinne Dolan Alzheimer Center provides day, respite, and long-term care for patients in the early and middle stages of dementia. It is part of a 234-bed multidisiplinary, multilevel healthcare complex. The center itself accommodates twenty-three residents, in addition to six to ten daycare clients. It also provides one respite bed.

The center is a single-story structure consisting of two triangular units with a shared support and bathing core. The units each house twelve beds, designed to allow staff visual access and to provide a continuous loop path for wanderers. The design eliminates dead ends—a very important feature in creating environments for dementia patients. Each unit has a residential-style kitchen and activity center, a dining room, and a program/activity room. The units are each designated a "household," or family cluster. The units include "family rooms" for small group activities and socializing.

The residents' rooms are arranged around the perimeter of the wandering path. These rooms are accessed through Dutch doors, so that the patient can, if she wishes, maintain contact and orientation with the outside corridor, while preserving privacy. Each patient room includes a locked display case for the patient's treasured items. This not only allows the patient to retain and view familiar, meaningful objects, it also keeps them secure, yet allows others (especially staff) to gain insight about the patient and what she values. Patients are encouraged to furnish their rooms with furniture from home. The toilet is visible from the room and may be shielded by a wrap-around curtain. With Alzheimer's patients, it is important that the toilet be visible, so that it can be found easily and quickly. In this way, the physically and emotionally debilitating effects of incontinence are greatly reduced, while a sense of independence is enhanced.

The center is beautifully sited and includes a wild flower field near the entrance, a natural area with seating and a view of a brook, a patio with seating and raised planters for patients' gardening activity, and gardens designed for wandering. A playground for visiting family children is provided.

■ Psychiatric Facilities

JOHN GEORGE PSYCHIATRIC PAVILION
ALAMEDA COUNTY DEPARTMENT OF HEALTH SERVICES
San Leandro, California

Ratcliff Architects created a 71,000-square-foot, five-building campus incorporating a short-stay acute care hospital, accommodating eighty

John George Psychiatric Pavilion, San Leandro, California. Floor plan, main level. *Courtesy Ratcliff Associates.*

1   Loading dock
2   Waiting
3   Nurses' station
4. Interview exam (typical)
5   Lounge/dining
6   Single (typical)
7   Double (typical)
8   Seclusion (typical)
9   Food service
10 Pharmacy
11 Delousing
12 Office (typical)
13 Conference
14 Group
15 Classroom
16 Multipurpose
17 Craft
18 Diet therapy
19 Courtyard

John George Psychiatric Pavilion, San Leandro, California. The lobby/ registration area of a facility designed to maintain a residential scale and a relaxed atmosphere. *Photo by Jane Lidz. Courtesy Ratcliff Associates.*

Right: John George Psychiatric Pavilion, San Leandro, California. The design is organized around a central courtyard in a campus setting. A colonnade connects the buildings, all of which give the Pavilion a strong community feel. *Photo by Jane Lidz. Courtesy Ratcliff Associates.*

patients, and a full outpatient treatment center. The goal was to design a non-institutional, villagelike environment intended to encourage social interaction among patients and between patients and staff. At the same time, the designers sought to promote maximum efficiency of staff operations.

The site, a prominent hilltop location in an area featuring Mediterranean-style structures, suggested the model of an Italian hill town. Accordingly, the "village" incorporates such themes as residential neighborhoods clustered around piazzas. A symbolic clock tower marks the main entrance to the facility and is connected to an administrative building by a large plaza. This building acts as the town center, with regular daytime activities (occupational and recreational therapy) concentrated here. Inside the "city wall," a "village green" provides space for outdoor community activities for residents. It affords both quiet and active areas. Under a curved arcade within the exterior courtyard, individual front doors mark entrances to three "neighborhoods" of living units.

The interior spaces are designed to enhance the flow of patients through the facility and present a transition from public to private spaces. Each of the three groupings of informal patient units—or "neighborhoods"—has a private courtyard, which projects into a secluded valley on the far side of the hilltop. All patient bedrooms feature volume ceilings and sixteen-square-foot windows, which look out onto the hillside.

Day rooms provide open spaces for social interaction. Structural frames and carpeted seating groups subdivide the day rooms into more intimate spaces, yet visibility is maintained for staff supervision. Skylights maintain contact with the outdoors, providing ample light that changes throughout the day. Windows are large, but an intimate scale is maintained through use of small panes. Warm-toned wall treatments, an abundance of natural lighting, and the maintenance of residential scale have created a relaxed atmosphere that, according to staff, has had a noticeable effect on reducing the incidence of violent behavior in patients transferred from older facilities.

HILLSIDE HOUSE AT FRIENDS HOSPITAL

Philadelphia, Pennsylvania

Friends Hospital was designed by Mirick Pearson Batcheler (MPB) Architects to provide long-term residential care for persons with chronic mental illness. Scaled residentially in a style that harmonizes with much of the finer prevailing architecture in suburban Philadelphia, the facility houses twelve residents in single or double bedrooms. Terraces and porches relate the building to a relatively secluded area of a landscaped hundred-acre campus.

Friends Hospital/Hillside House, Philadelphia, Pennsylvania. In a facility of long-term residential care for persons with chronic mental illnesses, the design encourages residents to develop a sense of community and to avoid the isolation of patient bedrooms. *Photo by Peter Olson. Courtesy MPB Architects.*

The building was layed out with dining and recreation facilities at opposite ends in order to promote use of the entire building. The entrance hall is two stories high, and living spaces are arranged with southern exposures to admit ample natural light and to establish a relationship with the exterior. Throughout, the purpose of the design is to promote a sense of community and contact with the world outside the facility and to avoid isolation of the bedrooms. In exterior appearance, siting, and layout, the friends Hospital facility is the antithesis of an institution.

■ Rehabilitation Facilities

INDEPENDENCE SQUARE

Inpatient rehabilitation facilities share many design characteristics of SNFs. Indeed, the trend in all long-term care is to emphasize rehabilitation, to the extent possible, over maintenance. As is also true of SNFs, the

Independence Square™, Northern Illinois Medical Center, McHenry, Illinois. A recent development in rehabilitation facilities design, Independent Square provides "architectural vignettes" that simulate daily experiences. *Photo by Guynes Design, Inc. Courtesy Guynes Design, Inc.*

prevailing trend in design is always to connect with "real life" and the "outside world." Perhaps the most exciting recent approach to this is the Independence Square (originally called Easy Street) environment concept pioneered by David Guynes Design, Phoenix, Arizona. Independence Square environments replicate, within a hospital context, "architectural vignettes" that simulate daily experiences: going to the post office, getting into a car, climbing a stool at a coffee shop, working in an office, operating a vending machine, and so on. Designed as discrete, fully customizable modules occupying 1,000 to 6,000 square feet each, the Independence Square environments can be adapted to existing hospitals or facilities can be designed specifically to accommodate them.

CRENSHAW CREEK REHABILITATION CENTER
Lancaster, South Carolina

Earl Swensson Associates' design for the Crenshaw Creek Rehabiliation Center, built in 1988, is a campus that combines siting for minimal travel distances between buildings, yet a relationship to the site that promotes healthy interaction with the natural environment. The goal was to combine a feeling of enclosure and security with a spacious, outdoors feeling that affords beautiful views and is separated from vehicular traffic. The effect is a recuperative transitional setting for the rehabilitation of people with traumatic brain injuries. Its ultimate purpose is to facilitate readjustment to life in the "real world."

Crenshaw Creek includes a residential building with a lounge and dining area, an administrative and physical therapy building, which includes a gym, pool, lounge, and facilities for occupational therapy, and individual living units—the final transitional step up from the residential building, before a patient leaves the facility.

Crenshaw Creek combines a residential feeling with the atmosphere of a wooded lodge or retreat. It is a resolutely non-institutional setting for

Rehabilitation Hospital of Indiana, Indianapolis, Indiana. One of the largest freestanding rehabilitation facilities in the Midwest, this hospital provides both inpatient and outpatient services. Therapy rooms provide a variety of stimulating environments. *Photo by Greg Murphey/Greg Murphey Studios, Inc. Courtesy Bohm-NBBJ.*

Crenshaw Creek Rehabilitation Center, Lancaster, South Carolina. In the lounge area, patients and visitors enjoy views of the facility's natural setting. The furnishings allow flexible seating in large groupings or smaller ones. *Photo by Gordon H. Schenck, Jr. Courtesy Earl Swensson Associates.*

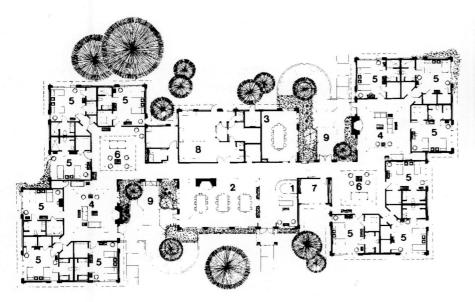

Crenshaw Creek Rehabilitation Center, Lancaster, South Carolina. The design of the center fosters easy mobility between buildings, yet encourages patients in a healthy interaction with the natural environment. *Photo by Gordon H. Schenck, Jr. Courtesy Earl Swensson Associates.*

Crenshaw Creek Rehabilitation Center, Lancaster, South Carolina. Floor plan, residential unit. *Courtesy Earl Swensson Associates.*

1 Reception
2 Dining
3 Conference
4 Lounge
5 Bedroom
6 Recreation
7 Family room
8 Kitchen
9 Patio

intensive physical therapy, making extensive use of natural light and interaction areas—lounges, dining areas—to promote rehabilitation and reintegration into "the world." Offering the comforts of home, the facility anticipated and surpassed subsequent ADA requirements and guidelines.

■ AIDS

AIDS is among the most visible, tragic, and intractable of those diseases that fall into the category of treatable but incurable. So far, the disease has proven 100 percent fatal, and while the course of the disease may be retarded for varying periods and symptoms treated, patients become candidates for hospice care.

BAILEY-BOUSHAY HOUSE
Seattle, Washington

This thirty-five-bed, twenty-four-hour care home for AIDS patients is a quiet, angled, three-story structure that blends into the surrounding mixed-use neighborhood. The street-level facade is commercial in appearance, but the upper stories are residential, featuring gables and single-hung windows. The building is topped by an octagonal greenhouse, and, indeed, the entire structure is designed to admit a maximum of sunlight. The thirty-five single rooms, on the top two floors, are divided into four "neighborhoods" separated by nurses' stations. The second floor also contains a meditation room, and the third floor the greenhouse. The work of some thirty artists decorates the interior, worked into architectural features and niches. The overall feeling is of a small residential hotel.

Bailey-Boushay House accommodates non-resident AIDS patients as well as residents. The ground floor is an adult daycare center for non-residents. Bailey-Boushay House is the work of Bumgardner Architects.

Bailey-Boushay House, Seattle, Washington. The home care facility for AIDS patients has the feel of a residential hotel. The third-floor greenhouse overlooks the Cascades Mountain Range beyond the city. *Photo by Michael Jensen. Courtesy Bumgardner Architects.*

EASLER HOUSE
Gloucester, Massachusetts

As part of an editorial initiative sponsored by *Interiors* magazine, Payette Associates contributed interior renovation services for this half-way house, transforming two suites into prototypical AIDS respite residences. The project was published in the December 1991 issue of *Interiors*.

Easler House was functioning as a halfway house for people in recovery from substance abuse. Clean and adequate, the seventeen-room facility was also rather grim. The challenge was to create a living space that respected the physical needs of AIDS patients while also respecting their dignity and enhancing their quality of life. The idea was to create an environment that offered the resident a measure of control and choice, yet also incorporated practical healthcare features.

Each suite has a private bathroom, which incorporates grab bars, stools, and built-in cupboards. In addition to a bed, a wide, comfortable sofa and an upholstered chair are provided. The upholstery covers zip on and off for easy cleaning or replacement. Built-in tables and beds fold out of the way, and lighting and window shades are remote controlled. The quartz lighting is dimmable.

The Easler House hospice emphasizes views to the outside, and a roof-level promenade affords fresh air and sunshine in a private setting. The use of large floor cushions provides comfortable, adaptable seating for guests.

Finishes were chosen for a light, warm residential look. Light maple panelling covers the lower half of the walls, and, above this, the walls themselves are light-colored. Upholstery colors are in warm earth tones.

■ Universal Design

While the concepts embodied in Crenshaw, Caretel, and Independence Square represent advanced thinking in architecture for the elderly and disabled, perhaps the future will be more thoroughly influenced by a design philosophy already prevalent in Sweden: universal design. As the word *universal* implies, this is design literally for everybody, a design philosophy that assumes that all people, at some time during their lives, will be more or less disabled, at least functionally. Good design should, therefore, incorporate this temporal reality as a fact and should not attempt to discriminate between the "able-bodied" and the "disabled." Barrier-free designs that facilitate way-finding and heighten sensual acuity are truly universal in that they serve the needs of anybody, anytime. If universal design becomes increasingly common, the architecture of SNFs, rehabilitation centers, and other long-term care facilities will, perforce, become more closely integrated with the surrounding community.

10

Ambulatory Care Design and Professional Offices

Not so very long ago, the medical world was neatly divided into hospitals on the one hand and doctors' offices on the other. Sometimes, for the sake of convenience, the doctors' offices were housed in a medical office building (MOB) attached to or adjacent to a hospital, but, basically, never the twain did meet. Some doctors performed minor surgery in their offices; "office surgery" it was called. Aside from this, surgery was the province of the hospital, and so was virtually any more or less complex procedure. The physician's office was primarily a place for examination, evaluation, and relatively simple routine procedures (inoculation, drawing of blood for lab tests, and so on). Anything beyond this was generally referred to a hospital, and that usually meant admittance to a bed, even if the condition or procedure did not absolutely necessitate an overnight stay.

For the simple reason that most of us grew up—as professionals or as patients—under that system, it seemed natural, inevitable, and right.

But, today and for the foreseeable future, this system is neither natural, inevitable, nor right. Depending on the course cost containment, managed care, and national health insurance take, it is a system that will likely become less and less viable, and perhaps, at some point, downright impossible.

There are two broad ways of looking at the paradigm shift that has been—and is—dissolving the barriers between "private" or "office" practice and the realm of the hospital. From the perspective of hospital professionals, the past decade or two have seen periods of boom in hospital construction, yet the more sustained trend has been toward vacancy of beds. Many administrators have viewed this with alarm. Others have been able to rethink the hospital beyond the overnight stay and successfully restructure for ambulatory care. In 1983, according to the AHA, fewer than 12 percent of total hospital revenues in the United States were outpatient related. Just four years later, by 1987, that figure had increased to 23 percent, reflecting a 92 percent growth in that segment of the market. By the beginning of the 1990s, a significant number of hospitals reported 40 to 60 percent of their revenues resulting from outpatient services. Today, the mix in the *majority* of hospitals hovers on either side of 50/50—half outpatient revenue, half inpatient revenue.

From the point of view of the physician, the day of the solo practitioner—long the virtually iconic norm in American medicine—is rapidly waning. The growth in the number of physicians has outpaced population growth, and increased competition and cost-containment pressures leading to more restrictive reimbursement practices, as well as the cost of maintaining malpractice liability protection have all contributed to a precipitous decline in the number of solo practitioners and a concomitant explosion in the number of group practices. Group practices—usually three or more physicians who share patient care and the business aspects of a practice—often have the combined financial clout to purchase the equipment and office facilities to render services that were once exclusively the province of hospital-based ambulatory care. During the 1980s, entrepreneurial physicians (and others) further challenged hospitals—as well as solo practitioners—by creating freestanding facilities to provide urgent, episodic, and primary medical care. In 1980, according to AHA figures, there were fewer than 300 such facilities nationwide. Seven years later, in 1987, the number had increased 400 percent to over 3,000. By the early 1990s, some 5,500 freestanding facilities were in operation, handling about 63 million patient visits annually—compared to five million in 1980. Despite this phenomenal growth, such freestanding "convenience" facilities have rarely attained financial viability. By the beginning of the 1990s, only some 30 percent were operating in the black. This did not discourage the concurrent development of freestanding ambulatory surgery facilities, which numbered about 1,200 at the beginning of the decade.

Increasingly, hospitals have shown an interest in affiliating with group practices or even acquiring them. Increasingly, too, hospitals have been expanding outpatient programs to offer the same kind of "convenience" care available from freestanding facilities. Since freestanding convenience care was originally perceived as directly competing with the hospital emergency department, these departments were expanded and upgraded—often simply to make an emergency department visit a more pleasant, less time-consuming, and less generally harrowing experience. More and more, emergency departments evolved into two separate and discrete operations: one to handle emergent care (trauma, sudden severe illness) and another for urgent and primary care (serving the kinds of patients who commonly visit a private physician or a freestanding convenience facility). In many hospitals nowadays, ambulatory convenience care is entirely separate from the emergency department. Finally, an increasing number of hospitals and hospital corporations are building freestanding community-based convenience facilities of their own. Beyond this, hospitals and hospital corporations are creating discrete ambulatory surgery departments within the hospital or even building freestanding ambulatory surgery centers.

Other freestanding facilities that have witnessed considerable growth during the 1980s and early 1990s are diagnostic—or imaging—centers and various specialized treatment centers: eye, heart, geriatric, cancer, women's centers, and so on. These may be physician owned, hospital owned, or the product of joint ventures undertaken by hospitals and physicians.

For the architect, designer, and planner, the proliferation of hospital-based and freestanding ambulatory services has resulted in a medical landscape more varied than ever before, and with increasingly innovative business relationships developing among hospitals, insurance providers, hospital corporations, group practices, and individual physicians, it is likely that the demand for ambulatory care facilities, both hospital-based and freestanding, will continue to grow.

■ MOBs/POBs

Other than the hospital, the most familiar medical building is the medical office building or professional office building: the MOB or POB. As traditionally designed, however, the physician office building is suited to solo practice and is not easily adaptable to the increasingly larger single and multi-specialty group practices. The MOB designed to accommodate solo practitioners is based on the solo practice unit, a 700- to 1,500-square-foot office or suite. Each practitioner shares central building support services, including elevators, toilets, HVAC, and so on. This simple arrangement was perfectly adequate for individual physicians, but it limits options for group practice. Most group practices are based around some shared procedure or piece of diagnostic equipment. It is, therefore, essential that the practitioners' suites be located around the shared resource and that the core services of the traditional building—elevators, toilets, mechanical equipment—be located to the side of the building in order to keep the floor plate unobstructed for flexibility of configuration that facilitates sharing resources. It is relatively easy to demonstrate to hospital administrators that a particular existing facility may be unsuited to emerging technologies or practices. More difficult to get across is the need for new MOBs to accommodate the new ways in which medical care is being delivered. But the fact is that the rigid design of traditional MOBs cannot readily support the following:

▲ *Sharing of clinical areas (exam, consultation, nurse support, procedure area)*
▲ *Sharing of diagnostics*
▲ *Sharing of reception*
▲ *Sharing of administrative and support services*
▲ *Sharing of office and conference space*

In addition to design for sharing facilities, the advanced MOB must appeal to the new medical consumer.

▲ It should accommodate a focus on wellness by providing space for fitness services and health maintenance, as opposed exclusively to the treatment of disease.

Southern Hills Medical Center MOB, Nashville, Tennessee. The new medical consumer looks for MOB facilities that focus on wellness and health maintenance in addition to facilities that offer treatment of disease. The MOB of the Southern Hills complex features hydrotherapy treatment in a pleasant setting. *Photo by K. D. Lawson. Courtesy Earl Swensson Associates.*

Southern Hills Medical Center MOB, Nashville, Tennessee. The muted colors, comfortable seating, plantings, and soft lighting of the waiting room recall a residential setting. *Photo by K. D. Lawson. Courtesy Earl Swensson Associates.*

▲ It should appeal to today's generally more sophisticated, more demanding, more questioning, and better-informed medical consumer.

▲ It should incorporate elements of universal design, particularly with the elderly in mind. This reflects the trend toward an aging medical consumer. Design elements to consider include lighting to eliminate glare, avoidance of strong contrasts, design to compensate for reduced color perception, furnishings that properly support an aging body, crystal-clear way-finding cues, and the like.

▲ It should be designed with women in mind. This is not the case with "women's centers" alone (which are treated in the next chapter), but with any MOB. Women make most of the healthcare decisions in the United States, including where to "shop" for their family's medical care.

The consumer and shopping metaphors have been incorporated into the "medical mall" concept discussed in Chapter 3. It is possible to conceive the MOB in these terms, and, in fact, some hospitals have renovated corridors as outpatient medical malls. The consumer model need not be taken so literally, but it is a design option that several hospital-related MOBs have exercised in order to make the facility serve as a transition or crossroads between physician care and hospital care. And the consumer model is also useful to help keep MOB design from degenerating into what noted medical interior designer Jain Malkin calls a "formula fast food restaurant." Retail merchants long ago learned the value of good design in marketing, and, certainly, prospective patients find an aesthetically attractive, distinctive design appealing and reassuring as a visible projection of an attitude toward quality and excellence. But effective design in medical office space goes deeper than this. For example, the office suite of an allergy practice should not be decorated with heavily textured surfaces, shag rugs, or nubby upholstery—no matter how elegant or "residential" looking. For this market, such harborers of allergens are not only inappropriate, they are downright repellant and even harmful. Similarly, a suite designed for a neurological specialty should avoid sharply contrasting surfaces, busy patterns, and vivid colors—design elements that may exacerbate the disorientation neurological afflictions may bring with them. Then there are certain specialties that employ equipment requiring special design provisions. Magnetic resonance imaging (MRI), discussed in Chapter 6, is one such specialty. If MRI equipment is to be housed in the MOB, shielding and other provisions must be designed in if the equipment is not self-shielded.

If there is one major identifiable trend in the design of medical office buildings it is what Jain Malkin calls "gourmet recipes" for design. Whereas hospitals tend to follow a relatively small number of design approaches, Malkin identifies nine distinct approaches to medical offices:

▲ Retail—the galleria or mall concept
▲ Hospitality—the luxury hotel approach
▲ Cultural—facilities designed with respect for the ethnicity of the patient community; for example, the use of indigenous materials or design motifs
▲ High technology—facilities that emphasize rather than disguise the high-tech nature of treatment
▲ Intellectual—architecture that expresses the patient's struggle against disease
▲ Entertainment or theater—an approach that is especially appropriate for pediatric practices, it entertains, amuses, distracts, and educates
▲ Comfort—design that emphasizes amelioration of intimidation; this would be especially appropriate, for example, in facilities that use ultra-high-tech equipment: MRI, linear accelerators for cancer treatment, and so on
▲ Corporate—businesslike and no-nonsense
▲ Residential—homey, familiar, comforting

Some of these approaches invite a design daring that would give many hospital administrators pause. For example, the Starbright Pavilion, currently being designed by Kaplan McLaughlin Diaz for the Los Angeles County USC Medical Center, is a radical healing environment for children with life-threatening diseases. The design is based on the findings and assumptions of the emerging research field of psychoneuroimmunology (PNI). The design goal is to create an environment that will make children happy and thereby boost their immunologic systems. Starbright uses bright, primary colors, simple geometric shapes, and Erector-set-like structural members to create a dazzling, brilliant, and mega-toylike environment. Provisions for video and live entertainment as well as imaginative play environments are also included.

In California's Simi Valley, a children's dental group designed an office facility around an outerspace concept. Patients arrive at a "Pre-Flight" check-in counter and then are led by a space-suited dental technician through a metallic "Time-Warp Tunnel" to procedure rooms equipped with "flight chairs."

Wild as some of the new approaches are, they gain ready acceptance in a pediatric context. No parent enjoys taking his or her child to the doctor or dentist, and these medical consumers welcome design strategies that allay their children's anxieties. Far more controversial are designs, for adult facilities, that convey strong messages.

Of course, all architecture speaks, albeit sometimes in confused and contradictory mumbles and shouts. As we explored in Chapter 2, the hospital design vocabularies most of us now think of as "traditional" evolved as an expression of a very powerful message, proclaiming, among other things, the majesty and supremacy of the Institution over the individual. Given sufficient thought, this message comes to seem as outrageous as any; it is just that familiarity and custom have inured us to the significance of that message. To new messages, however, messages that depart sharply from the old Institutional one, we are far more acutely sensitive.

The Cedars-Sinai Comprehensive Cancer Center in Los Angeles is a 53,000-square-foot, 24-hour facility designed by Morphosis Architects and Gruen Associates. Neither high tech nor deliberately hospitable—or "comforting"—the building is best described as "Deconstructivist" and almost allegorical. It is a geometrically bold and challenging structure that is built mostly below grade. Patients enter at street level and then descend. While this earth-hugging orientation is not unusual in facilities that employ radiation therapy, Cedars Sinai makes no attempt to disguise the patient's journey into the Underworld, as if to convey to him that this is part of actively combatting the disease. While some have described the building as hauntingly beautiful, others have seen in it associations with a tomb or crypt. Is this depressing? Or this a resolute refusal to condescend to and deceive the patient? Does the sense of removal from the world connote death? Or does it help channel energies into the self and against the disease? Does the architecture intimidate and oppress? Or, by expressing a certain degree of intimidation and oppression, does it make a spiritually liberating statement that is beneficial to the patient? By challenging the patient, does the architecture heighten stress, or does it encourage active engagement in the treatment process?

The proliferation of medical office buildings, whether associated with hospitals or not, seems certain to afford architects, designers, administrators, and caregivers greater and greater opportunity for expression. Indeed, care providers are likely to demand increasingly greater levels of thoughtful expression from architects, thereby multiplying the risks and rewards of design.

■ General-Purpose MOBs: Some Recent Projects

HARBOR-UCLA PROFESSIONAL BUILDING
Torrance, California

Employing manufactured construction (concurrent construction) techniques, Integral Environments/The Scotsman Group (Paramount, California) designed and built this 45,000-square-foot MOB in 220 days, completing it in 1989. The facility is divided into twelve specialized areas: clinic, offices of the Harbor UCLA Medical Foundation (which funded the project), pharmacy, medicine, neurology, obstetrics/gynecology, ophthalmology, pediatrics, psychiatry, surgery, and C.R.I.S.P. (cardiology, radiology, imaging, scanning, pulmonary). This imaging facility includes two nuclear radiation scanners, X-ray room, and MRI equipment—with a 22,000-pound magnet.

The Harbor U.C.L.A. facility is highly flexible, employing a steel-frame column and truss system to eliminate load-bearing walls, so that interior renovations can be made economically to accommodate expansion or new markets. These flexible elements were not allowed to compromise the aesthetic amenities of the facility, which include a 27-foot-high pyramid-shaped skylight over the main lobby. That lobby opens into a central courtyard enclosed by twelve-foot glass walls. This courtyard and two smaller ones greatly increase the amount of natural light that enters the facility.

Centennial Medical Center, Physicians Park, MOB, Frist Clinic, Nashville, Tennessee. In a clutter-free environment, a nursing station in the clinic features cubicles for completing paperwork and lighting suited to a variety of tasks. *Photo by Gary Knight. Courtesy Earl Swensson Associates.*

PHYSICIANS PARK
CENTENNIAL MEDICAL CENTER
Nashville, Tennessee

Physicians Park Medical Office Building, opened in 1992, was designed as the hub or catalyst of the large Nashville-based Centennial Medical Center designed by Earl Swensson Associates. This MOB functions as a main entry into the entire hospital complex. Its facade is delineated by a stately grid of precast and reflective glass enhanced by crossed window mullions and detailed with a diamond motif. The rounded canopy of glass and tubular steel is generously sized to accommodate up to twelve cars at a time and allows efficient and effective shelter for valet service.

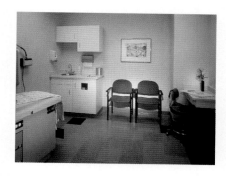

Centennial Medical Center, Physicians Park, MOB, Frist Clinic, Nashville, Tennessee. In a simple examination room, the color and pattern in the floor add visual interest to a utilitarian space. *Photo by Gary Knight. Courtesy Earl Swensson Associates.*

Centennial Medical Center, Physicians Park MOB, Nashville, Tennessee. The large canopy at an entrance that also serves the adjoining hospital accommodates patient pick-up and drop-off. The entrance is level for the convenience of walk-in and wheelchair-bound patients. The entire building is handicapped accessible. *Photo by Gary Knight. Courtesy Earl Swensson Associates.*

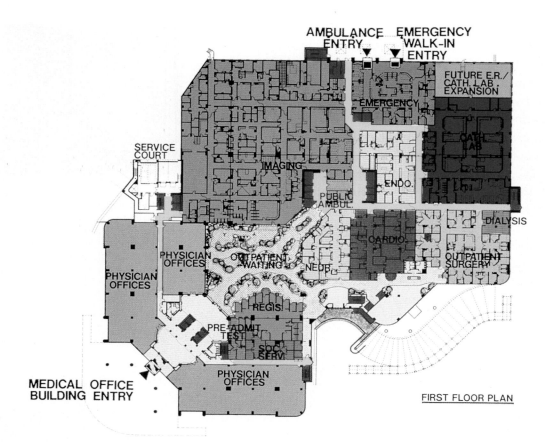

AMBULANCE ENTRY   EMERGENCY WALK-IN ENTRY

FUTURE E.R./ CATH. LAB. EXPANSION

EMERGENCY

CATH. LAB

SERVICE COURT

IMAGING

ENDO.

PUBLIC AMBUL.

DIALYSIS

PHYSICIAN OFFICES

CARDIO.

OUTPATIENT WAITING

NEUR.

OUTPATIENT SURGERY

PHYSICIAN OFFICES

REGIS.

PRE-ADMIT TEST

SOC. SERV.

MEDICAL OFFICE BUILDING ENTRY

PHYSICIAN OFFICES

FIRST FLOOR PLAN

Centennial Medical Center, Nashville, Tennessee. Floor plan, first floor. The ground floor of the center houses physicians' offices and some services shared by outpatients and patients in the adjoining acute-care hospital. *Courtesy Earl Swensson Associates.*

The Physicians Park is contextual with buildings on either side of it and was designed to relate to Nashville's landmark replica of the Parthenon, which is located in adjacent Centennial Park. The colonnade echoes the Parthenon, and its proportions as well as the rhythm of the columns and grid imposed on the entry portico suggest a modernist interpretation of the classical Greek temple.

The decorative elements established on the exterior of the building are repeated inside, giving its five stories and 200,000 square feet of space a pleasing continuity of design.

The lobby of Physicians Park is articulated by balconies and columns that effectively reduce the area to human scale, while soft colors and strong verticals create an open, uplifting effect. The MOB is designed with efficient traffic flow as a principal goal. Outpatient service areas are clustered on the first floor, and physician suites are located above. A two-story 1,000-space parking garage is located beneath the building and is invisible at ground level. Not only does Physicians Park serve as a main entrance to Centennial Medical Center, each floor of the office building is integrated by skyway connectors to the adjacent 239-bed acute care hospital.

The acute-care hospital features an eight-story atrium topped by a sloped, three-story skylight, under which lush plantings flourish and fountains flow. The colors used throughout the hospital and Physicians Park are designed to complement the atrium. Rich greens and warm tones with jewel accents predominate. While the atrium projects an image of some opulence, it actually functions as a cost-efficient, high-profile means of integrating a variety of medical services.

MT. SINAI INTEGRATED MEDICAL CAMPUS

Beechwood, Ohio

This project, designed by Earl Swensson Associates and opened in 1994, is a good example of building to accommodate the changing demographics of a region and to integrate new with existing facilities. Mt. Sinai Medical Center, located in downtown Cleveland, Ohio, found itself facing the serious problem of supporting suburban areas with outpatient services. ESa was assigned the task of designing an integrated medical center—in effect, a hospital without beds—to function in concert with an existing 120,000-square-foot medical office building in Beechwood, a prominent suburb. The objective was to site the new facility so that the entire campus would appear to be a single integrated complex, yet would allow for adequate parking and well-defined entries. Furthermore, state code regulations would have mandated costly upgrades to the existing structure if the new facility were built as a direct extension of it. The solution that best addressed all of these demands was to keep the new facility structurally separate from the existing building, but join the two by a spacious atrium lobby.

After the patient is dropped off underneath a ten-car canopy, the car is valet parked to a 700-vehicle underground garage, and the patient enters a one-story lobby, where he is greeted by a receptionist/information director. Proceeding into the atrium area, the patient experiences a dramatic change from the one-story lobby to a four-story glass-enclosed

Mt. Sinai Integrated Medical Campus MOB, Beechwood, Ohio. Patient education is an integral part of the facility. Accordion doors divide the classroom into smaller spaces as needed. *Photo by Gary Knight. Courtesy Earl Swensson Associates.*

Veterans Administration Outpatient Clinic, Los Angeles, California. Patients traverse a quiet plaza to reach the main entrance. Red granite decorates the lower floors that house support functions. The clinics of the upper floors are clad in gridded aluminum. *Photo by Michael Arden. Courtesy Bobrow/Thomas and Associates.*

Veterans Administration Outpatient Clinic, Los Angeles, California. The external corridors are for public use and feature plenty of light through glass block windows decorated with granite insets. Staff uses the inner corridors. *Photo by Michael Arden. Courtesy Bobrow/Thomas and Associates.*

space, approximately 200 feet long, flooded with light, and heavily landscaped. Within the atrium space are areas for patient registration and pre-hospital admission testing. There is also a deli/cafe with umbrella seating, medical retail space, a pharmacy, space for a 150-person auditorium, a childcare area, and entries to imaging and cardiopulmonary departments within the existing building and a planned women's center. The atrium area also provides a pleasant vista for physician offices in the old as well as new buildings and for the new outpatient surgical facility on the third floor.

VETERANS ADMINISTRATION OUTPATIENT CLINIC

Los Angeles, California

Physicians' offices and ambulatory facilities, particularly in large urban hospitals, are often designed as virtually undifferentiated spaces to be adapted and modified as necessary. The result can be undistinguished, anonymous, confusing, and inhumane. Bobrow/Thomas and Associates designed the 340,000-square-foot outpatient facility for this Veterans Administration hospital to be flexible, yet to maintain thoughtful connec-

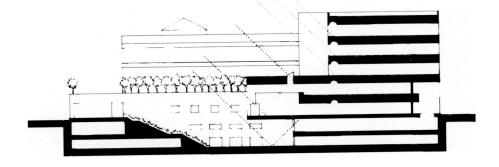

Veterans Administration Outpatient Clinic, Los Angeles, California. Diagram, light penetration. *Courtesy Bobrow/Thomas and Associates.*

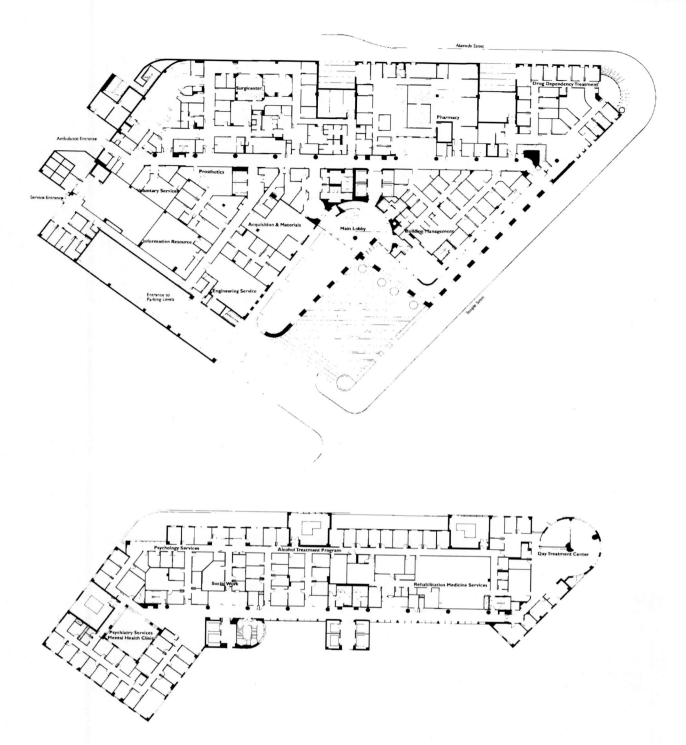

Top: Veterans Administration
Outpatient Clinic, Los Angeles,
California. Floor plan, first floor.
Courtesy Bobrow/Thomas and Associates.

tions with the outside. The entrance was oriented to the quieter side of
the facility and opens onto a sunny plaza. Waiting areas are likewise
oriented to the quiet side of the building, while physicians' offices face
busy Alameda Street. The lower floors of the facility contain most of the
support functions, while the upper floors, which are smaller and more
intimately scaled, house the clinics. These clinic areas look out onto roof
gardens. Generally, treatment areas are arranged in suites, with each suite
accessible from the public corridor. The suite arrangement provides
human scale, while the ease of access assists way-finding.

Bottom: Veterans Administration
Outpatient Clinic, Los Angeles,
California. Floor plan, fourth floor.
Courtesy Bobrow/Thomas and Associates.

■ Freestanding Clinics

TREATMENT CENTER
Jackson, Mississippi

Freestanding ambulatory care centers—for urgent and primary care—now dot the American landscape. For the most part, these are not upscale facilities, and few of them are distinguished architecturally. This need not be the case, since the market served by such facilities is an increasingly competitive one, and consumers look for an attractive care environment. On the other hand, these small-scale facilities must not be designed pretentiously. A design that balances economy, user-friendliness, and architectural wit is this freestanding ambulatory care center near Jackson, Mississippi, designed by Thomas Goodman and incorporating a number of architectural styles to create a visually reassuring as well as interesting general-purpose suburban clinic. The 2,600-square-foot facility combines the geometric planes of Modernism, the wit of Post-modernism, details that invoke the architecture of the Old South, and a residential touch in the use of clapboard. The same blend of styles is repeated inside, which includes traditional black-and-white checkerboard vinyl tile, a "southern-looking" plantation-type column, and a sleekly modern nursing station as well as registration desk.

Variations on the Outpatient/Freestanding Clinic Theme

MERRITT ISLAND MEDICAL CENTER
Merritt Island, Florida
and
HOLY FAMILY HOSPITAL AMBULATORY CARE CENTER
Wheeling, Illinois

Holy Family Hospital Ambulatory Care Center, Wheeling, Illinois. A clinic affiliated with Holy Family Hospital offers the services of a modest MOB which includes a community center for educational programs. Such human-scale facilities that extend hospital services into the community are a likely trend of the future. *Photo by Howard N. Kaplan. © HNK Architectural Photography, Inc. Courtesy Holabird and Root.*

These two facilities suggest innovative combinations of services that greatly extend a hospital's ambulatory outreach. The Merritt Island building, designed by Hansen Lind Meyer, is a 4,500-square-foot wood-frame facility located near Cape Canaveral and operated by the Cape Canaveral Hospital. Sited on a constricted lot, this simple building combines four physicians' offices with an outpatient clinic.

The Holy Family Hospital Ambulatory Care Center, designed by Holabird & Root, offers 24,000 square feet of space and combines a comprehensive, twenty-five-physician clinic—plus one dentist and dental assistant—with a community center, which features, among its community-oriented programs, medical education and outreach operated by Holy Family Hospital, which is located across the street from the facility.

Taking their cue from the proliferation of freestanding physician-owned and operated ambulatory centers, hospitals will likely build more of these modest, humanly scaled neighborhood facilities in the years to come.

■ Freestanding Diagnostic Facilities

Chapter 6 covers design considerations for diagnostic imaging and includes some freestanding as well as hospital-based facilities. Physician-owned freestanding diagnostic facilities are becoming increasingly numerous, but another trend is toward satellite facilities operated by hospitals. One such is the Samaritan North Health Center designed by Earl Swensson Associates in an affluent suburb of Dayton, Ohio. The 220,000-square-foot facility is a combination diagnostic center and medical office building—in effect, a hospital without beds, which is a building type likely to proliferate during the next several years.

The facility extends into the suburbs the healthcare reach of Samaritan's main hospital, located in downtown Dayton. A large facility, Samaritan North was designed to relate to its suburban ambience, so the look, therefore, is far more residential than institutional. This effect is enhanced by the use of brick and gentle arches, which contrast with the high-tech glass and a sloped standing-seam metal roof.

Walking in the front door, the patient has access to an open outpatient mall, which is illuminated by skylights flooding the central area. A daycare area is available for parents to leave their children. To the right is a community education center, with a subdividable conference area. The center is adjacent to an open courtyard, which is designed for preconference activities and mid-program breaks. Accessible from this

Samaritan North Health Center, Englewood, Ohio. The brick detailing and standing-seam metal roof give a residential character to this satellite facility of a major Dayton, Ohio, hospital. The center offers diagnostic services and an MOB. *Watercolor by Gerry Harvey. Courtesy Earl Swensson Associates.*

Samaritan North Health Center, Englewood, Ohio. Floor plan, first floor. *Courtesy Earl Swensson Associates.*

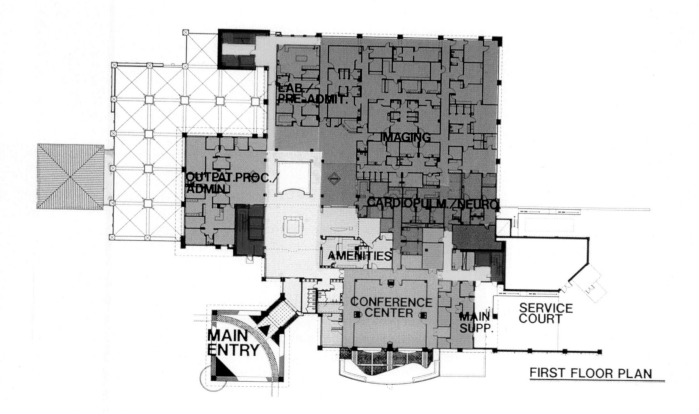

area is deli-style food service with inviting fun finishes and a pleasant location that takes advantage of abundant natural light. The outpatient mall houses a pharmacy, which serves the entire Samaritan North campus and is connected to all departments and the physician office space through a pneumatic tube system. The pharmacy area also offers a gift shop.

Departmental barriers do not exist at Samaritan North, and the major imaging facilities (plus a cardiopulmonary area) are located on the first floor, so that outpatients can wait in the airy, naturally lighted mall area.

In addition to imaging, Samaritan North offers an oncology service, a women's center, and physical rehabilitation and sports medicine facilities. In a later phase of development, facilities for ambulatory surgery are planned.

The site of Samaritan North is sloped, and ESa designed the facility to take full advantage of this challenging site, designing a multi-level building with separate entrances at varying levels. At the highest level are the principal areas, including imaging, community education, pharmacy, cafeteria, and administrative areas. The next lower level houses the oncology service and the physical therapy/rehabilitation/sports medicine facilities. At the lowest level is a dedicated staff parking area and staff entrance to the facility.

The medical office building that is part of the complex comprises three stories in addition to the first story of outpatient services. Because the MOB shares this first story with the imaging center, physicians can send their patients directly for diagnostic procedures without obliging them to reenter the system and register at a "main desk."

Samaritan North represents the kind of tight integration of individual physician, hospital facility, and the medical consumer that is a strong current trend and likely to prevail. "Samaritan North Health Center," Hospital Administrator Doug Deck offers, "will accommodate the major shift in healthcare delivery from the acute, inpatient services to a more innovative, cost-effective quality care in the most appropriate setting. In planning for this facility, we never even considered the inclusion of inpatient beds."

■ Ambulatory Surgery

Traditionally, physicians have performed minor surgical procedures in their offices, and it was only after World War II that a sizable number of such procedures were taken over by hospitals. Major procedures, of course, had been the province of hospitals since at least the later nineteenth century, and the prevailing philosophy of treatment placed great emphasis on postoperative recuperation. For example, the great surgeon William Halsted prescribed a twenty-one-day period of bed rest for hernia repair. However, it was anticipated that most of these long periods would be spent in bed *at home,* not in the hospital. As the twentieth century progressed, recuperative times shortened, but it was expected that the patient would be cared for during recuperation in a hospital bed. Thus post-surgical stays often occupied several days of uneventful hospital bed rest. Even relatively minor procedures, carried out in a hospital, mandated at least an overnight stay—whether or not this was strictly necessary for medical reasons.

At last, in 1961, the first modern ambulatory surgery program began at Butterworth Hospital in Grand Rapids, Michigan, and was followed the next year by a program at the University of California, Los Angeles. A decade later, early in 1970, Drs. Wallace Reed and John Ford opened Surgicenter in Phoenix, Arizona. Planned, built, and run by these two anesthesiologists, Surgicenter was a freestanding, totally self-sufficient unit. It sparked the development of additional such units nationwide. By the later 1980s, as cost containment and DRGs came increasingly to dominate medical reimbursement, the future of ambulatory surgery, whether in a hospital outpatient department or in a freestanding independent or hospital-affiliated setting, seemed to be one of growth. So far, this has proven to be the case. And even for procedures where a period of in-hospital recovery is still deemed necessary, the trend is toward short-stay surgery and early discharge.

As a consumer society, we are accustomed to expect that cost-saving measures must come at the expense of quality or convenience. The delivery of medical care has been challenged, perhaps more than most industries, to contain costs. The positive aspect of this pressure, however, is that the cost efficiencies do not necessarily come at the expense of the patient. In the case of the trend toward ambulatory and short-stay surgery, not only are costs substantially reduced, but patient care may actually be enhanced:

▲ Rather than experience a major, albeit temporary, change in lifestyle, ambulatory surgery patients are, at worst, minimally inconvenienced. The same holds true for their families—especially in the case of procedures performed on children and infants.

▲ Post-operative care is handled, to a great extent, by family members. This not only saves money, it almost certainly benefits the patient, especially children and infants, who do not have to endure anxiety-provoking separation from parents. No matter how dedicated a professional nursing staff may be, it is hard pressed to compete with a family's loving care.

▲ The patient receives more individual attention—not only from family member/caregivers, but from the staff of a center specifically set up to treat ambulatory surgery.

▲ Anxiety is reduced. The stress of a hospital stay is eliminated.

▲ There is less risk of nosocomial infection. Unfortunately, hospitalization exposes patients to hospital-borne infections. This is greatly reduced in same-day surgery.

▲ The perception of disability is decreased (After all, if I'm not in a hospital, how sick can I be?), and patients return to normal life more quickly.

▲ The physician retains more direct control of the patient in a setting devoid of red tape and large numbers of personnel.

▲ Finally, costs are reduced.

There are disadvantages to ambulatory surgery, but none are insurmountable:

▲ The patient may not follow preoperative instructions. This needs to be addressed through careful preoperative education. The most serious problem is failure to heed instructions about taking nothing by mouth overnight. Under general anesthesia, this could result in vomiting and aspiration of vomitus, followed by asphyxiation or pneumonia.

▲ The patient must ensure that he or she has transportation to and from the facility.

▲ Ambulatory surgery assumes that the patient has competent at-home assistance available. If such care is not available, professional home care is still probably less costly than an overnight stay in the hospital. Advanced planning is required, however.

▲ Although the circumstances, setting, and implications of ambulatory surgery usually act to reduce patient anxiety, some individuals may be concerned that ambulatory units, especially those that are physically independent of a major hospital, lack the advanced resuscitative support available in a hospital setting. Careful patient education is required to address these understandable concerns.

Ambulatory surgery is commonly performed in four types of settings:

1. Hospital-controlled integrated units. These are in-hospital units that share facilities with inpatient surgery. For smaller hospitals, this may be the only economically viable ambulatory surgery option available. Capital costs are, of course, relatively low for an integrated unit, but this must be weighed against the loss of market share among medical consumers who require or want ambulatory surgery. Treated in a setting that integrates them with inpatients, they tend to feel like second-class citizens. It is always clear that inpatient surgery has priority over them. Actual operating costs may also be high, since major surgical facilities and personnel are used for any number of relatively minor procedures. One final *advantage* of integrated units, however, is that surgeons may be willing to undertake in them more types of surgery than they would in freestanding ambulatory units. The surgeon may feel that his patient's risks are minimized by the immediate availability of full hospital surgical support.

2. Hospital-controlled autonomous units. This is a unit located within the hospital, but explicitly designed for ambulatory surgery service. Such units allow the hospital to capture important ambulatory markets while providing the backup of a fully equipped hospital, should these facilities be necessary. Depending on the community, however, licensing, code compliance, and certificate of need (CON) costs may be high.

3. Hospital satellite units. These are freestanding units located off the main hospital campus, but sponsored by the hospital. Using the staff expertise and good name of the sponsoring hospital, these

units can provide important outreach into areas more or less remote from the main hospital. Ambulatory surgery may be integrated into fairly large satellite facilities that function as virtual hospitals without beds, providing such services as primary care (often in an integral or adjacent MOB facility), urgent care, diagnostic imaging, wellness, fitness, and rehabilitation along with ambulatory surgery. Satellite units extend the suburban reach of established hospitals sited in downtown locations.

4. Freestanding ambulatory surgery units. These are independent facilities. They enjoy the advantages of hospital-sponsored satellite units and can often offer the same surgical services at lower cost. Depending on the patient and the type of procedure, such units are increasingly attractive in the presently emerging medical marketplace. However, some individuals may feel hesitant about undergoing a surgical procedure in a facility that has less extensive resuscitative equipment and, some say, a less thoroughly qualified staff than a major hospital. The actual performance record of freestanding ambulatory surgical facilities has been excellent.

COVINGTON MEDICAL PARK

Tacoma Park, Washington

Earl Swensson Associates and Giffin Bolte Jurgens Architects designed this hospital without beds, completed in 1993, to include a strong ambulatory

Covington Medical Park, Tacoma, Washington. Floor plan, first floor. *Courtesy Earl Swensson Associates.*

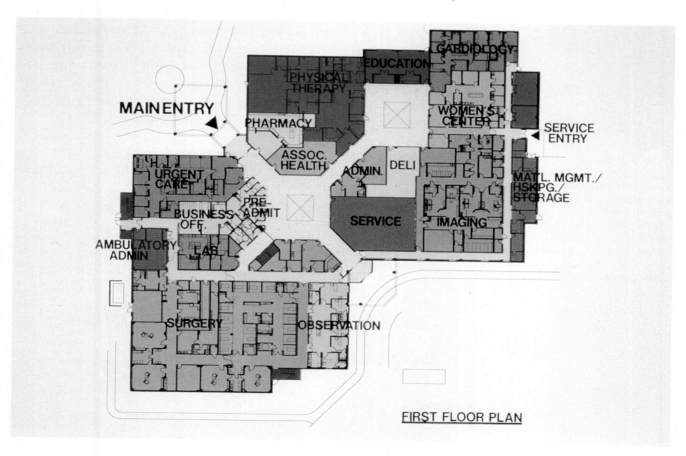

FIRST FLOOR PLAN

Covington Medical Park, Tacoma, Washington. Floor plan, outpatient surgery. *Courtesy Earl Swensson Associates.*

1 Entrance
2 Surgical waiting
3 Lobby
4 Men's locker
5 Women's locker
6 Operating room
7 Special procedures
8 Staging
9 Observation

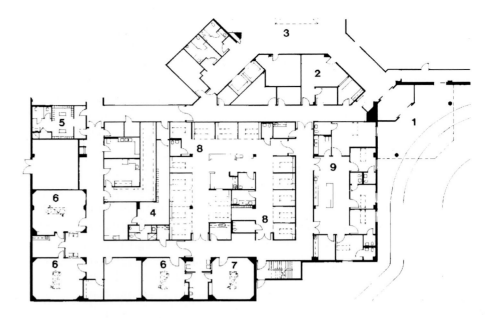

surgery component. Also housed on the first floor is a pharmacy, optometry area, physical therapy facility, a patient education area, cardiology, a women's center, radiology, laboratory, and an urgent care facility. A deli is available for dining. The second floor of Covington Medical Park is an MOB, offering family practice; obstetrics/gynecology; ear, nose, throat; and pediatrics. The third floor houses facilities for internal medicine, gastroenterology, dermatology, and urology, together with surgical facilities for plastic surgery and urological procedures.

This compact facility is designed around the concept of vertical integration, with all specialties sharing such services as accounting, billing, medical records, and so on. The principal first-floor surgery area is composed of two operating rooms, with recovery in the central core. Most patients recover here. Those requiring a longer stay are sent to the observation suite directly across the hall. A nurses' station is located here. The length of stay is always less than twenty-four hours.

Athens Regional Medical Center Surgicenter, Athens, Georgia. The 1910 Talmadge House serves as the entrance and reception and waiting areas through which patients pass to the new surgical area. Innovative design combines the warmth of a gracious residential building with a modern, same-day surgery facility. *Photo by Paul Ferrino. Courtesy Payette Associates.*

The following labels appear in the axonometric floor plan:

CLEAN UTILITY · STERILE ENCLOSURE · PACK PREP · CENTRAL STERILE STORAGE SUPPLY · FEMALE DRESSING · MALE DRESSING · STAFF LOUNGE · TOILET · TOILET · ELEC

CORRIDOR · JAN. · STOR. · STORAGE · OR 1 · STERILE CORE · STOR. · OR 3 · ELEC. · OR 2 · CORRIDOR

DARK ROOM · ANESTHESIA WORK · DICT. · S. UTIL. · HEAD NURSE · C. UTIL · OFFICE · ANES. MED OFF. · NURSES STATION · PREP 1 · DRESS 1 · RECOVERY · PREP 2 · DRESS 2 · PREP 3 · DRESS 3 · REFRESHMENT · PREP 4 · DRESS 4 · CORRIDOR · QUIET ROOM · QUIET ROOM · ENTRY

KITCHEN · TOILET · TOILET · CONSERVATORY · RECOVERY WAITING · EXAM · EXAM · OFFICE · CORRIDOR · SURGICENTER WAITING · RECEPTION · PRE-OP

Athens Regional Medical Center
Surgicenter, Athens, Georgia. Patients
recovering from surgery are bathed in
natural light. *Photo by Paul Ferrino.
Courtesy Payette Associates.*

ATHENS REGIONAL MEDICAL CENTER SURGICENTER

Athens, Georgia

This unique same-day surgery center was designed by Payette Architects.
The 1910 Talmadge House, a colonial-style mansion located near the
main campus of the medical center, was restored and renovated, and a

day surgery facility and parking garage were added. The colonnaded Talmadge House serves as the entrance through which patients pass to the new surgical area, which adjoins the house, extending from its rear. The parking garage is located beneath the new addition.

As restored and renovated, the ground floor rooms of the Talmadge House serve as the reception and waiting area, while the rooms to the right of the hall house preregistration, medical exam space, and laboratory testing. From here, patients move through the former conservatory and dining room to the new addition. Traffic flow here is arranged so that the patient moves from one stage of the procedure to the next in a continuous loop, without encountering other patients at various treatment stages. From preparation, the patient enters one of three operating rooms, which are arranged around a sterile core. Following surgery, the patient is transferred to a recovery room and then dressing rooms, where two-sided lockers allow the patient to retrieve the clothing left at the preparation area. From the quiet rooms where recovery is completed, the entrance to the parking garage is easily accessible.

Using the venerable Talmadge House, Payette has carried the residential model of healthcare design to a successful, innovative, and economical extreme.

PEDIATRIC AMBULATORY SURGERY FACILITY
VANDERBILT UNIVERSITY MEDICAL CENTER
Nashville, Tennessee

Earl Swensson Associates designed this pediatric ambulatory surgery facility—completed in 1991—for Vanderbilt University Medical Center, a major research institution in an urban area. The department consists of eight operating rooms, two minor procedure rooms, and thirty-two

Vanderbilt University Medical Center, Medical Center East, Pediatric Ambulatory Surgery, Nashville, Tennessee. Floor plan, third floor. Arrows indicate the linear path a patient follows through the surgical process. *Courtesy Earl Swensson Associates.*

1 Elevator lobby
2 Waiting/reception
3 Business office
4 Staging rooms
5 Nurses' station
6 Operating room
7 Clean procedure
8 Sterile storage
9 Equipment
10 Special procedure
11 Recovery
12 Physician's lounge
13 Women's lcoker
14 Men's locker
15 Connector to main hospital

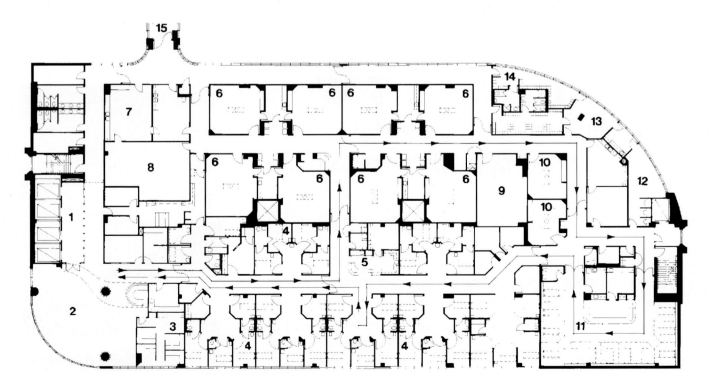

outpatient surgery staging rooms. The ORs are large—500 square feet—designed to accommodate high technology. Large operating rooms are an important trend.

Built atop a parking garage, the facility is tied to the surgery floor of the main hospital via an overhead connector. Thus the center is freestanding, but also fully supported by the resources of the hospital. This arrangement is ideal for ambulatory surgery facilities, providing the convenience of outpatient service with the emotional security offered by the proximity of a major hospital.

The front portion of the department houses preadmission testing. The patient does not have to enter the hospital or be shunted from department to department for testing. The traffic flow is set up so that the patient enters the suite, goes to surgery, then to recovery, then back to an assigned room—all without ever crossing other patients at various stages of their procedures. The assigned rooms are set up in pods of four or five beds per pod with either private or shared toilets. No patient has to walk down the corridor to find a restroom. The pod arrangement is also more efficient for the nursing staff, greatly reducing travel time to and from the nurses' station. In a straight-line arrangement, some rooms might be as much as 150 feet from the nurses' station. The pod arrangement means that no room is farther than seventy feet.

Families are accommodated in a large family waiting area on the perimeter of the unit, which has a beautifully curved glass lobby that admits daylight and affords a nice view. A specified companion may come back into the suite with the patient and wait in an assigned room during the procedure.

■ Concepts in Specialized Ambulatory Care

While the hospital without beds is emerging as a very important trend in healthcare facilities, freestanding and hospital-associated ambulatory facilities devoted to a single specialty are also in significant demand. Within the given area of specialization, such facilities offer the level of care traditionally found only in a hospital setting.

RESURGENS ORTHOPEDICS
Atlanta, Georgia

Farrington Design Group and Cooper Carry & Associates designed this 25,000-square-foot "one-stop-shopping" orthopedic facility as the penthouse suite of a medical office building in Atlanta. Resurgens Orthopedics is an upscale practice (its head, Dr. John Garrett, is team surgeon to the Atlanta Falcons football team), and the architects and designers created a space that elegantly expresses what that practice is all about. Neither corporate in appearance nor modeled after the increasingly familiar hospitality/residential paradigm, the intricate grid of exposed beams and columns symbolizes the mechanics of the human skeleton, while the exposed wiring and piping in the elevator lobby suggests how bones,

Vanderbilt University Medical Center, Medical Center East, Pediatric Ambulatory Surgery, Nashville, Tennessee. The large family waiting area features an attractive curved lobby, plenty of natural light, and pleasant views of the outdoors. *Photo by Gary Knight. Courtesy Earl Swensson Associates.*

Vanderbilt University Medical Center, Medical Center East, Nashville, Tennessee. In this image of the medical complex, Medical Center East, which houses the Pediatric Ambulatory Surgery among other services, occupies the building with the curved glass wall. Connectors from the East building direct patients and visitors from outpatient services to the corresponding inpatient services in the center's hospital. *Rendering by Gerry Harvey. Courtesy Earl Swensson Associates.*

Resurgens Orthopedics, Athens, Georgia. The unique design of this facility echoes the structure of the human body. *Photo by Jon Miller © Hedrich-Blessing. Courtesy of Farrington Design Group and Cooper Carry & Associates.*

muscle, and sinew work together. Yet, unlike the Cedars-Sinai Comprehensive Cancer Center in Los Angeles, discussed earlier in the chapter, this allegorical expression of the work that goes on in the space does not invite profound (and controversial) contemplation of disease, but, rather, is a witty, wry reflection on orthopedics. The effect is aesthetically stimulating and conveys the message that the medicine practiced here is at the cutting edge.

HEART CENTER OF SARASOTA

Sarasota, Florida

In an October 1992 *Contract Design* article on his Atlanta facility, Orthopedist John Garrett commented that "Orthopedics sits on the lighter side of medicine. There is no death and dying." Thus it was thoroughly appropriate to design a stimulating, exciting, even aggressive space for upscale medical consumers. In contrast, the design of the Heart Center of Sarasota, by Arthur F. Mead Architect and Donald J. Stanzione Associates, creates a soothing, residential environment intended to bring a measure of serenity and reassurance to cardiac patients, for whom anxiety can literally be deadly.

The first floor of this four-level, 40,000-square-foot facility houses a cardiac catheterization lab and a rehabilitation area. The lab is designed to create a residential feel, with peach-and-green carpeting that lends a soft tropical touch suited to the Sarasota location. The rehabilitation area includes space for patient education and is designed to resemble the fitness and locker room facilities of an upscale country club.

The main waiting area is on the second level, and it features gently curving walls as well as a custom-built 350-gallon aquarium. The curvilinear forms and the aquarium are both intended to soothe anxious patients, and, of course, the aquarium makes familiar reference to the kind of sea life with which Florida is associated. The second level also contains physicians' and administrative offices, as well as fourteen examination rooms clustered in four pods, color coded to assist way-finding.

The third floor comprises mainly laboratories. Since patients may spend up to an hour lying on their backs during testing procedures, the designers covered the wall facing the patient with a photomural of a tropical landscape, and they used a compatible backlit photomural on the ceiling. These pleasant, relaxing images are intended to ameliorate any feelings of intimidation and discomfort produced by the diagnostic machinery.

The fourth level houses a gym and walking track. It is decorated with painted murals of seaside activity and undersea life.

SHILEY EYE CENTER

University of California, San Diego

The California firm of Anshen & Allen designed this comprehensive ophthalmological facility in the Modernist mode inspired by Louis Kahn. The bold, if austere, exterior geometry is a dignified, but aggressive visual statement, which suggests the sharp focus and acuity of vision that are,

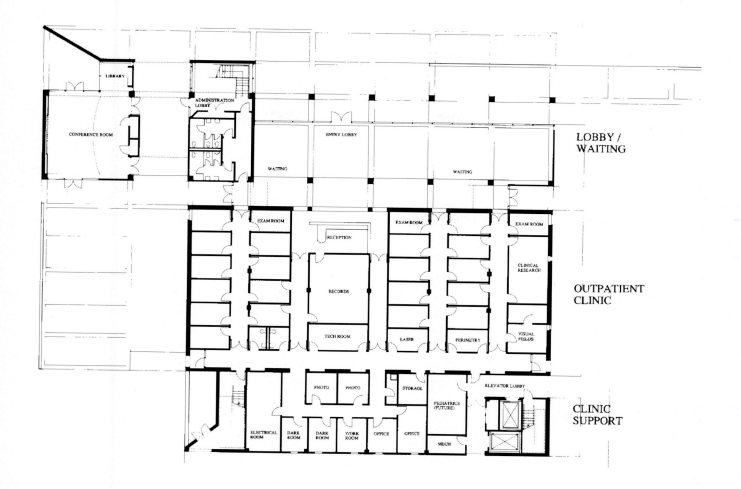

LOBBY /
WAITING

OUTPATIENT
CLINIC

CLINIC
SUPPORT

Shiley Eye Center, San Diego, California. Floor plan, first floor. *Courtesy Anshen & Allen.*

Left: Shiley Eye Center, San Diego, California. With a striking exterior made of precast concrete, the clinic makes a visual statement that suggests the sharp focus and visual acuity that is the purpose of an eye care center. *Photo by David Hewitt/Anne Garrison. Courtesy Anshen & Allen.*

Right: Shiley Eye Center, San Diego, California. The clean and simple use of materials and shapes gives the interior of this facility an austere appearance but a unique richness. *Photo by David Hewitt/Anne Garrison. Courtesy Anshen & Allen.*

after all, part and parcel of the goals of an eye center. Inside, the geometrical austerity is sharply punctuated and relieved by maple paneling, polished composition stone floor tiles, and custom-crafted furniture as well as fine artwork. Natural light is abundant through sloping skylights.

Beyond the aesthetic challenge presented by this project, the architects were also called upon to integrate a clinic, offices, laboratories, conference and library spaces, and a surgery center while simultaneously promoting the autonomy of each function and providing individual access for each. The building thus emerges as an aesthetically distinguished and highly practical facility devoted to the comprehensive practice of a single medical specialty.

MARQUETTE CANCER TREATMENT CENTER
Marquette, Michigan

This 50,000-square-foot facility, profiled in *Health Facilities Management* 2, no. 4 (April 1989), is an example of a medical building type intended to house a comprehensive multiplicity of treatment modalities directed against one type of disorder. Up until the mid 1970s, outpatient cancer treatment centers were essentially stand-alone radiation therapy buildings. Today, they are comprehensive facilities that offer screening and educational services, diagnostic services, and treatment services. Diagnostic services include: endoscopy, minor surgery (biopsy and needle aspiration), coloscopy, cystoscopy, and imaging (CT, MRI, and chest X-ray).

Treatment modalities include: chemotherapy, blood transfusion, radiation therapy, phototherapy, laser therapy, hysterectomy, minor surgery (excision of superficial lesions), maxillofacial reconstruction, and psychiatric therapy.

For disorders such as cancer, the one-stop approach makes for efficient, less stressful treatment, creating a sense that energy is being directed toward addressing the problem—the disease—rather than in bouncing the patient from one hospital department to another.

Scripps Clinic of Green Hospital, Fitness Center, La Jolla, California. The simple but sophisticated exterior of the facility fits in well with the region's architecture. *Photo by K. D. Lawson. Courtesy Earl Swensson Associates.*

Fitness and Sports Medicine Centers

As paradigms of caring shift from remediation to prevention, hospitals and other healthcare providers will call with greater frequency for health and fitness centers. In order to maximize revenue production from such facilities, they will most likely become increasingly similar to commercial health and fitness clubs—though, perhaps, with a stronger education program, ties to rehabilitation and cardiac departments, and sports medicine programs. The hospital fitness center will emerge as a holistic program, which includes exercise and recreation, as well as nutrition education and other education for wellness. We anticipate partnerships and joint ventures

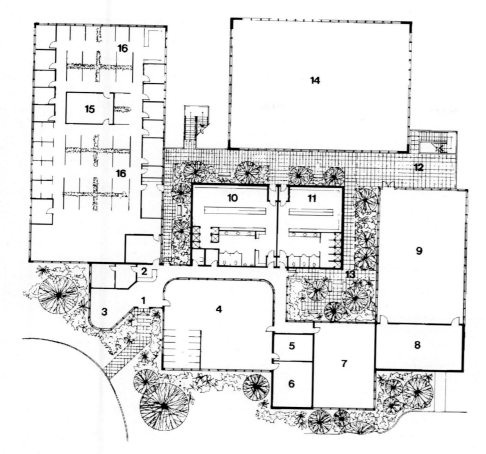

Scripps Clinic of Green Hospital, Fitness Center, La Jolla, California. Floor plan, first floor. Situated in pleasant Southern California climate, the fitness center provides both interior and exterior spaces for a variety of activities. *Courtesy Earl Swensson Associates.*

1 Entrance
2 Reception
3 Waiting
4 Strength training
5 Body
6 Stress
7 Indoor spa/therapy room
8 Kitchen
9 Dining
10 Men's locker
11 Women's locker
12 Outdoor dining
13 Outdoor living
14 Gym below
15 Hydrotherapy
16 Therapy

between hospitals, health clubs, and even country clubs, as well as such community organizations as the YMCA/YWCA.

SCRIPPS CLINIC OF GREEN HOSPITAL
FITNESS CENTER
LaJolla, California

Earl Swensson Associates designed this 22,000-square-foot 1989 adjunct to the Scripps medical campus as a combination public-use health and fitness center and cardio-pulmonary treatment and therapy facility. The Scripps Clinic of Green Hospital has a strong inpatient emphasis and a specialization in cardiac diagnosis and care. The fitness center, while it relates directly to the hospital's cardio-pulmonary focus, serves to extend its reach further into the outpatient market.

The fitness center houses sophisticated facilities for cardiac rehabilitation and sports medicine, as well as a general-use gymnasium, strength center, swimming pool, restaurant, lockers, changing rooms, and showers. Outside, in the midst of a beautiful Southern California landscape, there is a running track and a "human performance circuit," with designated stations for testing physical potential in a variety of activities.

Natural light and the landscape are extensively exploited in the facility. Skylights are used wherever possible, and space planning incorporates windowed "pods" to provide maximum exposure to views of the

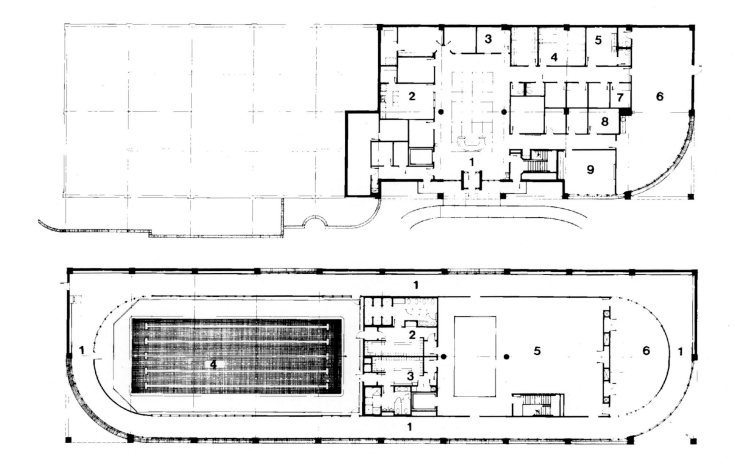

Top: Vanderbilt University Medical Center, Kim Dayani Human Performance Center, Nashville, Tennessee. Floor plan, first floor. *Courtesy Earl Swensson Associates.*

1 Lobby
2 Demonstration kitchen
3 Administration
4 Treatment
5 Procedure
6 Fitness evaluation
7 Exam
8 Office
9 Conference

Bottom: Vanderbilt University Medical Center, Kim Dayani Human Performance Center, Nashville, Tennessee. Floor plan, second floor. *Courtesy Earl Swensson Associates.*

1 Track
2 Women's locker
3 Men's locker
4 Pool
5 Rehab/exercise
6 Aerobics

rolling landscape. Additionally, the center is tied together by covered, open-air walkways, which reinforce the outdoor orientation.

KIM DAYANI HUMAN PERFORMANCE CENTER
VANDERBILT UNIVERSITY MEDICAL CENTER
Nashville, Tennessee

Completed in 1989, the Dayani Center is a state-of-the-art rehabilitation and wellness facility that serves as a treatment and a fitness center. Situated on a long, narrow, and slightly sloping site, the facility takes advantage of the grade by locating the lobby, administrative, and treatment spaces on a ground-level "half-floor," so that the structure's upper floor is freed for an olympic-length swimming pool, locker rooms, aerobic exercise areas, and a track for walking or running one mile every ten laps.

The building is planned so that circulation from one area to another never requires crossing the running track. A central atrium pierces the upper floor to illuminate the lower level, and interior and exterior walls are almost entirely glazed to enhance the visual experience of the walkers or runners. Natural light, views, high ceilings, and brightly painted mechanical systems greatly enliven the center's environment. The pool and an aerobics exercise room anchor each end of the building, with a cardiac rehabilitation area and a fitness center occupying most of the remaining corridor. All areas are open or completely glassed in order to open the track visually. The intention is to maximize the visual activity of

all users—runners, walkers, those in the pool, those in aerobics, those in treatment and rehabilitation areas.

At the north and south ends of the building, bold curves conform to the shape of the running track, but the external structure continues its long-span rectangular grid, producing attractive landscaped terraces at the two front corners as well as a visually interesting interplay of external surfaces.

TOM LANDRY SPORTS MEDICINE AND RESEARCH CENTER

BAYLOR HEALTH CARE SYSTEM

Dallas, Texas

This 330,000-square-foot project was designed by Healthcare Environment Design as a sports medicine facility combining medical treatment and rehabilitation of sports-related injuries with the preventive physical conditioning. Included in the project is a 124,000-square-foot, seven-story physicians' office tower adjacent to a three-level, 124,000-square-foot fitness center, and a 106,000-square-foot underground parking garage. The Landry Center's nine-acre site includes a six-acre running park. Most of the physicians working out of the office tower have practices related to sports or physical conditioning.

Tom Landry Sports Medicine and Research Center, Dallas, Texas. The second-floor running track overlooks the basketball court. The center provides facilities for exercise as well as for the treatment of sports injuries and rehabilitation. *Photo by Phillip J. Benoist. Courtesy Healthcare Environment Design.*

Essentially, the Landry Center was designed as a medically based fitness club, a rehabilitation services center, and a medical office building. Patients and the general public are served by the facility, which is focused on a central atrium, from which the medical office building, the fitness club, and the rehabilitation services are all accessible.

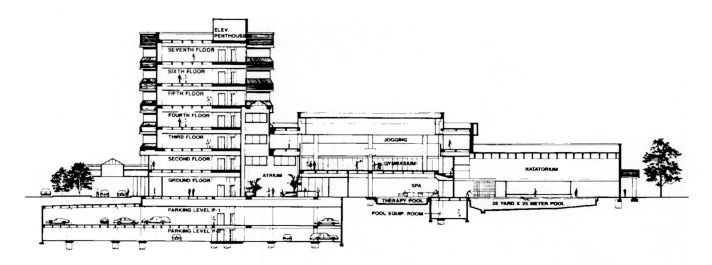

Tom Landry Sports Medicine and
Research Center, Dallas, Texas.
Building section. *Courtesy Healthcare
Environment Design.*

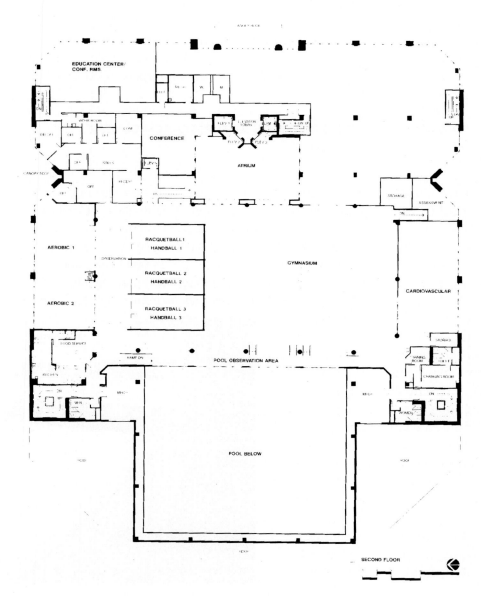

Tom Landry Sports Medicine and
Research Center, Dallas, Texas. Floor
plan, second floor. *Courtesy Healthcare
Environment Design.*

Not only did the architects wish to avoid a clinical look, they also wanted to steer clear of the harsh, cold-looking areas usually associated with fitness centers. The indoor running track is located on a mezzanine above the second floor to provide uninterrupted use of the track, locker rooms are extremely spacious, and color and ceramic tile textures add warmth. Perforated acoustical tile walls and colorful cloth banners damp down sound in the natatorium. Throughout, a combined feeling of privacy and spaciousness is achieved through the use of see-through walls, overlooks, and views opening on to activity areas. A member standing in the second-floor cafe can watch running on the third-floor track, watch basketball on the second-floor court, or observe swimmers in the ground-floor pool. Natural light is used in all exercise areas.

Other cutting-edge amenities in the Landry Center are a special copper ionization system to aid in killing pool bacteria. This significantly reduces the amount of chlorine needed, thereby virtually eliminating the strong chlorine odor usually associated with indoor swimming pools. Running track surfaces were planned with safety in mind. The outdoor track uses crushed bark and a synthetic rubber surface over concrete, while the indoor track, the gymnasium floor, and the floor of the aerobics studio are all suspended, resulting in a resilience that reduces shock and shock-related injury.

Education

Medical libraries have long been impressive, imposing places—and, usually, places that, to the "lay" public seemed forbidding. Indeed, as the once-pervasive "sacred" Latin vocabulary of medicine symbolized, the attitude was actively to deny public access to medical information. Architects and designers frequently credit the Planetree movement with focusing design on the patient. But perhaps even more than design, it is information that is central to patient-focused philosophies like Planetree. Medical facilities are now commonly being designed with provisions for caregivers as well as patients to access information: in books, periodicals, on video, CD rom, and "on-line" via computer terminal.

Design projects range from the inclusion of spaces—a room, even a mere alcove—in patient floor settings, where patients can access medical information through user-friendly on-line computer systems, to major library/information centers such as the Schaetzel Center for Health Education at the Scripps Memorial Hospital Campus, La Jolla, California. Designed by Perkins & Will Architects (interior designer, Jain Malkin, Inc.) and completed in 1993, this 44,000-square-foot facility combines cutting edge information technology with a design feeling of warmth and wellness. The building includes extensive medical library facilities open to care providers and the public, with reading rooms designed on an elegant residential model; meeting rooms; lecture rooms; and a 400-person-capacity multipurpose hall for major gatherings (convertible to auditorium or banquet-meeting use and linked to worldwide health resources via satellite).

Scripps Memorial Hospital, Schaetzel Center for Health Education, La Jolla, California. A unique, freestanding education building, by Perking & Will with Brown Gimber Park Rodriguez,the center houses a medical library, conference rooms, and a satellite link to worldwide healthcare resources. Jain Malkin, Inc. designed the interiors. *Photo by Steve McClelland. Courtesy Jain Malkin, Inc.*

The Schaetzel Center uses the same stucco-framed brick exterior as the rest of the medical campus of which it is a part, but it also incorporates large expanses of glass for an outdoor feeling and to set off the two- and three-dimensional artworks that decorate the facility. A skylit gallery, which serves as a corridor between the hospital's main parking lot and the rest of the campus, houses sculpture, art exhibits, and live plants. The architects intended it to serve as a kind of "piazza, with everyone greeting one another and admiring the art as they passed."

The Workplace-Based Healthcare Facility

Industrial plants and other industries have long maintained on-site clinics to treat work-related injuries, to evaluate workmen's compensation claims, to perform insurance-mandated physicals, and so on. The emerging trend is for companies of all kinds to develop partnerships with healthcare providers—either on-site or off-site—or to maintain their own medical staffs to treat not only work-related injuries and ailments, but to provide primary medical care of all kinds, with a very strong emphasis on preventive care and wellness programs.

In Plano, Texas, J.C. Penney recently opened a $1 million emergency department and daycare center in partnership with JVE, a joint venture of Presbyterian Healthcare System and 500 physicians. USX's U.S. Steel plant in Merrillville, Indiana, recently created a $1.2 million, sixteen-room clinic staffed by four physicians, who provide care for 35,000 active and retired employees and dependents. The Mayo Clinic manages the John Deere Family Health Plan clinic in Moline, Illinois, and, in 1993, was designing a primary care facility for 30,000 Deere & Co. workers in Waterloo, Iowa.

The movement toward employer-sponsored healthcare is spurred in part by the high and ever-rising cost of providing insurance coverage. But it is also a movement to promote wellness, thereby decreasing insurance claims (some providers rebate a portion of premiums in response to reduced claims) *and* increasing worker productivity. For example, in one major insurance company, employees who participated in a fitness program were absent 3.5 days in a year, compared to 8.6 absentee days for workers not enrolled in the program. Wellness programs have also been credited with reducing employee tardiness.

Homecare

As hospitals and other healthcare providers reach out into the workplace, they also reach out into the home. By the beginning of the 1990s, some 2,000 hospitals nationwide had extensive homecare programs in place—up from 700 in 1983. The trend is likely to continue. Although, traditionally, hospital homecare departments performed poorly in terms of generating revenue, in an epoch of cost containment, homecare can be extremely cost effective. An executive with Carondelet St. Mary's Hospital (Tucson, Arizona) stated in a January 25, 1993, *Modern Healthcare* cover story that his institution saves about $900 a day for each patient treated at home.

In writing about the future, there is a natural tendency to lead up to a grand vision or a vision of grandeur: some mega-superhospital, perhaps, that will dwarf present facilities. Indeed, it is possible that what we now think of as hospitals will become fewer, but those that remain will be huge comprehensive regional centers incorporating state-of-the-art technology and featuring a kind of medical park or medical village approach to multiple specialties.

But, currently, the more significant trend is toward decentralization and community outreach, including homecare. The continued development of electronic monitoring, treatment, and telemetry technologies will only encourage this trend. For planners and administrators who suffer from what Laurence J. Peter (*The Peter Principle,* 1969) called an "edifice complex," this trend can only seem disappointing and deflating. For those who see beyond the physical edifice, however, it is apparent that hospitals are on their way to becoming, in varying degrees, virtual entities: not so much buildings to which patients are brought, but networks delivering care through many venues, including hospitals with and without beds, freestanding clinics—some specialized, some providing general or family practice—workplace clinics, and the homes of individual patients. If this seems difficult to visualize, just think, for example, of the rapid revolution of the bank: from a Greek- or Roman-revival edifice surrounding a vault to a financial network of branches, ATMs, point-of-purchase cash registers, and home computers. For architects, designers, planners, administrators, and healthcare providers, the virtual hospital is an emerging reality that is at once wonderful and challenging in its implications.

11

Women's Health Facilities and Pediatrics

We have chosen to group women's health facilities and pediatrics into a single chapter, not out of any "politically incorrect" conviction that the two "naturally" or "inevitably" go together, but to reflect a leading-edge trend in planning such facilities. Responding to the marketplace, administrators, planners, and caregivers are asking for facilities in which OB/GYN and pediatrics care is delivered as a continuum. Let us begin with a look at two such centers, examples of a building type that will likely become an increasingly familiar feature on the healthcare landscape.

ORCHARD PAVILION
EL CAMINO HOSPITAL
Mountain View, California

Designed by Lee, Burkhart, Liu, Inc., this new 220,000-square-foot mixed-use facility provides perinatal services (labor, delivery, postpartum nursing, well-baby nursery, neonatal intensive care) as well as a pediatric nursing unit. In addition, there are two floors of medical office space and two levels of underground parking. While the center is freestanding, with its own entrance and street identity, it is also attached to the main hospital by a first-floor enclosed corridor and an underground service tunnel. This kind of relationship to the main hospital is becoming fairly common as a way of reaping the benefits of a stand-alone facility while retaining the supportive presence of a major hospital.

The center is part of the new El Camino Hospital wellness campus. Its low scale, pitched roofs, skylights, ample bay windows, and courtyard minimize any institutional feel and work together to suggest a family orientation. The nursing units provide homelike settings, with every four rooms clustered around a central skylit foyer/nursing alcove. The labor-and-delivery (LDR) rooms consist of an entry foyer, procedure area, and a family area. Finishes throughout are resolutely noninstitutional: maple floors and hand rails, brick walls, built-in seating upholstered in fabric. Artwork, including collages by neighborhood children, abounds.

Women's Health Facilities and Pediatrics

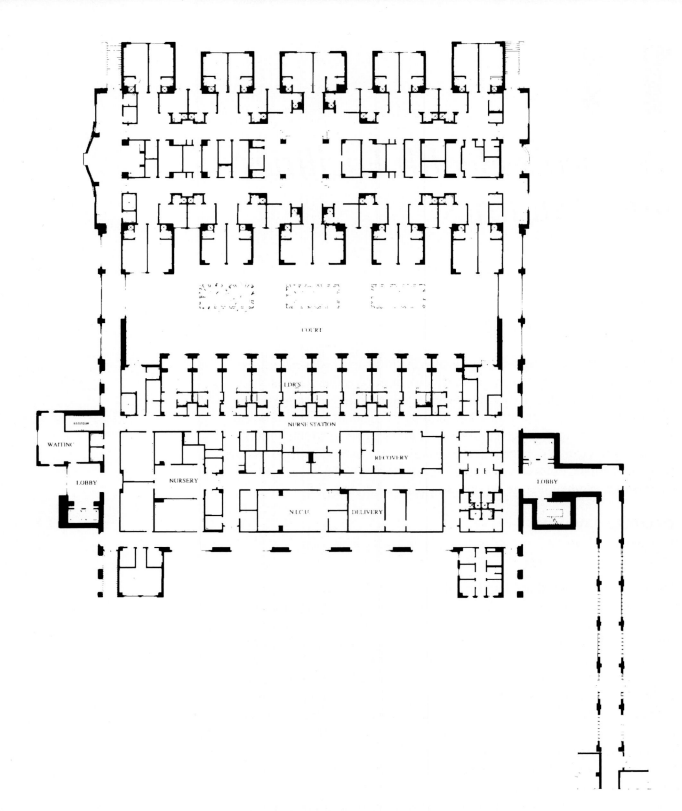

WAITING

LOBBY

NURSERY

N.I.C.U.

DELIVERY

RECOVERY

NURSE STATION

LDR'S

COURT

LOBBY

Orchard Pavilion, El Camino Hospital, Mountain View, California. Floor plan, first floor. *Courtesy Lee Burkhart Lui, Inc.*

The facility combines inpatient and outpatient women and children's services in a single building, along with private physicians' offices. Parking, a satellite laboratory, and a pharmacy increase the unit's convenience. Operationally, the facility is economical and flexible. Each four-room pod has its own satellite nursing alcove, which closes down at night when all nursing station functions are consolidated in a single central station.

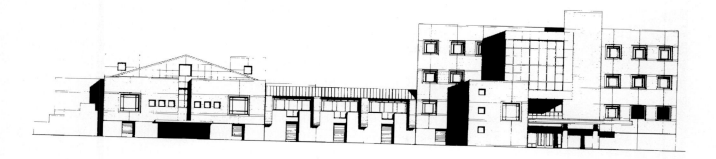

MATERNITY AND CHILDREN'S HEALTH CENTER

McKennan Hospital

Sioux Falls, South Dakota

Orchard Pavilion, El Camino Hospital, Mountain View, California. Elevation. *Courtesy Lee Burkhart Lui, Inc.*

Earl Swensson Associates added a third and fourth floor to an existing hospital to house this new mixed-use department, which was completed in 1993. Registration for the center is located in a two-story atrium, which is independent from main hospital registration.

McKennan Hospital, Maternity and Children's Health Center, Sioux Falls, South Dakota. In a two-story addition to an existing hospital, a separate registration lobby connects the third floor, which houses the single-room birthing facilities, and the fourth floor where services for high-risk deliveries and for neonates requiring special care are located. *Photo by Jonathan Hillyer. Courtesy Earl Swensson Associates.*

McKennan Hospital, Maternity and Children's Health Center, Sioux Falls, South Dakota. The center has a deliberate family-focus. Children whose mothers and siblings are patients of the facility have their own play area. The room was designed in playful colors and constructed of surfaces that are easy to clean. *Photo by Jonathan Hillyer. Courtesy Earl Swensson Associates.*

The third floor contains labor/delivery/recovery/post-partum rooms (LDRPs), for single-room birthing. The well-baby nursery is also located on this floor. The nicely appointed LDRPs feature custom headwalls and a whirlpool in each bathroom. While the rooms are intended to accommodate family members, niche seating is provided in the corridor for family members who wish to escape the birthing.

The other wing of the third floor houses the pediatric unit and the pediatric intensive care unit (PICU). Design is family-focused; two rooms are available for family members who wish to spend the night, and young children and adolescents have their own play areas. A roof courtyard is also available for play. Within the patient rooms, fold-out sofas provide a place for parents to sit or sleep.

The fourth floor of the facility contains the post-partum rooms, delivery rooms, and neonatal intensive care units (NICUs). This floor is principally for high-risk deliveries and for neonates requiring special care.

■ Marketing Epiphany

The *New York Times* for Saturday, November 7, 1992, reported on a movement within the medical community to create a new specialty focusing on women's health. Gynecology, advocates of the new specialty claim, is exclusively devoted to reproductive organs, whereas women's health would address the holistic treatment of women—"everything from managing menopause to spotting abuse, with a focus on the growing body of research on how diseases and drugs act differently in women than in men." In effect, the new specialty would be to women's health what pediatrics is to children's.

Even short of enacting this proposed specialty, during the later 1980s the healthcare industry seemed suddenly to awaken to an extraordinarily important market. After the age of fourteen, women visit the doctor 25 percent more often than men do. They are hospitalized 15 percent more often, and the surgical procedures peculiar to women—such as hysterectomies, tubal ligations, and cesarean sections—account for 11 of the 20 most frequently performed surgeries. Perhaps even more significantly, women make 60 to 75 percent of the healthcare decisions for all U.S. households. The implication for care providers is that they not only have an opportunity to capture the women's healthcare market, but in so doing, have an opportunity to motivate further decisions about healthcare for the family. If the female healthcare consumer is satisfied with the care she receives at a given facility, and that facility or its affiliates offer other kinds of care, she is likely to bring in other members of her family.

The conclusion: two cheers for the 1980s! The decade recognized a women's health market and its significance. But many of the answers that emerged from the 1980s were cosmetic: the same old programs in more attractive settings. To be sure, such cosmetic improvements are important—both in terms of attracting consumers and making patients feel more comfortable and empowered—but they are hardly the whole answer. Yes, women want healthcare delivery in an attractive setting, but their wants are also more complex, more profound, and more sophisticated.

To begin with, there is no single women's healthcare market. Needs vary with socioeconomic status, with level of education, with plans for a family, and with age. So the first thing any facility offering women's healthcare must do is become sensitive to the range of needs and desires that exist in what may seem, superficially, like a narrowly specialized marketplace. Nevertheless, certain common trends will continue to motivate planning and design for women's healthcare programs and facilities:

Convenience

▲ In 5 out of 6 households, both husband and wife work outside the home. Yet since 1960, when only 1 out of 3 women (aged 25 to 34) worked outside the home, men have picked up only about one-quarter of the domestic workload. This means that women are busy—at work and at home.

▲ Effective women's healthcare must accommodate difficult and demanding schedules, not only by offering extended hours of

Condell Intergenerational Day Care Center, Libertyville, Illinois. Floor plan, first floor. A convenience for busy women (and men), this center combines daycare for children and adults in the same facility. *Courtesy O'Donnell Wicklund Pigozzi & Peterson.*

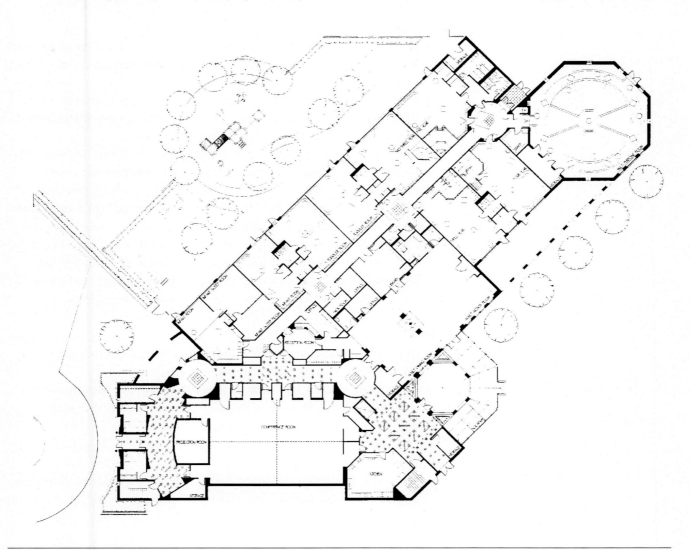

availability, but by decentralizing care through community-based programs and facilities and through self-help programs.

▲ Childcare should be available on-site.

▲ Comprehensive, one-stop care will have the edge. If and until women's health becomes an area of medical specialization, here is a marketing opportunity for women's health facilities associated with internal medicine or family practice. There is also an opportunity for association with pediatrics; the entire family can be cared for in a single visit.

▲ Medical mall designs may offer appealing convenience to these consumers.

Reasonable cost

▲ Ads in popular women's magazines and on television characteristically portray professional women as holding high-pay, high-prestige jobs. It is undeniable that the majority of women now work outside the home. But it is also undeniable that, on average, women are paid less than men and tend to hold lower-level positions. They are also frequently the heads of one-parent families. All of this adds up to a necessarily cost-conscious consumer.

Empowerment

▲ On average, all healthcare consumers are better educated and better informed, and nowhere is this more true than in the case of women.

▲ Women are taking—and will continue to take—a more active role in care decisions. Access to information will be an essential element in the design of women's healthcare facilities.

▲ Most women prefer female physicians, who, they tend to feel (with some degree of justification), understand and appreciate their concerns more fully than male physicians do. Women feel that female physicians are more likely to listen to them and respect their wishes as to courses of treatment.

▲ Nowhere are issues of patient empowerment more in evidence than in obstetrics. Women are looking for a wide range of obstetrical alternatives and are no longer willing unquestioningly to turn their bodies and their babies over to the care of their physicians.

Wellness and fitness

▲ In general, women are more willing than men to participate in preventive, wellness, and fitness programs.

▲ In general, women are far more likely than men to participate in health education programs, including nutritional information programs.

Do-it-yourself

▲ The self-help market is particularly active among women, providing opportunities for educational outreach programs.

Older women underserved

▲ The healthcare needs of older women are currently underserved, especially where health education is concerned.

▲ Like other care providers, women's healthcare professionals must take into account an aging population.

■ Hospital Women's Centers

In the 1980s, a number of hospitals rushed to get on the women's healthcare bandwagon by cosmetically renovating existing OB/GYN spaces and calling them "Women's Centers." When many of these failed to generate the revenues anticipated, planners reached the conclusion that women's health centers should be freestanding. Yet when the Omicron Group, a consulting firm in Omaha, Nebraska, conducted a nationwide survey in 1989 on what women want in healthcare centers, they discovered that the majority of women actually want facilities that are physically connected to a hospital. However, women also said they wanted a center that had an identity separate from the hospital, and three-fourths of the respondents wanted to access the center through an entrance separate from that of the hospital.

The message is that hospital-based women's centers can succeed, provided they are legitimate entities with an individually established identity. A comprehensive, hospital-based women's center should include

▲ *Complete OB/GYN services,* with access to LDR/LDRPs (labor and delivery rooms—that is, single-room maternity care)

▲ *Diagnostic screening services* (mammography, ovarian, osteoporosis screening, etc.)

▲ *Fertility clinic services*

▲ *Fitness and exercise programs* (in a dedicated space)

▲ *Education programs* (in a dedicated space)

▲ *Psychological/sociological counseling service* (in a dedicated space); this service includes general psychological counseling as well as intervention in cases of child or female abuse

In addition, the hospital-based women's center should provide an avenue to such other hospital services as plastic surgery (the third most widely used medical service for women) and cardiology (the fourth most widely used medical service for women).

GREATER BALTIMORE MEDICAL CENTER
OBSTETRICS/ACUTE CARE EXPANSION
Baltimore, Maryland

RTKL Associates, Baltimore, designed this 180,000-square-foot addition to the Greater Baltimore Medical Center for completion in 1993 (Phase I) and 1995 (Phase II). An enclosed four-story courtyard links the new and existing facilities. The primary focus of the new addition is the Women's Center, which provides a full complement of obstetrics/labor/delivery/

Greater Baltimore Medical Center, Baltimore, Maryland. The design and furnishings of the four-story lobby in the obstetrics/acute-care expansion recall the ambience of a fine hotel. *Photo by Maxwell MacKenzie. Courtesy RTKL Associates, Inc.*

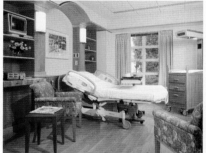

Greater Baltimore Medical Center, Baltimore, Maryland. In the labor/delivery/recovery (LDR) room, residential finishes overcome the array of technological equipment. *Photo by Maxwell MacKenzie. Courtesy RTKL Associates, Inc.*

recovery services. The acute levels of the addition house the departments of surgery, medicine, and cardiology, as well as coronary, medical, and surgical ICU; and nursing units and support facilities.

Throughout the Women's Center LDR Suite, attention is devoted to creating a homelike atmosphere as well as an ambience reminiscent of a fine hotel. Materials, finish, casework, and artwork are residential rather than institutional. The four-story interior courtyard, covered by a glass canopy roof, serves as a lobby and family waiting space for the Women's Center. It is planted with trees, flooded with abundant natural light, and furnished with residential-style chair groupings and intimate table and floor lamps.

The LDR suites have all services built into the head- and footwall millwork, and the delivery light is recessed into the ceiling behind closure panels. Thus the equipment required for delivery is hidden until it is needed. This is a typical solution to providing single-room labor and delivery. During labor, the room appears to be a comfortable residential or

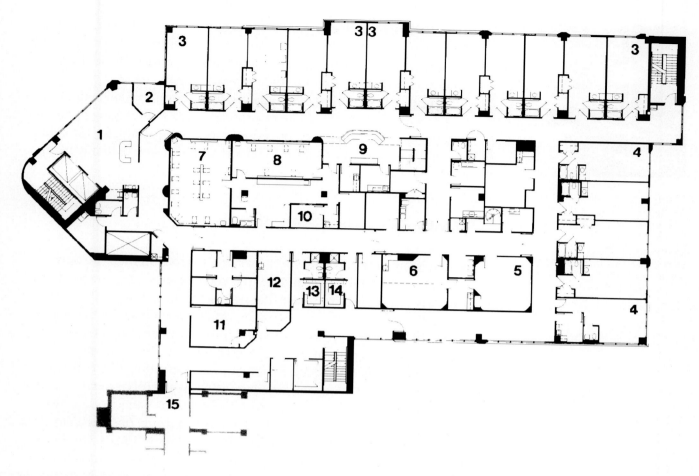

hotel room, complete with such traditional aids to easing labor as a rocking chair. Lighting is soft and relaxing. There is plenty of room for the father or other birthing partner. When the delivery phase begins, the room quickly converts to a fully equipped delivery room. The bed becomes a delivery chair, exam lighting emerges from the ceiling, and headwall casework is opened to access medical gases and electrical outlets.

NORTH FLORIDA WOMEN'S CENTER
NORTH FLORIDA REGIONAL MEDICAL CENTER
Gainesville, Florida

Earl Swensson Associates designed the 133,000-square-foot comprehensive women's facility as a new addition to the existing North Florida Regional Medical Center. The old building was renovated and reclad in keeping with the image created by the new structure. A freestanding women's center, the new, 1990 facility is linked to the main hospital for ancillary support and staff and patient convenience.

The Women's Center houses under one roof virtually all of the services and resources necessary for the treatment of female patients. The prevailing look is noninstitutional, with residential-style furnishings, ample natural light, and extensive outdoor landscaping. The first floor is a woman's resource center, which incorporates diagnostic services—mammography, ultrasound, and lab—psychological and nutritional counseling, educational programs, and a women's health and fitness

North Florida Regional Medical Center, Women's Center, Gainesville, Florida. Floor plan, third floor. *Courtesy Earl Swensson Associates.*

1   Waiting
2   Play
3   Birthing room
4   Mother's lounge
5   Delivery/C-section
6   Recovery/Emergency delivery
7   Level I nursery
8   Level II nursery
9   Nurses' station
10 Isolation
11 Education
12 Nurses' lounge
13 Women's locker
14 Men's locker
15 Existing hospital

North Florida Regional Medical Center, Women's Center, Gainesville, Florida. The use of residential-style furnishings, ample natural light, and extensive plantings—evident in the waiting area—is carried throughout the center. *Photo by K. D. Lawson. Courtesy Earl Swensson Associates.*

Mary Birch Hospital for Women, Sharp Memorial Hospital, San Diego, California. In the atrium/lobby of a state-of-the-art facility, warm rose, plum, and teal hues create a relaxed and inviting atmosphere. *Photo by Building Images, Inc. Courtesy Stichler Design Group/HKS, Inc.*

library. The second floor contains ambulatory surgery facilities, and the third floor holds the LDRPs. The LDRPs are residential in decor—instantly convertible for the delivery phase of birthing—and they overlook a beautiful lake and park within the hospital campus.

The gracious, comfortable, and even luxurious home ambience of this facility is a thoughtful response to a special event: the bringing of new life into the family. In obstetrics, the trend is toward providing for the comfort of the mother as well for the comfort and inclusion of family members.

■ Women's Hospitals

While many hospitals offer special services to women, there are only about twenty women's hospitals in the United States. This is down from the forty or fifty such hospitals that were active in the late 1970s. Some are affiliated with acute-care hospitals; others are independent facilities. As might be expected, obstetrics is the core of women's hospital, accounting for at least 75 percent of patient discharges. However, as Mark Wietecha of Hamilton/KSA (an Atlanta-based consulting firm) observes in an August 26, 1991, *Modern Healthcare* article, women's hospitals' reliance on obstetrics could prove disastrous for them if no changes occur. More acute-care hospitals are "getting back into the birthing business," and that is likely to draw patients away from some women's hospitals. On the other hand, as more women's hospitals offer increasingly comprehensive care, such as plastic surgery and cardiology—two areas extensively used by women—it is likely that competition between acute-care and women's hospitals will intensify even further. At minimum, some women's hospitals are branching into such services as high-risk pregnancies, perinatology, and neonatology; breast and uterine cancer detection and treatment; in vitro fertilization; urodynamics (focusing on urinary incontinence); urinary reconstructive surgery; cosmetic surgery; and psychiatry. A few of these hospitals offer general surgery, cardiology, and other mainstream services.

THE MARY BIRCH HOSPITAL FOR WOMEN
San Diego, California

Opened late in 1992, this new, state-of-the-art facility was designed by the Stichler Design Group and HKS, Inc. It is a six-story, 197,000-square-foot facility, which houses a 60-bed NICU (divided into a 30-bed acute NICU, a 24-bed intermediate care unit for growing, premature infants, and a 6-bed "transition to life" unit for infants whose status is uncertain. Mary Birch has 22 LDRs, a triage room and early labor lounge, and 108 adult beds. Twelve beds are designated as a perinatal special care unit (PSCU), with centralized fetal and cardiovascular monitoring. Ten beds are designated for special circumstances: for women whose babies have died or those who have placed their babies for adoption. Twenty-six beds are dedicated to surgery. Each mother's room has 30 square feet dedicated to the infant's

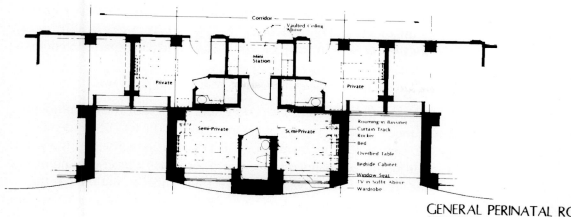

GENERAL PERINATAL ROOM CLUSTER

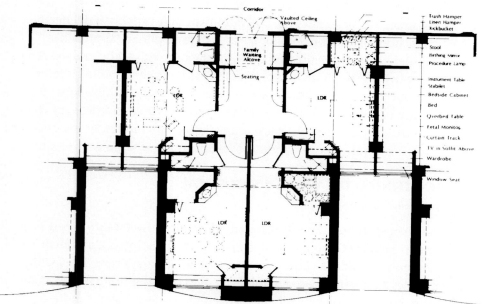

TYPICAL LDR ROOM CLUSTER

care, but two central nurseries are also available, containing 48 bassinets.

The surgical unit has 9 ORs—4 dedicated to cesarian section and high-risk vaginal delivery, 5 dedicated to inpatient and outpatient women's surgery. The 16-bed recovery room is divided by a central nursing station and provides separate care for maternity and gynecological patients. The nursing station serves both groups of patients.

In addition to these basic services, Mary Birch includes

▲ *A resource library* adjacent to the main lobby. This facility is also equipped for small-group discussions.

▲ *A breast center,* which serves as a postmastectomy and lactation clinic.

▲ *A parent living area* adjacent to the NICU: two bedrooms and a livingroom area for parents whose infants are in NICU.

▲ *A laboratory, pharmacy, and radiology department.* The latter includes mammography, ultrasonography, and general radiology facilities.

▲ *A 12-bed antenatal testing area,* which also includes ultrasonography.

Mary Birch Hospital for Women, Sharp Memorial Hospital, San Diego, California. Floor plan, LDR room cluster and perinatal room cluster. *Courtesy Stichler Design Group/HKS, Inc.*

▲ *Psychological counseling* is available in a dedicated first-floor space to inpatients and outpatients.

▲ *Cafeteria* for staff, outpatients, visitors, and participants in educational programs.

▲ *Multipurpose conference room* for educational programs.

Half the patient rooms are private, and half semi-private—although these are designed so that a bathroom separates the two beds, thereby giving each patient her own space and a heightened sense of privacy. The patient rooms are designed in clusters of four, each cluster containing two private and two semi-private rooms. A "mini-nursing" station is at the core of each cluster, supporting a nurse-to-patient ratio of 1 to 4. Supplies and linen are contained in the mini-nursing station.

Admitting, business, records, and a birth certificate office are centralized, as are medical, nursing, and administrative offices—a deliberate design step intended to encourage an interdisciplinary approach.

Interiors have been designed to create an inviting and relaxed atmosphere, with teal, plum, and rose tones predominating, and carpeting in all public areas. The LDRs are set up to convert quickly from labor to delivery function, with the bed instantly convertible to a delivery chair, and medical gases and electrical outlets discreetly hidden in the casework of the headwall. An exam light is available in the ceiling when required.

CENTENNIAL: THE WOMEN'S HOSPITAL
Nashville, Tennessee

Earl Swensson Associates integrated West Side Hospital into a new Centennial Medical Center, transforming the hospital into Centennial: The Women's Hospital, a center of excellence in women's care. The facility provides a patient-focused, family-oriented birthing unit, as well as the entire range of women's services. This includes gynecology and a Women's Imaging Center, which is separate from the hospital proper, but adjacent to it. In addition, the Women's Hospital offers counseling programs, educational programs, minor ambulatory surgery, plastic surgery, a Breast Center, urology, and diagnostic services that target heart disease, stroke, and cancer—leading causes of death among women, which, however, are not encompassed in the traditional gynecological specialty. The Women's Hospital directly interfaces with a cancer treatment center. As part of the services offered, the hospital maintains one of the most successful in-vitro fertilization programs in the country. A women's resource library is located in an adjacent medical office building and offers books, videotapes, and pamphlets, which can be examined at the center or at home. Since the Women's Hospital is part of the Centennial Medical Center, a pediatric unit is located nearby, which, like the Women's Hospital itself, is family-oriented.

The Women's Hospital has two floors of residential-style labor/delivery/recovery (LDR) rooms. All of the rooms feature birthing beds, a stabilization bed for the newborn, designer decor, and soft lighting. The eighth-floor LDRs are larger, and they are equipped with such luxury features as whirlpool baths. After recovery, mothers are transferred to fourth-floor post-delivery rooms, which, like the LDRs, are designer-decorated and feature whirlpool baths. The room becomes the setting for a candlelight dinner for the mother and father. The average length of stay is only 2.1 days—1.5 for vaginal deliveries.

A well-baby nursery is located on the same floor as the post-delivery suites, and the neonatal intensive care unit (NICU)—discussed in Chapter 8—is located on the seventh floor, for adjacency to the LDRs and other birthing facilities. A lactation clinic completes the menu of birthing services. This is an important service, one that not only promotes the health of the newborn (no artificial formula is superior to mother's milk), enhances the mothering experience, and strengthens the bond between mother and child, but also is highly cost-efficient.

■ Freestanding Ambulatory and Birthing Centers

During the 1980s, it seemed to many caregivers, administrators, and entrepreneurs that women wanted women's services outside of a hospital setting. The Omicron Group's 1989 nationwide survey, just mentioned, suggested that, in fact, women actually prefer women's healthcare centers that are within a hospital setting but retain a separate identity from the hospital, including provision for a separate entrance. Nevertheless, there are many freestanding women's health centers across the nation, and the most successful of them offer a convenience and cost-effectiveness that may be difficult to obtain in a hospital context. For insance,

▲ *Office hours are flexible and extensive*
▲ *Parking is readily available*
▲ *Waiting is kept to an absolute minimum*
▲ *A community-based approach is taken*
▲ *Prices of services, including lab tests, are quoted in advance*
▲ *Often, the staff is female*

It is possible to design a freestanding women's center primarily as OB/GYN space. But the trend is to make such centers genuine *centers*— devoted to the traditional OB/GYN functions, but also making educational materials and programs available, including dedicated space for women's support groups, and offering psychological counseling.

Design considerations for the self-standing women's center include:

▲ *Sophisticated decor.* It is a mistake to assume that designing for women automatically means a faux French Provincial look, with ruffles and lace. The typical women's center client is likely to be sophisticated and non-traditional in orientation. Color and design, accordingly, should be both comfortable and sophisticated.
▲ *Design space for education,* including a few private study carrels and, perhaps, a multipurpose room for lectures and seminars. Such programs not only serve the community, they also focus attention on the facility as a genuine center for women's health concerns. If possible, modest library space should be allocated.

Vanderbilt University Medical Center, OB/GYN Services, Nashville, Tennessee. The decor of a women's center must appeal to discerning consumers. The colors and finishes of this patient room give a pleasant, residential feel to the center. *Photo by Gary Knight. Courtesy Earl Swensson Associates.*

▲ *In examination rooms,* the emphasis should be on comfort and amenities. Provide dressing cubicles for privacy and hanging clothes. Provide attractive casework to store medical instruments out of sight. Provide artwork and a mirror. Carpet exam rooms, except for those in which surgery is performed.

▲ *Provide the physician's consultation room/office with desk, lounge chairs, and a coffee table.* This should be a relaxed, inviting area for consultation.

▲ *Provide a breast exam room,* furnished with a divan or high bed. The room could be equipped with a video monitor for viewing instructional tapes.

▲ *Provide specimen pass-through* between the restroom and the lab. This obviates the necessity of walking through a public area armed with a specimen.

▲ *Bear in mind that the facility will be used by women and, likely, in large measure staffed by women.* Standardize countertops height and the height of X-ray view boxes, etc. on a five-foot-four woman, not a six-foot-tall man. "Normal" work-counter height is 36 inches; consider 32- to 34-inch heights instead, to adjustable work counters.

Even before freestanding women's centers began to appear, alternative birthing centers—alternatives to hospital births—commanded a good deal of press coverage. In the early 1990s, more birthing centers opened and accounted for one-third of non-hospital births, or less than one-half of 1 percent of births in the United States. As of late 1993, there were 135 birthing centers in the United States, with another 60 under development. These are primary-care facilities for women who are able and willing to practice natural childbirth. Licensing regulations require that no center may be more than thirty minutes from a hospital, and most are within ten minutes of one. If any medical complications arise during labor, the patient is rushed to the hospital.

WILLIS-KNIGHTON CENTER FOR WOMEN'S HEALTH
Shreveport, Louisiana

VHA Health Facilities Group (Irving, Texas) and Page Southerland Page designed the renovation and expansion of a 71-bed acute satellite facility that is part of the Willis-Knighton Medical System. The renovated and expanded facility includes OB/GYN services as well as neonatal care. The updated look includes such consumer-oriented design amenities as a three-story entrance porch with a dramatic arched window, which becomes the striking visual focus of the new center. An atrium entrance, featuring a "water wall," leads to the admissions area, an education and conference center, meeting rooms, a gift shop, and an aerobic exercise studio. A library contains books, magazines, and audiovisual equipment. The facility provides dedicated space for childcare, and the childcare area is provided with a one-way window that allows parents to observe child-development activities conducted by professionals. Thus the childcare area is designed to serve a dual purpose.

Finishes throughout are hospitality-styled, as are furnishings.

The center includes two traditional labor/delivery rooms and five labor/delivery/recovery/postpartum (LDRP) rooms, as well as an early labor lounge. The LDRPs are designed to accommodate family members, including children. Between the two traditional labor/delivery rooms is an infant resuscitation treatment room, and the NICU is nearby. A lounge overlooking the atrium provides a pleasant place for visitors to relax.

Willis-Knighton also includes a dining room, overlooking the atrium, for patients and families, a VIP patient room, and a room specially equipped for handicapped patients. Each patient room is equipped with a whirlpool bath. A videotaping/filming area is provided for taking pictures of families and their new additions.

The third floor of the facility houses the full-term nursery, pharmacy, and nineteen patient rooms. Skylights provide ample natural light.

■ The Future of Obstetrics

While hospital-based and freestanding women's health centers will probably be increasingly popular during the coming century, these no longer represent the *radical* alternative to conventional hospital-based OB/GYN care that they once did. This is because the conventions of conventional OB/GYN care have changed and have increasingly embraced the kinds of alternatives the alternative health centers offer.

Nowhere is this more true than in birthing. Despite the proliferation of birthing alternatives, including home births, it is likely that, for some time to come, most births will continue to be in hospitals—but that hospital obstetrical practices and accommodations will continue to evolve according to the birthing center model. After all, a hospital-based birthing center can offer mother and child the best of the alternative and conventional worlds: a comfortable, homelike setting that encourages natural childbirth *and* instant access to the emergency backup available in an acute-care setting.

Why are hospitals moving in these new directions?

Because that's where the market is. Obstetrics can be a major source of hospital revenue, but it's also the kind of service consumers very deliberately shop for, looking not only for medical competence but for the most supportive and attractive setting for what is a momentous experience—and one that should be joyful.

The trend in hospitals is two variations on homelike birth: the labor/delivery/recovery room (LDR) and the labor/delivery/recovery/postpartum (LDRP). The second alternative, which is truly single-room maternity care, is the more radically patient-focused of the two, and it is gaining in popularity. In the LDRP setting, labor, delivery, recovery, and postpartum recovery and care all take place in the same room. A 1991 AHA survey found that only 10 percent of reporting hospitals offered LDRPs, while 20 percent offered LDRs. However, a survey by Ross Planning Associates of Columbus, Ohio, that year revealed that of forty-eight hospitals with LDRP facilities, 69 percent reported that the number of births increased

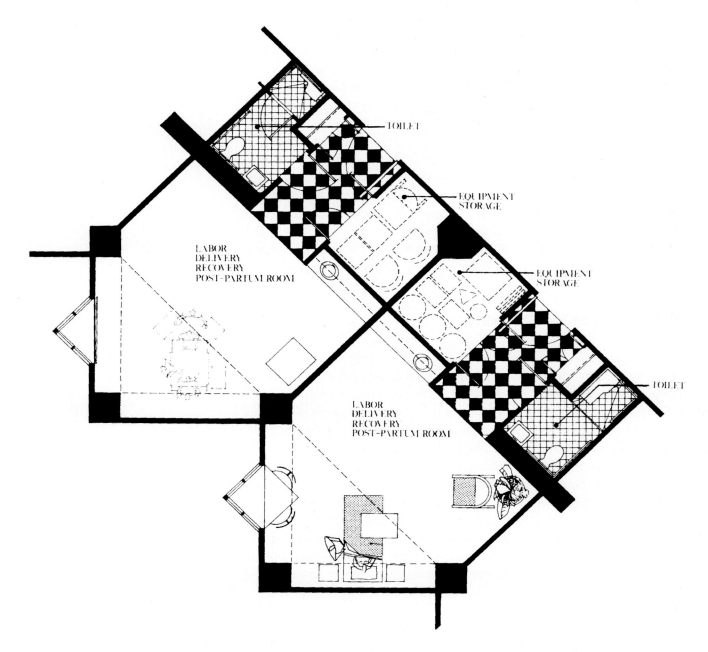

TOILET

EQUIPMENT STORAGE

LABOR
DELIVERY
RECOVERY
POST-PARTUM ROOM

EQUIPMENT STORAGE

TOILET

LABOR
DELIVERY
RECOVERY
POST-PARTUM ROOM

Sharp Chula Vista Medical Center, Chula Vista, California. Floor plan, LDR rooms. *Courtesy Stichler Group, Inc.*

during the program's first year. The average increase was 43 percent. Only 45 percent of hospitals with LDRs reported increases, and the average increase was only 12.5 percent. The LDRP, then, is very well received by patients.

LDRPs are essentially oversized patient rooms that are convertible from labor to delivery functions. We have already reviewed some examples of the headwall that conceals medical gases and electrical outlets, the bed that converts to a delivery chair, equipment that can readily be wheeled in and out, and the ceiling-mounted, fully adjustable exam light. For the postpartum function, the LDRP must be spacious enough to accommodate family members; it might include a window seat, which can be quickly converted to a bed for overnight family stays. A wall-mounted, fold-down table for in-room dining encourages the mother to get out of bed more quickly. If the room is large enough, a small stand-

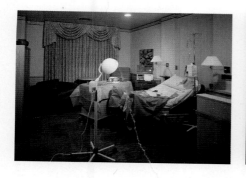

PineLake Medical Center, Mayfield, Kentucky. Two views show the functions of an LDRP (labor/delivery/recovery/postpartum) room. In one view the room is readied for labor and delivery. The second view shows the room as set up for recovery. *Photos by Gary Knight. Courtesy Earl Swensson Associates.*

alone table can be included for dining. One facility, the Washoe Medical Center in Reno, Nevada, features the Stork Club, an elegant dining room for new parents. In general, the hospitality or residential model is most appropriate for LDRPs.

LAKE PAVILION/FAMILY BIRTH CENTER
BAPTIST HOSPITAL OF MIAMI
Miami, Florida

This addition to the Baptist Hospital of Miami was designed by the Ritchie Organization. Because obstetrics has come to represent such a significant market, the 50,000-square-foot facility was designed to occupy a highly visible site at the hospital's front door. The addition conforms to the Miami-style Italianate coral-pink stucco of the original hospital, and the effect is that of a fine hotel.

Inside, the layout is highly logical, with staff support spaces separating the Family Birth Center from the rest of the hospital, and delivery (LDR) and nursery facilities located between the support area and patient rooms. The LDRs as well as the patient rooms are custom-furnished with armoires containing the television, music equipment, and a small refrigerator. Oversized sleeping chairs can accommodate the father overnight, and a rocking chair is provided for the mother.

HOLY CROSS JORDAN VALLEY HOSPITAL
West Jordan, Utah

Holy Cross Jordan Valley Hospital had a half-dozen delivery rooms and recognized a need to expand its obstetrics service. Earl Swensson Associates designed the new unit on top of the existing hospital building, creating a state-of-the-art birthing unit and a completely new facade for the entire building. Together, these create a distinctive, upscale image for the hospital in the community.

The new facility features large LDRPs outfitted with such amenities as stereos, VCRs, Jacuzzis, and custom-designed furniture. Colors of fabrics and finishes are muted and designed to enhance skin tone. Each LDRP room is entered through its own small alcove, thereby greatly reducing noise and enhancing privacy. An elegant lounge for the exclusive use of mothers is located down the hall from the LDRPs, and two baby nurseries are provided for varying levels of care. Specialized rooms accommodate surgical deliveries.

Left: Holy Cross Jordan Valley Hospital, West Jordan, Utah. Creating a state-of-the-art facility with an upscale decor, the architects supplied the hospital with a distinctive image in the community, an important consideration where medical facilities must compete for discerning consumers. The fireplace of the waiting area imparts a warm, inviting atmosphere—and one particularly suited to cold Utah climes. *Photo by Gary Knight. Courtesy Earl Swensson Associates.*

Right: Holy Cross Jordan Valley Hospital, West Jordan, Utah. The special pattern in the ceiling over the bed adds visual variety for the patient. The LDRP room provides lighting for delivery and softer lighting for recovery. The finishes have been designed to appeal to the feminine mind. *Photo by Gary Knight. Courtesy Earl Swensson Associates.*

The unit is laid out in a triangle plan, with nurseries and nursing stations in the center, thereby minimizing travel time between nursing stations and patient rooms. There is also an education area for pre- and postnatal classes. The large family waiting area is complete with fireplaces.

The obstetrics unit is tied to the original hospital by a two-story atrium with plantings, a fountain, and a barrel-vaulted skylight. The

Holy Cross Jordan Valley Hospital, West Jordan, Utah. The patient bath area features lever handles and grab bars that make access easier. The wall sconces, mirror, and other touches give the room a nice homey feel. *Photo by Gary Knight. Courtesy Earl Swensson Associates.*

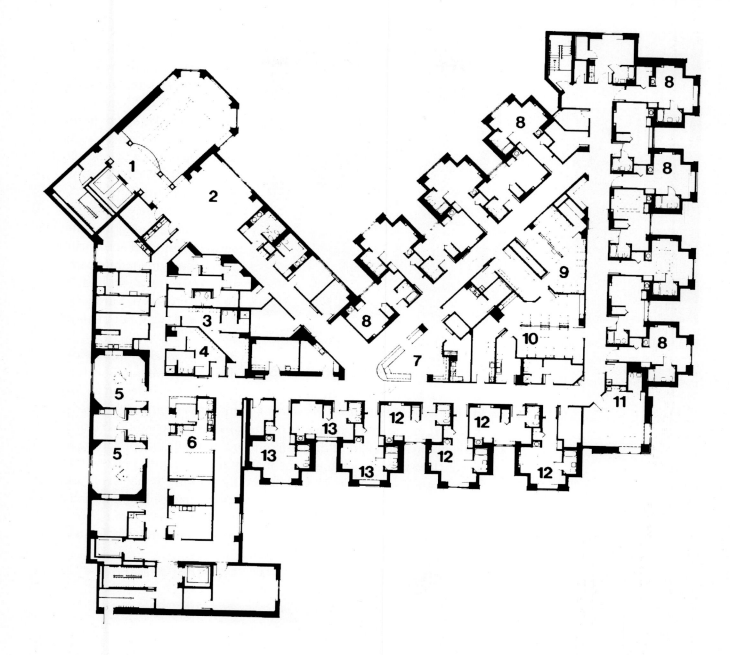

atrium serves as an entry area for the first-floor hospital and the second-floor obstetrics area. The atrium includes new administrative areas, a medical records area, a chapel, and a gift shop.

■ Pediatrics

In this book of new directions, trends in pediatric design occupy a some-what paradoxical position. There are no clear "new directions" to report in pediatric care design—but that is largely because the dazzling variety of design options presently seen in advanced pediatric facilities are already markedly forward-looking and imaginative. Perhaps this is because the world of childhood naturally invites daring, fantasy, and innovation.

Holy Cross Jordan Valley Hospital, West Jordan, Utah. Floor plan, second floor. *Courtesy Earl Swensson Associates.*

1 Elevator lobby
2 Family waiting
3 Women's locker
4 Men's locker
5 C-section
6 Recovery
7 Nurses' station
8 LDRP room
9 Nursery
10 Continuing care nursery
11 Mother's lounge
12 Private gynecological
13 Private acute partum room

HealthPark Florida, Ft. Meyers, Florida. The inclusion of play areas for children is an important consideration in the design of advanced pediatric facilities. The imaginative design of this playroom offers areas for a variety of activities. *Photo by Robert Ames Cook. Courtesy HKS, Inc.*

Childhood and its needs are, by their very nature, anti-institutional. The enlightened children's hospital does more than meet a child's medical needs. It creates an environment that addresses physical, social, developmental, and emotional needs. Moreover, it takes into account not only the child's needs, but those of his or her family. More and more children's hospitals and pediatric facilities are encouraging family participation in the treatment and healing process not just as a matter of policy, but by providing for families in the design of the facility.

Indeed, most healthcare facilities are just now awakening to the importance of providing for families. In the case of children's healthcare facilities, providing for the family should not be considered an add-in design feature, but rather the starting point for planning any child-oriented medical environment. This means making parental sleeping accommodations part of the design from the beginning, providing a family lounge and, perhaps, a meditation room—a quiet place to take a break from the emotionally and physically draining demands of caring for a seriously ill child. Sleeping accommodations may be as simple as a chair that opens out into a bed, placed, of course, in a patient room large enough to accommodate it. Or the facility may offer full guest suites. The

Office of Dr. Gordon Bellah, Pediatric Practice, Nassau Bay, Texas. "Playful, geometric shapes penetrate an interactive wall between the parents' waiting area and the children's play area." *Photo by Jud Haggard. Courtesy Watkins Carter Hamilton.*

needs of siblings, too, should be remembered. Childcare resources for siblings might be made available in a dedicated space. At the very least, a playroom should be part of the family accommodations.

Other key design goals include

▲ *Interaction with peers.* The inclusion of playrooms, lounges, and classrooms do much to enhance social interaction among children. Even well-designed corridors, especially those with bays or alcoves, invite such interaction. Depression and a sense of isolation are major psychological factors in any seriously ill person. They are often most intense in a child. Peer interaction does much for morale and, therefore, promotes healing.

Armstrong World Industries, ABPD Cirrus Themes: Trains. Incorporating fantasy and imagination into hospital design helps to develop chidren's physical, social, developmental, and emotional needs. A ceiling design, copyrighted by Armstrong, offers bed-ridden patients a bit of whimsy. *Photo courtesy of Armstrong World Industries.*

▲ *Territory.* Anyone who has children knows how they feel about their rooms. To the child, her room is a nest, a refuge, a special place that empowers her in ways denied in other parts of the house. Patient room design should enhance this sense of territoriality. This begins with the orientation of furniture. The child's back should be against the wall, not toward the center of the room. When people enter the room, they should face the child, not approach her from behind. Children have the same privacy needs as other patients—it's just that, in an adult world, this need is not always respected. Finally, it is useful to provide pediatric rooms with space—a shelf, an alcove— for a child's treasures and toys. A closet, or some other secure place to keep things, also adds to her sense of territorial security, a feeling that the items she loves and is familiar with will be safe.

▲ *Independence.* The environment should promote a sense of independence, including (to the degree possible) freedom of movement and a sense of competency. Color coding can aid both by assisting way-finding.

▲ *Access to outdoors.* Children love to play outdoors. Design should include such amenities as a patio, deck, or solarium.

▲ *Fantasy and stimulation of imagination.* This is one area in which architects and designers have excelled. The Starbright Pavilion (Los Angeles), discussed in the previous chapter, is a particularly ambitious example of fantasy and imagination applied to a hospital setting. Of course, it is not necessary to structure the entire facility as a fantasy environment, but elements of fun can be worked into any design.

Children's Hospital and Health Center, San Diego, California. Taking cues from architectural styles of the area, this children's hospital projects a playful, almost fairytale character. *Photo by David Hewitt/Anne Garrison. Courtesy NBBJ.*

■ Four Pediatric Care Facilities

CHILDREN'S HOSPITAL AND HEALTH CENTER
San Diego, California

NBBJ Architects designed this 190,000-square-foot facility to combine elements of indigenous Spanish mission-style architecture with broad elements of childlike fantasy and fun. The result is a cohesive, decidedly non-institutional and non-intimidating massing of surprises, including downspouts that empty into concrete collector cubes decorated like tic-tac-toe boards, interactive art, and playfully landscaped courtyards. Inside, the patient rooms are grouped into clusters designed to evoke cozy neighborhood feelings. The overall effect is of a fairytale mission/castle nestled amid the more imposing buildings that constitute the rest of this large medical campus.

Visitors to the hospital enter through the base of a large clock tower. The lobby is also the reception area and waiting room for families of children visiting outpatient clinics, which are located on the first floor. Also on the first floor, but separated from these reception and ambulatory areas, is San Diego's only children's emergency department. The second floor contains patient rooms, and the third floor contains critical care rooms and pediatric intensive care facilities.

The patient floors consist of 10-bed neighborhoods arranged around a nurses' station. The stations are made to look like garden walls and fences. Columns are fashioned to resemble lampposts. Green carpeted areas imitate lawns. At night, fiber optics provide the illusion of twinkling stars in the vaulted ceilings over the nurses' stations.

The patient rooms themselves are designed to resemble a child's bedroom and include brightly painted cabinetry for clothes and personal belongings. Children are offered a catalog from which they may select toys and art prints to decorate and personalize their room. The rooms on

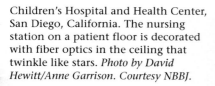

Children's Hospital and Health Center, San Diego, California. The nursing station on a patient floor is decorated with fiber optics in the ceiling that twinkle like stars. *Photo by David Hewitt/Anne Garrison. Courtesy NBBJ.*

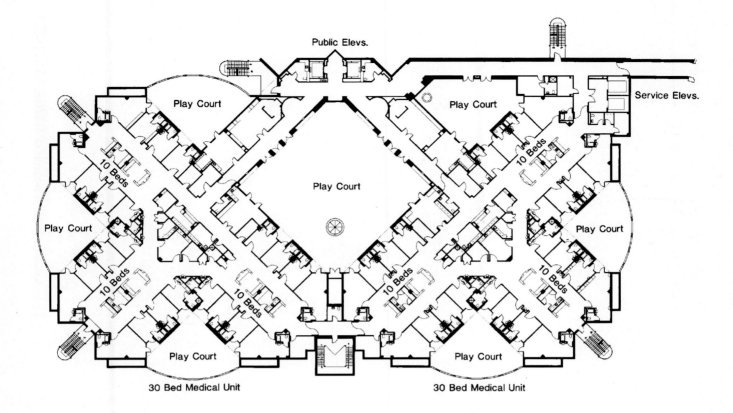

Public Elevs.

Service Elevs.

Play Court

Play Court

Play Court

10 Beds

10 Beds

Play Court

Play Court

10 Beds

10 Beds

10 Beds

10 Beds

10 Beds

Play Court

Play Court

30 Bed Medical Unit

30 Bed Medical Unit

Children's Hospital and Health Center, San Diego, California. Floor plan, patient floor. *Courtesy NBBJ.*

the second floor have exterior doors that lead to six perimeter courtyards, each of which is landscaped thematically. There is, for instance, a Sensory Court (includes plants of varied textures, smells, and appearance) and a Court of Names (featuring plants with children's names, such as Johnny Jump-Up and Creeping Jenny). A large central court is available to staff, families, and patients. Covered by a conical skylight, this court features a large patch of lawn for picnics.

CHILDREN'S MEDICAL CENTER OF ISRAEL

Petah Tikva, Israel

The Cannon architectural firm designed this major 390,000-square-foot facility, which in late 1992 opened its doors to all children of the Middle East, regardless of nationality, race, or religion. The owners and architects had two major goals: to create a building that would effectively house very advanced care and medical research and to create a building that is in itself a healing environment for children. "We want to create a setting that . . . allows children to react only to what is bothering them," said project director Jerry Switzer, "not to emotional stress or the conditions typically associated with a hospital. . . ."

Stress is minimized, in part, by maintaining contact with the outside. Daylight is abundant, as a main circulation path leads through a five-story, skylight-capped atrium, which is at the core of the inpatient area. The atrium is decorated with large trees and comfortable, casual furniture, suggesting a village square rather than a hospital lobby. The object is to maintain a comforting feeling of being outdoors, so that (as Switzer

Children's Medical Center of Israel, Petah Tikva, Israel. The center's atrium is designed to resemble a village square rather than a hospital lobby. *Photo courtesy Cannon, Inc.*

remarked in *Facilities Planning News* [January 1993]) "you get almost to a patient room before you feel like you've entered the building." Patient-room windows look out onto the atrium, and glass-enclosed elevators allow children to watch visitors come and go, including parents. By being able to observe the parents as they leave the building, the child feels less alone, less abandoned.

In contrast to one current patient-focused strategy, which concentrates as much patient treatment in the patient room as possible, the Children's Medical Center of Israel clusters fifteen patient rooms around a central treatment room. Children are brought here for most procedures. The object is to preserve their own room as a safe haven, a place for rest and comfort, not pain and anxiety. Switzer remarked: "Children always know that when someone enters their room, they will not be hurt." Likewise, while patient-focusing emphasizes privacy, the rooms at the medical center actually have windows along the *inside* corridor—not so much for the nurse to look in, as for the child to gaze out.

Bathrooms are located on the outboard (external) wall rather than the more conventional inboard (interior) wall. This not only provides a clear line of sight into the corridor, it provides an alcove that can serve as private space for parents who choose to remain in the room with the child. The alcove has a reading lamp and a lounge chair that converts into a sleeper.

Color schemes are appropriately bright throughout, and magnetic chalkboards are available in each room so that children can personalize their space.

CINCINNATI BURNS INSTITUTE
SHRINERS HOSPITALS FOR CRIPPLED CHILDREN
Cincinnati, Ohio

The critical care aspects of the Shriner burn facilities in Galveston and Cincinnati were discussed briefly in Chapter 8. The Cincinnati Burns

Cincinnati Burns Institute, Cincinnati, Ohio. Large numbers and individualized images identify rooms in a "language" familiar to young patients. *Photo by James Wilson. Courtesy HDR, Inc.*

Institute, designed by HDR, is also a fine example of an environment created for severely injured children—aged two to eighteen—who may be confined to the hospital for as much as a month, depending on the severity and extent of their burns.

The Cincinnati Burns Institute creates a comforting fantasy world by evoking a Victorian "old town," complete with turn-of-the-century buildings arranged around an atrium. The town square is equipped with gazebos, a video arcade, a baby crawl area, and a jungle gym, as well as an old-time toy store to browse in. Each patient room is designed as a safe haven. Instead of a room number, each door is decorated with a different toy. A wipe on-and-off board is positioned next to the door and allows the child to personalize his room. As in the Children's Medical Center of Israel, no painful procedures are performed in the patient rooms. The room is to be associated exclusively with comfort and security.

Except for the ICUs, patient rooms are adaptable for parent rooming-in. The parent bed is built in. In addition to this feature, there is a separate area for parents to stay with their children before discharge, so that the parent can learn how to care for and work with the child to promote rehabilitation.

As comfortable and reassuring as the patient rooms are, play areas, located throughout the patient areas, are designed to draw children out of their rooms as much as possible.

The Cincinnati Burns Institute is an advanced and comprehensive facility. The lower level of the five-story building contains support services, records storage, a medical library, administrative office, and a lecture hall. Radiology, orthotics (where special masks, body braces, and garments are fabricated and fitted), and an outpatient department are located on the first floor. The outpatient clinic is designed like an old town toy square and includes a nurses' station, fourteen single-bed examining rooms, and a treatment room.

Baylor University Medical Center, Pediatric Center for Restorative Care, Dallas, Texas. The chapel in the center addresses the spiritual aspects of healing. *Photo by Michael Lyons. Courtesy Healthcare Environment Design.*

The second floor is a child life area, with sixteen reconstructive beds and fourteen ICU beds, as well as a parent care unit, rehabilitation for former patients, gymnasium, physical therapy, occupational therapy, and a school. The parent care area consists of six hotel-like rooms, meant to accommodate parents and their children.

The third floor contains surgery, acute care, respiratory services, hydrotherapy, and a chapel. The fourth floor is devoted to laboratory and research space, and the fifth floor is divided into research areas and dining—including an outdoor rooftop dining area—and a rooftop play area. The sixth floor contains housing for experimental animals.

PEDIATRIC CENTER FOR RESTORATIVE CARE

Baylor University Medical Center
Baylor, Texas

This facility, designed by HED, is a new kind of freestanding pediatric medical center. Its object is to integrate physician, nurse, parent, and child in order to provide the most effective and most cost-effective care for children with multiple medical problems, who range in age from newborn to three years old. The idea is to create a transition from hospital to home care. Parent education is, therefore, a crucial element of the care program.

To facilitate this collaborative care effort, HED designed a comfortable and non-institutional facility that emphasizes a family feeling. The Victorian facade of the building not only harmonizes well with the surrounding neighborhood, it in effect broadcasts and fosters the warm family feelings that are essential to this type of collaborative care.

The layout of the center is organized to encourage parent education and participation by emphasizing the relationship among the sleep, social, and therapy areas rather than centering design on the traditional staff, material, and patient areas. There is no central nurses' station but, rather, a number of small workstations. Long corridors have been replaced by shorter, more varied spaces. Everything contributes to working together, rather than separating staff, family, and patients.

12

Trends for 2000 and Beyond

When most of us think about the future of medicine, architecture is not the first thing that comes to mind. And this is true whether we are healthcare providers, administrators, or even planners, designers, or architects. We think first and foremost of advances in diagnostic imaging, in electronics, robotics, in biotechnology, in genetics. We think, too, of the current healthcare crisis: the inescapable reality that many people cannot afford good basic medical care, let alone gain access to the technological wonders now in existence and yet to emerge.

Toward the beginning of this book, we mentioned two plays by the great nineteenth-century dramatist Henryk Ibsen: *An Enemy of the People* and *The Master Builder.* The hero of one is a physician; of the other, an architect. Both men find themselves faced with similar tasks: to diagnose and heal the ills of their community and their society. Physician or architect, both promote the health of humanity and civilization. For us, this concept drives our practice as architects—especially as healthcare architects—and it has driven us as authors of this book. But it is more than a talisman or metaphor. It is a reality. And it is not just *our* reality. If there is one trend that overrides all others in shaping the future of hospital and healthcare facility design, it is the emergence of architects and designers as full partners in planning and delivering medical care.

■ A Catalog of Trends and Developments

Throughout this book, we have tried to balance ourselves on the cutting edge, delineating trends for which those concerned with hospitals and healthcare facilities are currently building or currently planning, or *should* be currently building or planning. In this final chapter, we take a somewhat longer view and attempt to outline the trends and developments likely to shape healthcare and, therefore, the practice of healthcare architecture, well into the twenty-first century. The discussion naturally falls into three broad areas:

1. A catalog of medical trends and developments
2. How architecture will address and facilitate these trends and developments
3. The practice of architecture as the practice of medicine

With some justification, medical historians regard all healthcare prior to the later 1930s as the Dark Ages. To be sure, many advances in diagnosing and describing illness had been made before that time, but for the most part, until an arsenal of antibiotic drugs became available, doctors really could do relatively little to combat disease. They could palliate, and they could support, but they could offer little in the way of aggressive, effective treatment. Antibiotics cured an array of diseases—although it is now apparent that these drugs have created an environment in which new, drug-resistant strains of bacteria have also been produced. Tuberculosis, for example, the grim reaper of the last century, is reemerging as a scourge at the end of this one.

In fact, while it is undeniable that modern medicine has relieved some suffering, has given us all the feeling that we are no longer helpless in the face of disease, it is by no means certain that medicine has done very much to lengthen the span of human life. True, in 1940, the average American life expectancy was sixty-three years, and it is now seventy-six. However, most authorities ascribe this increase not to medical science but to such wealth-linked factors as improved sanitation, better nutrition, better housing, improved working conditions, and even the virtually universal use of household refrigeration, which has greatly reduced the incidence of food-borne bacteria contamination.

Looked at from a world perspective, rather than that of one wealthy industrial nation, the human population is not, in fact, getting healthier, according to a 1992 report from the United Nations World Health Organization. The failure of medicine—if that is how one chooses to view it—is not just a failure to defeat disease once and for all, but a failure even to treat disease at a reasonable cost, to provide cost-effective healthcare.

Three megatrends will shape the future of medicine during the next century:

1. Medicine will address the causes of disease, which means that medicine will dig to the roots—or, more properly, the seeds—of life itself, "engineering" human genes, chromosomes, and molecules in order to eliminate rather than attempt to cure disease.
2. For those diseases and disorders that cannot be engineered out of existence and in the case of injury and accident, non-invasive treatments (especially drug therapies) and minimally invasive procedures will extensively replace surgery. Such procedures will be performed at home or in outpatient settings rather than in hospitals.
3. Genetic engineering, insofar as it succeeds, will be the most cost-effective way of dealing with disease: not repeatedly to plug, and patch, and repair, but to prevent. For those disorders (and injuries) that cannot be prevented, however, treatment will be judged on a cost-versus-benefit basis.

These are sobering trends, particularly the first and the third. Some may even find them terrifying. Genetic engineering presents a vast field for abuse by governments and individuals. After all, if diseases can be engineered *out* of genes, can't other "desirable" qualities be engineered *in*—blue eyes, blond hair, a tendency toward absolute obedience? What will genetic engineering do to the human gene pool? How will it affect human ecology and evolution? Will such engineering create new "super" strains of disease, just as the indiscriminate use of antibiotics has created new strains of resistant bacteria? Finally, is human genetic engineering morally desirable?

These are all valid and highly disturbing questions. Yet we already know the consequences of the failure to eliminate disease: high-cost medical care of questionable effectiveness. If genetic engineering proves to be the most effective medicine, would it be morally defensible to ask caregivers to deliver *less* effective medicine? Is there a qualitative moral difference between intervening in a disease process at the genetic level and intervening at a later stage in the disease? Is genetic engineering any less "natural" (and therefore less "moral") than vaccination? Is vaccination any less natural than confinement to an "iron lung"? Is death, in fact, the most natural—and, therefore, most moral—outcome of disease?

Our answer to these questions? It seems to us that genetic engineering is inevitable.

Scarcely less disquieting in its implications is the third megatrend: healthcare based on a cost-versus-benefit equation. The physician's vaunted Hippocratic Oath harmonizes with the Judeo-Christian ethic of universal charity and a revulsion from putting a price of any kind on human life. However, the Hippocratic Oath is the product of an age of cheap—and, in any case, limited—medical treatment. Until rather recently, to do "everything possible" for a patient cost very little more than to do nothing at all, simply because there was not much that *could* be done.

To be sure, the ambition to do all one could to save a life was and remains a noble one. In the past, it was also economically feasible. Today, however, there is much, much more that *can* be done for any given patient—and each of these procedures, drugs, and interventions comes with a price tag, which the individual and, ultimately, society must pay. Indiscriminately paying "for it all" has already become crippling to society, and most insurance providers and government agencies are now acknowledging that paying for it all is not *merely* crippling, but fatal.

Diagnosis Related Groups (DRGs) are already expressions of judgment about the effectiveness of procedures. Insurance providers and government agencies are saying that they will pay for procedures proven to be effective, but they will not pay for unproven or marginally effective treatments. Such cost-versus-benefit judgments will play a greater and greater role in the delivery of healthcare, no matter who is paying for the treatment. Whether the consumer is the government, an insurance provider, or the patient, questions will center on value, on cost versus benefit. No longer will care providers have sacrosanct license to do "whatever is necessary" in each and every case.

Healthcare reform is still very much in flux, but healthcare planners and hospital administrators are already reacting in at least five ways:

1. Some are rapidly shifting their institutions from an inpatient to an outpatient orientation.
2. Some are facing with dread the prospect of capitation—a system in which reimbursements are fixed by contract rather than paid on a fee-for-service basis.
3. Some are desperately resisting the tide of the trend by clinging to licensed beds.
4. Some are expanding ambulatory services and decentralizing, working to bring hospital-based facilities into the community, providing educational and other preventive services in neighborhood settings.
5. Some are planning and creating healthcare systems in which payers, providers, patients, and physicians are elements of a single coordinated continuum—a genuine *system*.

The cost-versus-benefit equation goes beyond dollars and cents. Healthcare consumers will increasingly weigh the prospective benefit of a given treatment against the quality of life they may expect as a result of it. It is not only likely that more patients will opt out of treatments that prolong misery in order merely to prolong basic life processes, but that life termination will become a viable medical option.

These megatrends may embody wonders and horrors, but they come as no surprise. Truly, they are *trends*—continuum extensions of things that have already been set into motion. The lesser trends, which are part and parcel of these megatrends, likewise represent continuing developments of current technological and demographic facts.

Imaging

CT scanning. Like other imaging technology currently in place, CT scanning is becoming more flexible, more portable, and cheaper. It will become increasingly available in ambulatory facilities, and, as fiber-optic transmission technology continues to develop, CT data will be, as a matter of routine, instantaneously transmitted to hospitals or to the offices of specialists.

High-speed CINE-CT devices will continue to improve, providing effective real-time observations of bodily processes, including the heart, thereby offering a less costly, safer alternative to angiography. Real-time CT is finding its way into the operating room, where it is currently used to monitor such procedures as stereotactic neurosurgery. A new CT application—the CT Xenon Cerebral Blood Flow Imaging System—furnishes images of the brain that were previously available only through costly nuclear medicine studies and PET scans.

CT will continue to make sophisticated imaging modalities available in settings outside of the hospital.

Magnetic Resonance Imaging (MRI). While, in some areas, costly MRI competes with far cheaper CT technology, it is still more effective than CT in imaging soft tissue, and therefore enables very early—pre-symptomatic or asymptomatic—diagnosis of such illnesses as multiple sclerosis, stroke, and brain tumors. MRI will become less expensive and will continue to take the place of invasive procedures such as myelography and angiography. MRI can be performed on an ambulatory basis, while myelography and angiography require a hospital stay. Mobile MRI, currently available, may become more prevalent. Real-time MRI is under development, and more powerful MRI units (4 tesla as opposed to the current 1.5-tesla standard) will make complete metabolic mapping possible.

Positron Emission Tomography (PET). A very high-ticket technology, PET is largely confined to major research centers, although its use is more widespread in Japan. Because of the support required—an adjacent cyclotron, and the availability of a "hot lab" to process isotopes with extremely brief half-lives—PET will not become a mobile technology and will, for the foreseeable future, be confined to larger institutions. It allows observation, evaluation, and diagnosis on the cellular level, providing a detailed picture of metabolic processes unavailable through other diagnostic modalities. As medicine continues to zero in on smaller and more basic biological elements, PET and related technologies (such as the far less expensive SPECT) are likely to develop further. It will almost certainly require greater practical, clinical experience with PET—an indisputable demonstration of its clinical effectiveness in diagnosis—before a greater number of non-research institutions can justify acquisition of the technology.

Single Photon Emission Computerized Tomography (SPECT). Another modality for imaging soft tissue, SPECT is currently seen as a lower-cost alternative to PET. Its ultimate utility is linked to the further development of isotopes. These may, in turn, be enhanced by the development of monoclonal antibody (MAbs) "site finders," which use the body's own natural defense system to trace such disorders as cancer to their points of origin, while nuclear medicine (except for SPECT) will likely yield increasing ground to CT, MRI, and PET.

Ultrasound. Ultrasound applications should become cheaper and more plentiful.

Digitized Radiographic Imaging and Digital Archiving. In healthcare, as in many other areas, the digital processing and storage of data, including image data, continues to increase in importance. Digitized images can be stored cheaply and retrieved as well as compared readily. They can be transmitted, and they can be enhanced to delineate various anatomical features and disease processes more fully. In some cases, digital imaging quality is greater than imaging by conventional analog methods. Digitized radiographic imaging and digital archiving of diagnostic imaging of all kinds will continue to gather momentum as individual hospitals evolve into genuine healthcare networks.

Fiber Optic Endoscopy and Laser Imaging. Endoscopy, already widely used, will continue to grow as a minimally invasive diagnostic and surgical technique. Lasers, currently in wide use as surgical instruments, may also be developed as an alternative to X-ray, especially for extremities.

Treatment Modalities

In general, surgery, as we understand it today, will increasingly come to be regarded as crude and brutally invasive. Lasers, already extensively used in neurosurgery, vascular surgery, ophthalmology, laparoscopic procedures, and dental surgery, has expanded into orthopedic surgery and angioplasty. Photodynamic therapy, using site-specific dyes to color a tumor so that only it (and not surrounding tissue) will be destroyed by laser light, is currently under development. Endoscopic surgery will continue to develop as a minimally invasive alternative to conventional surgery.

Wherever possible, wholly non-invasive alternatives will replace even minimally invasive surgery. Lithotripters, an acoustic alternative to surgery in the treatment of kidney and gall stones, are not likely to find their way out of hospitals due to cost; however, the procedure will probably become an outpatient treatment.

A panoply of new drugs will reduce the necessity of surgery in such applications as

▲ *Dissolving vertebral disks*
▲ *Reducing coronary artery blockages*
▲ *Dissolving blood clots*
▲ *Dissolving gall stones*

Currently under investigation are the therapeutic effects of electromagnetic fields. Until very recently, medical attention was focused exclusively on the potentially harmful effects of EMFs generated by such items as household wiring and power transmission lines. At selected frequencies, however, EMFs can accelerate the healing of fractured bones; stabilize irregular heart rhythms; aid in the control of seizures; accelerate healing of skin, tendons, and nerves; retard bacterial growth; and so on. It is difficult to say just how far-reaching EMF therapy will become.

Robotic Surgery

Will surgery, as we know it today, ever become totally obsolete? We don't think so. To begin with, accidents and traumatic injury are part of life and often require surgical intervention and repair. Also, most authorities believe that, as immunosuppressive therapies become increasingly effective, transplant surgery will become increasingly routine.

But the mechanics of surgery are likely to change. Robotics are already being used in rigid endoscopy, and there is currently under development a device called Robodoc, a joint project of IBM and Integrated Surgical Systems of Sacramento, California. Robodoc is a robot surgeon designed to perform a highly specialized task in a very common kind of surgery: precisely milling out a cavity in the thigh bone in order to accommodate it to the prosthesis used in hip replacement. The tolerances involved are better suited to a precision machine shop than an operating room: a few thousandths of a centimeter. Robodoc, which is linked to a CT scanner, mills out the required cavity with twenty times the accuracy of even the best human orthopedic surgeon.

Doubtless other surgical robots will be developed, especially in conjunction with 3-D digital-imaging devices, which can provide continual feedback to the robot. Surgical robots introduce yet another possibility: remote-control surgery. It will be possible for an eminent surgeon in, say, Chicago to operate via remote control on a patient in Los Angeles.

Finally, some medical futurists have speculated as to the possibilities of subminiature surgical robots. It is now feasible to manufacture electric motors less than a millimeter in size, etched onto a silicon crystal. Using various monitoring and control devices, it is possible that a patient might swallow such a tiny surgical robot, which would be directed to do its work—say, in the patient's gut—thereby performing invasive surgery without an incision having been made.

Genetic Engineering

As mentioned earlier, genetic engineering may provide the most profound alternatives to the conventional treatments of today by obviating the need for treatment altogether. Genetically engineered agriculture is already a reality, and work is proceeding apace to map human chromosomes thoroughly. For the practice of preventive medicine, the first major step in genetic engineering will likely be population screening for certain genetic markers that indicate susceptibility to various diseases. Once these have been identified in an individual, preventive measures—drugs, change in lifestyle, and so on—can be prescribed in order to head off disease before it actually manifests itself. Beyond this, it is probable that techniques will be developed to manipulate genetic material on the level of the gene, chromosome, and even molecule in order to produce desired results.

Decentralized Care and Self-Care

Forbidden Planet, a popular science fiction movie of the 1950s, featured a lost civilization of an advanced race who had developed a technology free from "instrumentality"; they had only to *think* into existence whatever item they wanted or activity they wished to perform. Unlike the Krell (such was the name of this extraterrestrial people), we have not yet eliminated "instrumentality." But, since the invention and subsequent proliferation of the integrated circuit—the silicon "chip"—we have certainly made "instrumentality" small.

Just fifty years ago, ENIAC, the first fully electronic computer, unveiled at the University of Pennsylvania, weighed in at thirty tons and occupied three thousand cubic feet of space. Running on 18,000 notoriously undependable vacuum tubes, having cost millions to develop, it required highly trained specialists to operate. Today's handheld calculators (let alone even modest desktop or laptop personal computers) easily outstrip ENIAC's calculating power. Transistors are already microscopic, with millions arrayed on the central processing chip of a desktop computer. Quite likely, the size of the individual transistor will continue to shrink, even down to the molecular level, so that billions and billions of transistors might be accommodated on a single chip. The result will be further miniaturization and enhancement of computing power, making electronics-intensive medical equipment ever more portable and cheaper than ever.

At the very least, smaller, cheaper electronics will mean further decentralization of sophisticated diagnostic imaging equipment. No doctor will need to be on-site to operate or monitor the equipment, since data can be transmitted anywhere. At some point, monitoring devices will likely be so portable that they can be attached to, implanted in, perhaps even injected into the body. A computer can monitor vital signs and other data continuously and in real time, alerting caregivers as well as the patient to any problems. This means that the patient being monitored can be physically independent of any central facility. Most likely, many of the problems to which the monitoring system may alert him can be self-treated at home.

Procedures such as dialysis, which now tether a patient to a machine for protracted periods, will also become increasingly miniaturized and manageable at home. Chemotherapies that now require the aid of a technician to administer will be infused by portable devices linked to biosensors that allow metered doses of a drug, the doses regulated by continuous feedback from the sensor.

We could go on listing developing and likely-to-develop devices, but the point is that miniaturization, exponential increases in computing power, decreasing cost, and the universal ease of data transmission (something that has already made "telemedicine" an emerging reality) all

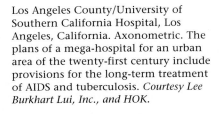

Los Angeles County/University of Southern California Hospital, Los Angeles, California. Axonometric. The plans of a mega-hospital for an urban area of the twenty-first century include provisions for the long-term treatment of AIDS and tuberculosis. *Courtesy Lee Burkhart Lui, Inc., and HOK.*

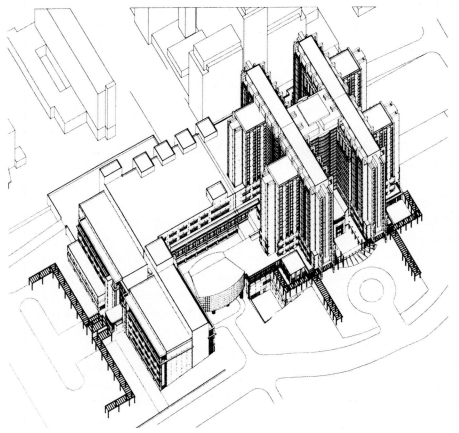

point to the decentralization of care: a continued decrease in inpatient care, a concomitant increase in ambulatory care, an increase in visitation to freestanding and satellite clinics, and an increase in self-care administered at home—perhaps the greatest growth market of all.

A Caveat

The foregoing trends are real, and their single most profound implication for architecture is obvious: acute-care hospitals will be fewer in number and, in general, smaller. (Another scenario sees acute-care hospitals as far fewer in number, but those few that are built will be "megaplexes"—very large regional facilities.) Even in the relatively near term, acute-care hospitals will likely shed beds, converting significant portions of their operations to ambulatory care.

But what if—and that is *always* the controlling question in formulating scenarios—what if a disease epidemic surfaces that requires a high volume of protracted traditional acute care? Or, for example, what if an effective treatment for AIDS is discovered—but one that requires significant acute care? In the rush to get rid of empty beds, it is possible that we may find ourselves critically short of acute-care facilities. The period of greatest vulnerability will be whatever transitional span may stretch between the ongoing reduction of acute-care beds and the development of the preventive, diagnostic, and treatment techniques just discussed.

Going Farther Out

The catalog we have just paged through is, at most, only a step or two ahead of today's cutting edge. Since the 1980s, Earl Swensson Associates has been conducting research with assistance from Ken Barker of the Department of Pharmacy Care Systems of Alabama's Auburn University on a picture of the healthcare system of the future. Let's leave the catalog and look at some scenes—scenes from a probable future.

Do you think healthcare is a central issue now? Wait until 2020! By then the tumult and panic and crisis in healthcare will have been largely resolved into a healthcare system intimately bound up with the community system. The healthcare system will be evaluated in terms of the quality of *community life,* and in a world where telecommuting will have removed the majority of the workforce from the necessity of living even relatively near their place of employment, people will move to communities with the healthiest reputations. What are the most important considerations in real estate? Real estate moguls—now and in 2020—will answer: *Location, location, location.* But what's a location worth? In 2020, those moguls will answer, *Wellness, wellness, wellness.*

The revolution in patient-focused care that began in the 1980s and 1990s will have culminated by 2020. Truly, the patient will be at the center of it all. Here are ten hypothetical patients from the next century.

William. William is a retired politician from Arkansas. The Human Genome Project has identified a gene that indicates a high potential for coronary artery blockage. Furthermore, this genetic abnormality can be corrected by gene-transfer therapy. In the case of William, who has the abnormality, such therapy is strongly indicated because his Atherogenic Lipoprotein Profile reveals that he has three times the normal risk for heart attack. If—and only if—the gene-transfer therapy should fail, will William become a candidate for the second-best treatment: minimally invasive rotablator coronary artery surgery.

Merina. After breakfast one morning, Merina received a phone call from her wellness technician. Early signs of cardiac arrhythmia triggered an alarm on her telemetry unit during the night. In response, a technician transmitted a signal to her implanted drug pump to correct the problem temporarily. However, her dosage requires fine tuning. The wellness technician instructs Merina to follow Care Plan #3 (she looks this up on her personal computer), a series of simple diagnostic tests, that Merina performs herself at home.

Merina transmits her urine lab test results from a "smart toilet" analysis. Analysis is electronic, and the data is sent via modem (perhaps the device that is part of the "smart toilet" will be called a "commodem"?) over the telephone line. Next, she dons her functional jewelry—an earring consisting of biosensors that will run an eight-hour bloodless blood test. After eight hours, the earring is dropped off at a conveniently located diagnostic lab. Merina also wears a "hospital on a wrist"—a wristwatch-like device that monitors and transmits her heart rhythms to her wellness technician. The device has other monitoring modes available, and it also allows two-way audiovisual communication with her doctors.

The next day, Merina's cardiologist, a Dr. Hill, who lives halfway across the country, calls to tell her that her cardiac instability was due to a malfunction in her implanted pump. He recommends upgrading to a more advanced biocontroller—a drug delivery system small enough to be injected into a vein. The injection of the biocontroller and the removal of the malfunctioning pump will be carried out by a Mobile Surgery Unit. Her corner pharmacare provider meets her in the unit to program the biocontroller and explain precautions and possible side effects. The biocontroller requires maintenance and refilling annually.

Eleanor. Eleanor is one hundred years old. In 2020, that is old—but it is hardly newsworthy. By the year 2015, 20 percent of the population was elderly. People are living longer. Still, Eleanor has outlived most of her family.

Eleanor participates in the City Block Nurse Program, in which neighbors have been trained to perform some basic care activities. This has meant that Eleanor did not have to retire to a nursing home. Each week, the neighbor-nurse who has the most advanced level of training visits Eleanor and enters information about her status into a computer. The data is transmitted to technicians, who relay anything unusual to her doctor.

Ryan. Ryan is married to Bonnie, who works at the medical center on the Hospitalization Prevention Team. Bonnie delights in needling her husband about his high-risk behaviors, and she wonders what his wellness counselor will have to say about them. For example, while the couple relaxes in a local bar (last bastion of publicly permitted cigarette smoking), Bonnie scolds Ryan for exposing himself to secondary smoke—something prohibited by his health contract. In a data-intensive society, the speeding violation Ryan received was not only transmitted to his automobile insurance carrier, but may also result in a doubling of the deductible on his *health* contract. And it gets worse. Ryan has been eating too many fatty foods. His health plan administrator will learn of this via the garbage monitor Ryan agreed to install as part of his health-plan agreement. The wellness counselor will help Ryan to come into more thorough compliance with his agreement.

Rita Ann. This healthcare consumer is in the process of selecting a Health Optimization Organization (HOO) plan. She is assisted in her selection by PICSEL, the Public Interest Communication Systems and Electronic Libraries, which she accesses through her home computer. Each HOO also has an access manager, who helps to simplify the complex nature of the healthcare system. One plan (the access manager explains) offers a Designed Experiences Department, which creates special healing environments in hospital rooms—for example, recuperation in a Hawaiian Vacation Room. Other HOO services include

▲ Telehealth, for home-based healthcare. Tele-obstetrics offers help with self-delivery of children at home.
▲ A genethicist helps with fetal evaluation and embryonic correction of such diseases as cystic fibrosis and hemophilia.
▲ The HOO offers school system clinics, Emergicare centers, neighborhood health centers, sports medicine, and mobile mammography.
▲ Each HOO presents a comprehensive "report card," which measures quality, including patient satisfaction, access to care, outcomes, and health promotion activities.

Janet. Janet is a professional mother—a full-time surrogate mother, who is salaried and is pampered at a special Surrogacy Spa nine months out of every year. Fertility problems and an increase in career-minded women have made parenting services a big business.

Brutus. Brutus is a diabetic who finds it difficult to comply with his prescribed diet, lifestyle, and medication regimen. His wellness counselor has tried various methods of educating him into compliance, warning that amputation is a possible consequence of unchecked diabetes. The counselor finally fits a virtual-reality helmet on Brutus, who is treated to the frighteningly real sights and sounds of a surgical saw about to be applied to his foot.

This extreme form of aversion therapy is followed by an educational program, which not only shows Brutus how to monitor himself and manage his diet, lifestyle, and medication, but informs him that, within a year, it will be possible to transplant into his system healthy pancreatic cells, which will produce insulin. He is a good candidate for such a procedure—if he can control himself until it becomes available.

Colin. Colin has been hospitalized for a kidney transplant in a regional mini-hospital "sharecare" unit, which makes extensive use of family members as part of the care team. Wife and son help with custodial care and the administration of medication. Organ transplantation procedures have become more common by 2020. Instead of signing an organ donor consent form, consent, by federal law, is now presumed; those who do not wish to become donors must fill out a form that says they do *not* want to donate organs. Even though transplant surgery is common, the next few years beyond 2020 will see transplantation and implantation of organ cells rather than entire organs.

Besides his own family, Colin's care team consists of a nurse, physician, pharmacist, and support service assistant. His primary caregivers are a "care pair": a nurse and the assistant. All charting is done electronically, most lab procedures are done with hand-held equipment at the bedside, and medications are dispensed from a machine controlled by the pharmacist and maintained by an outside drug wholesaler. Physician dictation is digitalized and saved as part of the patient's electronic record. Colin also makes entries into his own chart, answering questions relating to a Quality of Well-Being Scale.

Colin's patient-focused hospital room is the locus of all activity related to him. Members of the care team don't have to leave the room to do their jobs.

Brandon. Brandon has a cancer with a very low survival rate. His health insurance has a buyout option. He can choose whether to undergo painful, sickening, and costly treatment or to accept cash in lieu of treatment.

Brandon's oncologist has suggested adoptive therapy. This biotherapy involves removing a portion of the tumor and cooking it in a test tube with a drug called Interleukin-2. The resulting custom-tailored medication is administered and—theoretically—the tumor cells are killed off by multiplying tumor-killing cells. In effect, the patient's own tumor kills the tumor. The catch is that Brandon will have to pay for the treatment himself, since his insurance plan excludes experimental therapies.

Mohammed. A champion soccer player, Mohammed requires advanced orthopedic knee surgery. He reports to a hospital in Riyadh, where a robot, operated from the workstation of an orthopedic surgeon in the United States, performs the surgery. The remote-control operation is made possible through an international healthcare provider, Global Health Alliance.

A Pack of Predictions

The hypothetical patients just discussed will reap the benefits—and submit to the intrusions of—a healthcare system that will likely include

▲ *Primary care-based multispecialty medical groups* operated by managed-care corporations or community health networks
▲ *Community-based diagnostic clinics,* which will form partnerships to share new, expensive technology
▲ *A National Center for Health Assessment,* which will receive and interpret data from the Community Diagnostic Clinics—but only for tests whose interpretations have not already been computerized

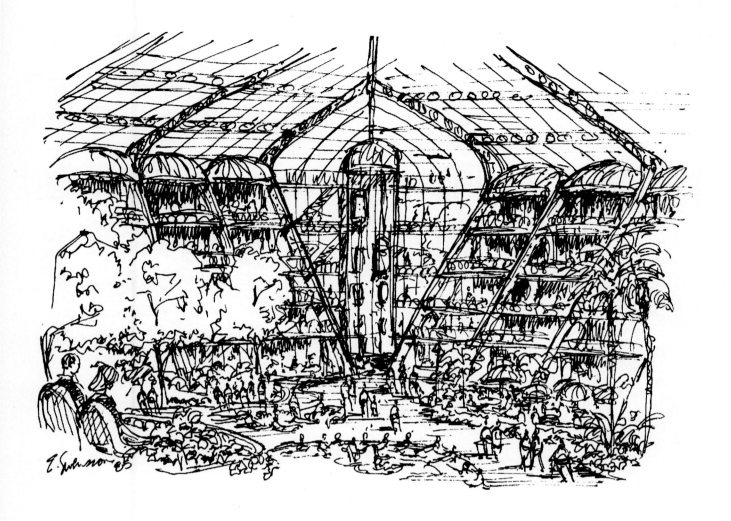

and entered into a vast databank accessible through the worldwide information superhighway

▲ *Physician specialty networks,* which will become increasingly prevalent; with the successful conversion to primary care in the future, a smaller percentage of physicians will specialize. The specialists will likely form nationwide consulting groups, something made possible by advances in telecommunications.

▲ *A Life Quality Optimization Community for Incurables,* which will offer a quality environment for people afflicted with terminal diseases

▲ *Parenting services,* including professional surrogates, surrogacy spas, genetic counseling, and in vitro fertilization clinics, which will become a major set of healthcare services

▲ *Medical Cyberspace:* health-oriented telecommunication (HOT) systems that are part of the information superhighway now under development in the United States and elsewhere; medical cyberspace will be a computer-centered virtual community of patients, healthcare providers, and payers

▲ *Treatment adherence clinics* as replacements for addict recovery facilities; medications that correct genetically based addictions will become the treatment of choice over psychotherapy

Extended Care Center of the Future. Perspective. Incorporating all the activities necessary for rehabiliation and recuperation, this facility accommodates not just the patient but his spouse as well. Each patient's living quarters includes a balcony that overlooks the therapy facilities and amenities on the ground floor. *Sketch by Earl S. Swensson. Courtesy Earl Swensson Associates.*

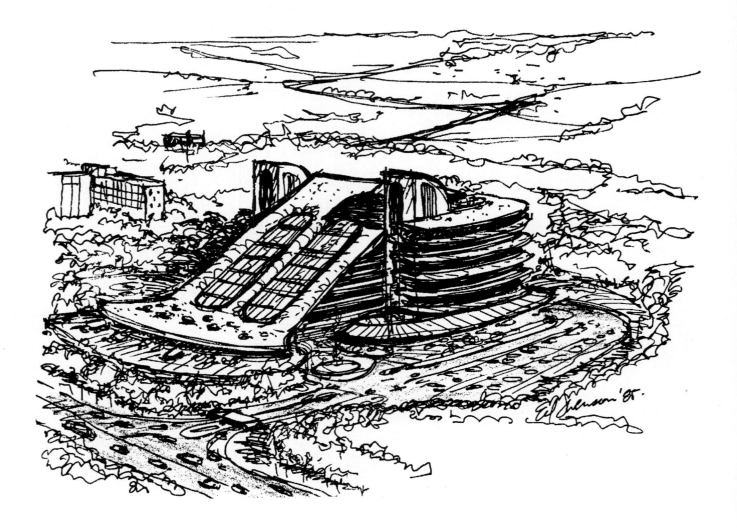

Acute Care Center of the Future. Perspective. Upon entering the registration area (small building at the driveway in the foreground) patients present their personal data card containing all the information needed for check-in. An attendant directs the patients to the appropriate department. Patient rooms occupy the periphery of the building. Ancillary areas are located in the core. The sloped area at the front of the facility houses shafts for the transport of supplies; mechanical, electrical, and plumbing lines; and staff circulation. Supplies are received at the base of the sloped area, then distributed as needed. The building is organized vertically by department--one floor for cardiology, one for neurology, etc. Floors can be reconfigured as demand requires. *Sketch by Earl S. Swensson. Courtesy Earl Swensson Associates.*

▲ *Intensive Hospice facilities*

▲ *Centers for Restorative Care*—intermediate units between skilled nursing facilities and acute-care hospitals

▲ *A demographic ensuring that eldercare* will continue to be a growth market

▲ *Community birthing centers* as popular alternatives to hospitals

▲ *Mobile medical services,* which will become widespread comprehensive providers of primary and specialized care

In addition, hospitals will continue to be restructured, so that

1. Access-management divisions will combine such disparate departments and functions as admitting, referrals, and finance.
2. A Hospitalization Prevention Team will promote strategies to avoid costly hospitalization.
3. Distinctions among doctors, nurses, pharmacists, and others will tend to blur. All will be regarded as caregivers, members of a care team.
4. Diagnostics will include imaging and a central lab. Biosensor and bedside technologies will proliferate, and the central lab will shrink in size as a result.

5. Bioengineering will be a growth area, especially in the development of electronic prosthetic devices.

6. Resource management will be emphasized, the management both of human and material resources.

7. The mission of the hospital-based Research Department will encompass not only clinical drug trials but outcomes research, including patient satisfaction.

8. Patient advocacy will become an important caregiving role. Advocates will include bioethicists, religious counselors, translators, and so on.

9. The medical mall of today will become the Medical Mall Biocampus, offering such services as health food restaurants; daycare for sick children; schools for people with disabilities; educational programs; vaccination clinics; sports medicine and rehabilitation; fitness and wellness centers; and diagnostic centers.

■ New Roles for Architects

Designers of healthcare facilities for the next century will probably be asked to create fewer hospitals and more ambulatory facilities, including freestanding clinics, medical office buildings, and specialized freestanding diagnostic centers. In addition, some futurist/architects see an increased demand for healthcare facilities on the retail model—medical malls, even the biocampus, perhaps in parklike settings.

One possible scenario is a system consisting of specialty hospital facilities —probably on the retail model—and strategically placed regional complexes: very large, very comprehensive hospitals in which specialized facilities and specialist practitioners are concentrated. For many patients, even those with serious or complex disorders, an actual trip to a major regional complex will be unnecessary, because remote monitoring, telemetry, and sophisticated data transmission will link the local specialty hospital to the more distant comprehensive facility.

If, for the most part, medical architectural commissions will be smaller—save, perhaps, for the comparatively few regional major complexes—there may well be new opportunities for expanded vision in healthcare hotels and healthcare communities. Healthcare hotels are proposed alternatives to acute-care hospitals, many of which are already borrowing much of their design from the hospitality industry. Healthcare hotels would be places for convalescence and supervised care—really, hybrid crosses among hotel, spa, and hospital.

Healthcare communities are another possible direction, especially as a larger percentage of the population ages. By 2020 almost one-third of the U.S. population will be at least fifty-five, and some nine million Americans will be over eighty-five. Planned communities focused on wellness, and providing various levels of assisted living, may—for a significant segment of the population—take the place of hospitals, skilled nursing facilities, *and* "retirement villages."

Synergenial Continuing Care Retirement Community (CCRC)/320 2000 Complex. This design for the future integrates a healthcare-oriented facility for the elderly in a community that includes 1.3 million square feet of office space; a 800-room hotel; a covered shopping galleria; a medical center with 320 acute-care rooms, a medical office building, a diagnostic center, and outpatient services; and educational, fitness, cultural, and recreational facilitites. *Sketch by Earl S. Swensson. Courtesy Earl Swensson Associates.*

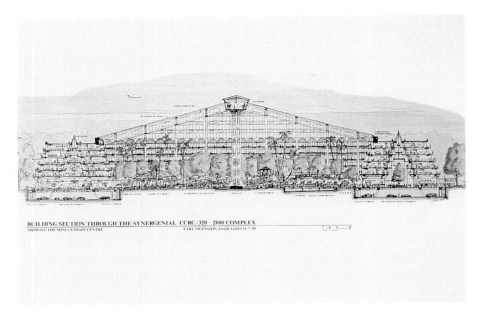

Synergenial Continuing Care Retirement Community (CCRC)/320 2000 Complex. The Synergenial community of the future is standardized on a seventy-five-year-old female rather than the thirty-year-old male of most architectural designs. *Sketch by Earl S. Swensson. Courtesy Earl Swensson Associates.*

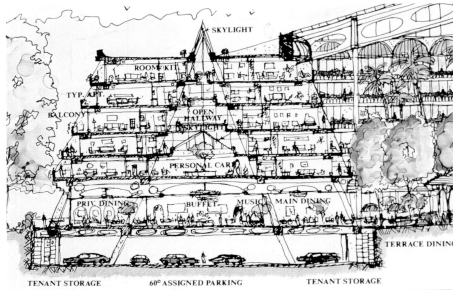

Such communities, as exemplified by the "Synergenial Suburban Village" designed by Earl Swensson Associates, may become as pervasive in the twenty-first century as the development of planned suburban communities was in the early postwar period. The Synergenial Suburban Village integrates healthcare-oriented eldercare into the heart of a community that would include 1.3 million square feet of office space; an 800-room hotel; a covered shopping galleria; continuing education and conference facilities; recreational, fitness, cultural, and amusement facilities; and a medical center with 320 acute-care rooms, a medical office building, a diagnostic center, and full outpatient facilities. The entire Synergenial Suburban Village would be standardized on a seventy-five-year-old female rather than the customary thirty-year-old, five-foot-ten male.

Maybe, at some point in the future, anything even remotely resembling today's hospitals will have ceased to exist. But for at least much of

Synergenial Continuing Care Retirement Community (CCRC)/320 2000 Complex. Site plan. The plan includes a chapel, lap pool, activity center, carillon, small pond, and various services such as restaurant, pub, research libary, computer center, and investment club. *Courtesy Earl Swensson Associates.*

Synergenial Continuing Care Retirement Community (CCRC)/320 2000 Complex. Village perspective. Within the CCRC complexes, all design accommodates the physical, social, and emotional needs of residents, ranging in age from 75 to 110. The two CCRC structures are six stories tall, situated on ten acres, and offer 320 apartments to accommodate a population of approximately 800 individuals. *Courtesy Earl Swensson Associates.*

the coming century, there will be hospitals—in addition to other, smaller healthcare facilities. What will administrators and planners look for in hospital buildings that are built, say, in the first quarter of the twenty-first century?

To begin with, there are indications that, during this period, there will be a demand for rural or ex-urban hospitals with strong ambulatory and primary care components. The overwhelming trend up to the present has been the decline of the rural hospital, but in many areas rural populations are actually growing, yet still remaining ex-urban as opposed to becoming suburban. If, in some regions, these markets are currently underserved, demand for ex-urban healthcare is likely to increase even more during the early part of the next century, as telecommuting and home businesses proliferate. As it becomes increasingly unnecessary to live near an urban center, the ex-urbs and outright rural population will increase.

As for the buildings themselves, the key word will be *flexibility*. In fact, Thomas F. Frist, Jr., chairman of Columbia/HCA Healthcare Corporation, has observed, "The hospital for the twenty-first century will serve as a nerve center for a fully integrated health delivery system. As a template, it must have built-in flexibility to adjust to its ever-changing network." Buildings will be designed to accommodate rapidly changing technologies and patient populations. Docking of mobile and plug-in modules will be particularly important. It is likely that specialized major diagnostic and diagnostic-surgical equipment will be manufactured in self-contained, preconstructed modules intended for docking at strategic points— "ports"—in the building. Such mountable and demountable building components can be readily downloaded to other facilities—for example, an ex-urban satellite of the main hospital.

HVAC systems will be modularized and zoned, with vertical circulation, mechanical shafts, and transport systems moved from the core of the building to the perimeter in order to create free fields within the core floor plate for easy adaptability to many configurations. Interstitial concepts, which seemed promising in the early 1980s but for the most part were judged to require excessive capital investment, may well return in the next century as a strategy for bringing building flexibility to a maximum. Within the first quarter of the twenty-first century, flexibility may loom as so crucial a consideration that the initial capital costs of interstitial design will be deemed justifiable.

Certainly, other structural strategies that maximize flexibility and adaptability will be used, including moment-resisting steel frames instead of braced frames or shear-wall structural systems. Floor systems will have to allow for multiple penetrations for plumbing and electrical lines, column spacing will need to be optimized so that departmental redesigns will not be cramped by structural requirements. Earl Swensson Associates designed the Centennial Medical Center project in Nashville on a true-grid system for maximum flexibility.

Other strategies for maximizing flexibility will likely include the deliberate specification of "swing" space to allow temporary relocation of departments during renovations and retrofits, and to allow greater flexibility in adapting to changes in patient populations. Low-tech departments can be zoned in "soft" spaces adjacent to high-tech departments, in order to allow relatively easy expansion of the latter when required. It may be desirable to separate diagnosis and treatment areas from patient care and ancillary areas, in order to achieve simpler and more economical integration of HVAC and structural systems. In diagnosis and treatment areas, these systems often have more demanding needs than in other hospital areas.

Finally, some facilities may require the development of "universal floor plans," which can be adapted—and readapted—to accommodate virtually any need. Bedside computing and its equivalents will facilitate the introduction of such universal floor plans, since the nurses' station—a traditional fixture on patient floors— will no longer be necessary. That is, each patient room will, in effect, be a nurse's station—and the nurses' role will be expanded beyond the monitoring and hygiene duties that comprise it now. Assisted by an artificial intelligence (AI) computer system, the nurse—or a nursing team—will take over more and more of the primary care of the patient.

The concept of flexibility extends beyond what the architect designs to the architect him- or herself. The architect will provide a range of services beyond the traditional architecture and engineering (A & E) tasks, including strategic business planning, evaluation of lease-versus-build options, financial planning, mechanical and electrical systems evaluation, space planning inventories, furniture inventories, long-range planning, and master planning. Once the building has been completed, the architect will remain in contact with the owners for the life of the facility, providing a full range of services on a contractual basis. These services will include ongoing evaluation and planning for expansion, contraction, and adaptation to changing needs.

■ Practice Architecture, Practice Medicine

Architects will be called in on planning processes earlier, they will be asked to contribute a very broad range of expertise, and they will be active during the entire lifespan of the building. In this sense, then, architects will serve as caregivers, practitioners of medicine, members of the patient-care team. But there is a more profound dimension of this new role as well.

The present cutting edge and the future of healthcare architecture are being driven by economics, as well as by two imperatives usually assumed to be antagonistic: high technology and high humanity. We hope this book has demonstrated that these two drivers need not be mutually exclusive at all. Quite the contrary, high technology can be designed to foster a higher and higher degree of humanity in healthcare.

Still, while these two imperatives are not inevitably antagonistic, they do lead us to a paradox, which, we believe, penetrates to the heart of the future of hospital and healthcare facility design.

In ancient Egypt, Greece, and India—and, doubtless, in other venerable cultures as well—healing was associated with temples and with magical spaces. We who have built our own temples to science and technology and commerce have long looked on such magical, mystical notions with a mixture of wonder, envy, and contempt, judging them as the nineteenth-century British critic and essayist Matthew Arnold judged them: the delightful products of humanity's "childhood." Yet (as they say in fairytales) "lo and behold!": Our science has led us, through a long and meandering course, back to a concept very like that behind those healing temples of old. We now know that *places* can make you sick, and they can also help to make you well. The hospital can no longer be thought of as a shelter—a mere shell—within which some healing activity takes place. The healthcare environment is integral with that healing, an instrument of that healing as surely as is a scalpel, or a laser beam, or an electromagnetic field, or the human touch of a dedicated caregiver.

The current dominant trend toward hospital environments modeled after hotels and residences has its critics, and, to be sure, we claim no single design mode or building type as *the* pattern for effective healthcare design. But the more profound message of such designs is not reference to luxury on the one hand or homeyness on the other, but healing and humanity, solace, respite, recovery, and health. The point is not to disguise this or that piece of medical hardware inside elegant casework or within a hotel-style armoire, but to provide an environment in which the human body's own vital energies can be activated, nurtured, fostered, replenished, and refreshed. This was the idea behind both the ancient Temple of Aesculapius and the more modern European spa, and by a protracted roundabout, this is the idea to which we are now returning.

Everything in the healthcare environment of the future will be directed toward healing and rejuvenating. In an article in *Advance for Respiratory Therapists,* Dirk W. van der Vaart evoked a scene from the coming century:

> In the year 2121, inpatients are likely to wake up in the morning and find a friendly attendant entering their luxury room, bearing breakfast on a bed tray, complete with a rose and champagne.
>
> From their sunny window, the inpatients will be able to get out of their beds and walk out onto a climate-controlled balcony to luxuriate for a moment in the warm tropical air while the sounds of birds and gurgling water ease them into wakefulness.
>
> . . . Everything is an isolated paradise. Just outside the medical complex, snowplows might be starting their morning routines on what is just another blustery winter day in the snow belt states.

Maybe it will be like that. Maybe not. As in any work of art or architecture, the details are bound to vary. But, we believe, the healthcare environment of the future, whatever else it will incorporate, will be an expression of what we call Synergenial Design: a new direction in architecture based on human-inspired design, state-of-the-art engineering, and sound economics to create spaces that evoke positive human responses, appeal to the senses, are task-oriented, and function well both physically and emotionally. Synergenial Design is *healing* design: the orchestration of all elements for the purpose of bringing about well-being. This is a holistic approach to healthcare, and a holistic approach to architecture as the facilitator of health. We do not intend it to be our *prescription for* the future, but we earnestly believe and we ardently hope it is a *description of* the future. For we do not see how our society can—quite literally—afford any less, or any more.

BIBLIOGRAPHY

BIBLIOGRAPHY

"A Healing Place: Kaneko Ford and Bobrow Thomas Team Up to Create an Oasis for Children in L.A.'s Inner City," *Contract Design* 31, no. 2 (February 1989), pp. 106-107.

"A Walk Down Easy Street," *Design Solutions* 9, no. 1 (Spring 1989), pp. 20-22.

"Acute Care Stacked on Public Uses: Marin General Hospital Addition," *Architectural Record* 178, no. 7 (June 1990), pp. 94-97.

Aging Design Research Program. *Design for Aging: Strategies for Collaboration Between Architects and Occupational Therapists.* Washington: ADRP, 1993.

Ahuja, Jan, et al. "IRIS: An Experimental Multimedia Workstation Linking the Departments of Emergency Medicine and Radiological Sciences," *The Journal of Emergency Medicine* 11 (1993), pp. 219-28.

Aldridge, Eva, et al. "VIP Suites: A New Trend," *Journal of Health Care Interior Design* 3 (1991), pp. 85-95.

Allen, David, and Margaret Davis. "A Computerized CIS Enhances Bedside Intensive Care," *Nursing Management* 23, no. 7 (July 1992), pp. 112I-112P.

Alt-White, Anna C., et al. "Selection and Development of a Critical Care Bedside Computer," *Nursing Management* 23, no. 7 (July 1992), pp. 112A-112H.

Altenhoff, Jenifer. "Hospes," *Ekriture* 3 (July 1993), pp. 18-23.

American Academy of Pediatrics Committee on Fetus and Newborn. *Guidelines for Perinatal Care.* 2d ed. Elk Grove Village, Ill.: American Academy of Pediatrics; Washington, D.C.: American College of Obstetricians and Gynecologists, 1988.

American Association of Retired Persons and Stein Gerontological Institute. *Life-Span Design of Residential Environments for an Aging Population.* Washington, DC: AARP, 1993.

American Hospital Association. *AHA Hospital Statistics, 1993-94.* Chicago: American Hospital Association, 1993.

American Hospital Association/American Society for Hospital Engineering. *1993 International Conference and Exhibition on Health Facility Planning, Design and Construction: Proceedings Manual,* vols. 1 and 2. Chicago: American Society for Hospital Engineering of the American Hospital Association, 1993.

American Institute of Architects Building Performance and Regulations Committee/Committee on the Environment. *Designing Healthy Buildings: Indoor Air Quality.* Washington, D.C.: American Institute of Architects, 1992.

American Institute of Architects Committee on *Architecture* for Health (with U.S. Department of Health and Human Services). *Guidelines for Construction and Equipment of Hospital and Medical Facilities.* Washington, D.C.: American Institute of Architects Press, 1993.

American Institute of Architects Committee on *Architecture* for Health. *Design Considerations for Mental Health Facilities.* Washington, D.C.: American Institute of Architects Press, 1993.

American Institute of Architects Committee on the Environment. *Energy, Environment, and Architecture.* Washington, D.C.: American Institute of Architects, 1991.

American Institute of Architects in cooperation with the American Association of Homes for the Aging. *Design for Aging: 1992 Review.* Washington, D.C.: American Institute of Architects, 1992.

American Society for Hospital Engineering. *The Fourth Annual National Conference on Health Facility Planning, Design and Construction.* Chicago: American Society for Hospital Engineering of the American Hospital Association, 1992.

American Society for Hospital Engineering and Society for Ambulatory Care Professionals. *Planning and Design of Outpatient Facilities: Flexibility for the 90s and Beyond.* Chicago: AHA, 1992.

Anderson, Howard J. "Are Hospitals Prepared for More Growth in Ambulatory Care?" *Trustee* 44, no. 9 (September 1991), pp. 16-17.

————. "Improving Access to Care Drives Updated ED Designs," *Health Facilities Management* (March 1993), pp. 42-46.

————. "Survey: Equipment Budgets Up; Use in Outpatient Areas Growing," *Hospitals* (September 20, 1992), pp. 38-44.

————. "Survey Identifies Trends in Equipment Acquisitions," *Hospitals* (September 20, 1992), pp. 30-35.

Anderson, John W. "Nursing Facility Design Offers Residential Look, Fell—Inside and Out," *Health Facilities Management* (November 1993), pp. 14-15.

Anderson, Neil. "The Medical Office Building: A Strategic Key to the Future," *Trustee* 42, no. 2 (February 1989), pp. 15, 19.

Anderson, Rebecca Cogwell, and Kim Edward Anderson. "Worksite Health Promotion," *AAOHN Journal* 39, no. 2 (February 1991), pp. 57-61.

Angier, Natalie. "Patients Rushing to Alternatives," *New York Times* (January 28, 1993), sec. A, p. 12.

Aquavella, James V. "Ambulatory Surgery in the 1990s," *Journal of Ambulatory Care Management* 13, no. 1 (1990), pp. 21-24.

Archer, Benjamin R., et al. "Protective Barriers for X-Ray Facilities," *The Construction Specifier* 46, no. 8 (August 1993), pp. 82-90.

Arcidi, Philip. Linear Nursing Unit: Cardiac Patient Tower, St. Luke's Medical Center, Milwaukee, Wisconsin," *Progressive Architecture* 72, no. 3 (March 1992), pp. 94-95.

Ardron, M. E., and A. Finneston. "Use of Rehabilitation Apartments for Elderly Patients," *Age and Aging* 19, no. 3 (1990), pp. 195-98.

Ashley, Mary Holt. "Discharge Holding Area: Using Inpatient Beds More Effectively," *JONA* 19, no. 12 (December 1989), pp. 32-35.

Association for the Care of Children's Health. *Construction Projects at Child Health Facilities: A Resource Directory.* Washington, D.C.: Association for the Care of Children's Health, n.d.

Bailey, Laura, et al. "Wellness Centers," *Journal of Healthcare Design* 5 (1993), pp. 105-14.

Baker, Carol F. "Discomfort to Environmental Noise: Heart Rate Responses of SICU Patients," *Critical Care Nursing Quarterly* 15, no. 2 (August 1992), pp. 75-90.

Balsano, Armand E., and Frances J. Fowler. "Subacute Care as a New Source of Revenue," *Healthcare Financial Management* 47, no. 7 (July 1993), pp. 56-62.

Bame, Sherry I. "Design Research: Ambulatory Clinic Design: The Case of Dialysis Facilities," *Journal of Healthcare Design* 5 (September 1993), pp. 125-33.

Barber, Janet M. "Key Considerations in Emergency and Trauma Unit Design," *Critical Care Nursing Quarterly* 14, no. 1 (1991), pp. 71-82.

Bardoczi, Stephen J. "Dual Alzheimer's Unit Sensitively Carved Out of X-Shaped Floor Plan," *Health Facilities Management* 3, no. 10 (Spring 1990), pp. 14-15.

Barilla, David J., et al. "Utilization of the Burn Unit for Nonburn Patients: The 'Wound Intensive Care Unit,'" *Annals of Plastic Surgery* 23, no. 5 (November 1989), pp. 426-29.

Barker, David. "Design Guide—Radiotherapy," *Hospital Development* 24, no. 9 (October 1993), pp. 19-22.

Barker, Kenneth N., et al. "Effect of Technological Changes in Information Transfer on the Delivery of Pharmacy Services," *American Journal of Pharmaceutical Education* 53 (Winter Supplement, 1989), pp. 27S-40S.

Barton, Anne K. "Mainstreaming Inpatients and Outpatients: Modifying Systems to Everyone's Advantage," *AORN Journal* 41, no. 2 (February 1985), pp. 386-88.

———. "Swing Beds: A Nursing Challenge," *Nursing Management* 21, no. 8 (August 1990), pp. 34-35.

Bauer, Suzanne. "A Sense of Wonder: Interiors at a Children's Hospital Spark the Imagination of Its Patients," *Hospitality Design* 14, no. 8 (September 1992), pp. 36-38.

Beale, Craig. "Medical Mall Conveys a 21st Century Image with Room to Expand," *Health Facilities Management* 1, no. 1 (September 1988), pp. 16-17.

Beck, Melinda, et al. "State of Emergency: *Hospitals* Are Seeking Radical Solutions to Ease Walk-In patient Overload," *Newsweek* 118, no. 16 (October 14, 1991), pp. 52-53.

Beckham, J. Daniel. "Beating the Box: Those Who Have Predicted the Demise of the American Hospital Have Missed the Point—They Are Focused on a Hospital as an Edifice," *Healthcare Forum Journal* 35, no. 2 (March/April 1992), pp. 55-58.

Beckwith, Deanne. *The Coherence of Color: A Palette for Health Care Designers.* Zeeland, Mich.: Milcare, 1993.

Behar, Richard. "Medicine's $10 Billion Bonanza: Fitness Centers," *Forbes* 141, no. 13 (June 13, 1988), pp. 101-106.

Behar, Susan. "Making Accessibility Easy on the Eye," *The Construction Specifier* 45, no. 6 (June 1992), pp. 114-19.

———. "Universal Design Blends Function with Form," *Group Practice Journal* 40, no. 4 (July/August 1991), pp. 87-88.

Benya, James R. "Advanced Health Care Facility Lighting Design," address delivered October 15, 1993.

———. "The Lighting Design Professional," *Architectural Lighting* 3, no. 1 (January 1989), pp. 44-48.

———. "Lighting for Healing," *Journal of Health Care Interior Design* 1 (1989), pp. 55-58.

Bergman, Rhonda. "Quantum Leaps: A Look at the Health Care Delivery System in Twenty Years," *Hospitals and Health Networks* 67, no. 19 (October 5, 1993), pp. 28, 31-35.

———. "Letting Telemedicine Do the Walking," *Hospitals and Health Networks* 67, no. 20 (October 20, 1993), pp. 46-48.

Bergoust, Donald G. "St. Patrick Hospital: Innovations in HVAC and Plumbing," *The Construction Specifier* 40, no. 10 (October 1987), pp. 101-107.

Bergstrom, Ebba. "Bathrooms Designed for the Disabled," *Nursing Mirror* 160, no. 5 (June 19, 1985), pp. 21-24.

Berman, Rhonda. "Integrated Information Paves the Way to Better Decision Making on Patient Care," *Hospitals and Health Networks* 68, no. 1 (January 5, 1994), p. 56.

Biner, Paul M., et al. "Inside Windows: An Alternative to Conventional Windows in Offices and Other Settings," *Environment and Behavior* 23, no. 3 (May 1991), pp. 359-82.

Birdsong, Craig, and Cynthia Leibrock. "Patient-Centered Design," *Healthcare Forum Journal* 33, no. 3 (May/June 1990), pp. 40-45.

Birren, Faber. *Color Psychology and Color Therapy.* New York: Carol, 1992.

"Birth of Universal Health, Inc.," *The Economist* 330, no. 7856 (March 26, 1994), pp. 73-74.

Blaese, R. Michael, et al. "Gene Therapy: Sci-Fi No Longer," *Patient Care* 27, no. 11 (June 15, 1993), pp. 24-27, 30, 35, 38-39, 42.

Bleeker, Nick. "Well-Lighted: Health-Care Environments Can Benefit from Technology That Delivers High-Quality Light at Low Cost," *Construction Specifier* 46, no. 8 (August 1993), pp. 92-95.

Blyth, Pamela L., ed. *Health Care Interior Finishes: Problems and Solutions—An Environmental Services Perspective.* Chicago: American Society for Healthcare Environmental Services of the American Hospital Association, 1993.

Bodnar, James. "Prescription Flooring," *The Construction Specifier* 44, no. 8 (August 1991), pp. 74-81.

Boerger, John, and Mardelle Shepley. "Mental Health Design: A Case Study," *Journal of Health Care Interior Design* 3 (1991), pp. 149-57.

Bonge, Lynn E., et al. "A Vision of the Future: The Intelligent Hospital and Health Care System." White paper prepared for 1994 Annual HIMSS Conference and Exhibition. HDR, 1994.

Bonine, Bruce R. "Alternative Futures in Health Care," *Health Care Strategic Management* 8, no. 1 (January 1990), pp. 12-15.

Bosker, Gideon. "Architecture as an Asset in Health Care," *Architecture* 76, no. 1 (January 1987), pp. 35-39.

Borzo, Greg. "New Hospitals May Resemble Malls," *Health Care Strategic Management* 10, no. 11 (November 1992), pp. 17-19.

———. "Patient-Focused Hospitals Begin Reporting Good Results," *Health Care Strategic Management* 10, no. 8 (August 1992), pp. 1, 17-22.

Brantley, Angela. "Rising Violence in ERs Cause Hospitals to Redesign Security," *Modern Healthcare* 22, no. 40 (October 5, 1992), pp. 44-45.

Bray, Karen A., and Kathryn Hearn. "Critical Care Unit Design, Part I: Organizing Plans," *Nursing Management* 24, no. 1 (January 1993), pp. 80A-80H.

———. "Critical Care Unit Design, Part II: Monitoring Operations," *Nursing Management* 24, no. 2 (February 1993), pp. 80J-80O.

———. "Critical Care Unit Design, Part III: Establishing Operations," *Nursing Management* 24, no. 3 (March 1993), pp. 64A-64H.

Brock, John E. "Solving Difficult Site Problems for MRI and PET," *European Journal of Radiology* 16 (1992), pp. 30-34.

Brown, George. "Construction Alternatives for Free-Standing Facilities," *Radiology Management* 12, no. 1 (Winter 1990), pp. 27-30.

Bucci, Ronald. "Positron Emission Tomography Executive Update," *Administrative Radiology* 12, no. 5 (May 1993), pp. 51-59.

Buckley, Jean Amerault, et al. "Medical Office Design: Brigham West Medical Office Campus," *Journal of Healthcare Design* 4 (1992), pp. 87-92.

"Building a Caring Community: Freeport Hospital Health Care Village," *Architectural Record* 178, no. 7 (June 1990), pp. 90-94.

Bulkeley, William M. "Get Ready for 'Smart Cards' in Health Care," *Wall Street Journal* (May 2, 1993), sec. 3, p. 8.

Burda, David. "Total Quality Management Becomes Big Business: But All the Hype May Actually Be Adding to Hospitals' Operating Costs," *Modern Healthcare* 21, no. 4 (January 28, 1991), pp. 25-29.

Burke, Marybeth. "New Surgical Technologies Reshape Hospital Strategies," *Hospitals* 66, no. 9 (May 5, 1992), pp. 30-42.

Burnette, Sam. "Gearing Up for the Outpatient: A Masterplan for the Year 2000," *Nashville Medical News* (February 1994), pp. 13-15.

Burns, John. "Long-term Chains Post Strong Growth in Subacute, Specialty Care," *Modern Healthcare* 23, no. 21 (May 24, 1993), pp. 63-69.

———. "Market Opening Up to the Non-Traditional," *Modern Healthcare* 23, no. 9 (August 9, 1993), pp. 96-98.

———. "Move to Outpatient Settings May Boost Medical Hotels," *Modern Healthcare* 22, no. 23 (June 8, 1992), pp.57-58.

———. "Special Units Aim at Dementia," *Modern Healthcare* 22, no. 46 (November 16, 1992), pp. 26-30.

———. "Subacute Care Feeds Need to Diversify," *Modern Healthcare* 23, no. 50 (December 13, 1993), pp. 343-38.

Bush-Brown, Albert, and Dianne Davis. *Hospitable Design for Healthcare and Senior Communities.* New York: Van Nostrand Reinhold, 1992.

Butler, Darrell L., et al. "Wayfinding by Newcomers in a Complex Building," *Human Factors* 35, no. 1 (1993), pp. 159-73.

Calkins, Margaret P. *Design for Dementia: Planning Environments for the Elderly and the Confused.* Owings Mills, Md.: National Health publishing, 1988.

———. "Designing Cues for Wanderers," *Architecture* 78, no. 10 (October 1989), pp. 117-18.

———. "Designing for an Aging Population," *Healthcare Forum Journal* 35, no. 5 (September/October 1992), pp. 22-23.

———. "Executive Forum: The Corinne Dolan Alzheimer Center," *Journal of Healthcare Design* 4 (1992), pp. 17-23.

Canter, Eric W. "Structuring Freestanding Diagnostic Imaging Centers for Profitability," *Radiology Management* 12, no. 2 (Spring 1990), pp. 29-34.

Carlson, Leanne Kaiser. "Creating Designs That Heal," *California Hospitals* 6, no. 3 (May/June 1992), pp. 12-14.

Carpman, Janet R. "Wayfinding in Health Care: 6 Common Myths," *Health Facilities Management* 3, no. 5 (May 1991), pp. 24, 26-28.

Carpman, Janet R., and Myron A. Grant. *Design That Cares: Planning Health Facilities for Patients and Visitors*. 2d ed. Chicago: American Hospital Publishing, Inc., 1993.

Carr, Tony, and Carolyn S. Webster. "Recovery Care Centers: AN Innovative Approach to Caring for Healthy Surgical Patients," *AORN Journal* 53, no. 4 (April 1991), pp. 986-95.

Carter, Edward, et al. "Acute Care Design: San Diego Children's Hospital and Health Center Addition," *Journal of Healthcare Design* 5 (September 1993), pp. 25-31.

Ceder, Ken. "Design Technology: Lighting for Health," *Journal of Healthcare Design* 4 (1992), pp. 145-48.

Centers for Disease Control. "*Healthy People 2000:* National Health Promotion, Disease Prevention Objectives for the Year 2000," *JAMA* 264, no. 16 (October 24/31, 1990), pp. 2057-58.

Centers for Disease Control and Prevention. *Vital and Health Statistics: Chartbook on Health Data on Older Americans: United States, 1992*. Washington, D.C.: U.S. Department of Health and Human Services, 1993.

Ceol, Dawn Weyrich. "Total Quality Management," *Provider* 19, no. 9 (September 1991), pp. 35-48.

Cerne, Frank. "Homeward Bound: Hospitals See Solid Future for Home Health Care," *Hospitals* 67, no. 4 (February 20, 1993), pp. 52-54.

Chapman, Robert H. "Thoughts for the Day: The Shift Towards Day Surgery . . .," *Hospital Development* 24, no. 8 (September 1993), pp. 21-22.

Chernow, Bart. "The Bedside Laboratory: A Critical Step Forward in ICU Care," *Chest* 97, no. 5 (May 1990, supplement), pp. 183S-184S.

Chicago Health Executives Forum. *The Hospital of the Future: Can the Patient-Focused Model Really Work?* Chicago: CHEF, 199).

"Child Kingdom," *Contract* 31, no. 2 (February 1989), pp. 110-111.

"Children's Medical Center of Israel," *Facilities Planning News* 12, no. 1 (January 1993), n.p.

Chu, Stephen. "Part I, Clinical Information Systems: A Fourth Generation," *Nursing Management* 24, no. 10 (October 1993), pp. 59-60.

"Clinic Plus Doctor's Office," *Architectural Record* 173, no. 12 (October 1985), pp. 132-33.

Cohen, Uriel, and Kristen Day. *Contemporary Environments for People with Dementia*. Baltimore: Johns Hopkins University Press, 1993.

Cohen, Uriel, and Gerald D. Weisman. *Holding On To Home: Designing Environments for People with Dementia.* Baltimore: Johns Hopkins University Press, 1991.

Coile, Russell C., Jr. "The Megatrends—and the Backlash," *Healthcare Forum Journal* 33, no. 3 (March/April; 1990), pp. 37-41 .

———. "Six Predictions for the Nineties," *Healthcare Forum Journal* 33, no. 3 (May/June 1990), pp. 69-70.

Coker, Robert H. "Modular Facility Grafts Speed with Lower Costs in Customized Skin Clinic: University Medical Center Dermatology Clinic, Tucson," *Health Facilities Management* (April 1992), pp. 18-19.

Collett, Howard M. "1990 Helipad Survey," *Journal of Air Medical Transport* 9, no. 8 (August 1990), pp. 20-21.

Committee on Architecture for Health. *The Health-Care Architect of Tomorrow.* Washington, D.C.: American Institute of Architects, 1991.

Committee on Health Care Delivery of the Ambulatory Pediatric Association. *Guidelines for Pediatric Health Care Delivery in Academic Ambulatory Care Settings.* N.p.: Ambulatory Pediatric Association, 1990.

Committee on Hospital Care and Pediatric Section of the Society of Critical Care Medicine. "Guidelines and Levels of Care for Pediatric Intensive Care Units," *Pediatrics* 92, no. 1 (July 1993), pp. 166-75.

Conlin, D. Walters. "Future Health Care: Increasing the 'Alternatives,'" *The Futurist* 22, no. 3 (May-June 1988), p. 15.

Cooper, Helene. "Offering Aerobics, Karate, Aquatics, Hospitals Stress Business of 'Wellness,'" *Wall Street Journal* (August 9, 1993), sec. B, p. 1.

Coster, Ronald L. "Substance-Abuse Centers," *Journal of Health Care Interior Design* 2 (1990), pp. 55-63.

Council on Tall Buildings and Urban Habitat. *Building Design for Handicapped and Aged Persons.* New York: McGraw-Hill, 1992.

Cowan, Timothy J., et al. "Intensive Care Design," *The Construction Specifier* 46, no 8 (August 1993), pp. 48-59.

Cowley, Geoffrey, with Pat Wingert. "Trouble in the Nursery: Are Hospital Lights Blinding Premature Babies?" *Newsweek* 114, no. 9 (August 1989), p. 52.

Cox, Anthony, and Philip Groves. *Hospitals and Health-Care Facilities: A Design and Development Guide.* London: Butterworth Architecture, 1990.

Craig, Sanna. "Consumer Clout: Healthcare Customers," *Healthcare Forum Journal* 31, no. 2 (March/April 1988), pp. 10-20.

Cramer, Carol, and Virginia R. Renz. "Preoperative Care Unit: An Alternative to the Holding Room," *AORN Journal* 45, no. 2 (February 1987), pp. 464-72.

Crosbie, Michael J. "Universal Hardware: Simplicity Is the Key to Specifying Hardware for the Disabled," *Architecture* 80, no. 7 (July 1991), pp. 88-89.

Cruz, Laurie D. "Ambulatory Surgery—The Next Decade," *AORN Journal* 51, no. 1 (January 1990), pp. 241-47.

Dancer, Gail E. "Automated Transport Systems," *Hospital Management International 1991*, pp. 264-65.

Davis, James E., "Ambulatory Surgery . . . How Far Can We Go?" *Medical Clinics of North America* 77, no. 2 (March 1993), pp. 365-75.

Deliganis, Sam G. "Maternity-wing 'Face-lift' Becomes Big Renovation to Recoup Market Share," *Health Facilities Management* 3, no. 12 (December 1990), pp. 10-11.

DeLong, Deanna L. "Preoperative Holding Area: Personalizing Patients' Experiences," *AORN Journal* 55, no. 2 (February 1992), pp. 563-66.

"Design for Living: At a New York City Hospital, Artists Create an Oasis for AIDS Patients," *American Craft* 51, no. 3 (June/July 1991), p. 8.

Devlin, Ann Sloan. "Psychiatric Ward Renovation: Staff Perception and Patient Behavior," *Environment and Behavior* 24, no. 1 (January 1992), pp. 66-84.

DeWitt, Paul Mergenhagen. "The Birth Business," *American Demographics* 15, no. 9 (September 1993), pp. 44-49.

———. "In Pursuit of Pregnancy," *American Demographics* 15, no. 5 (May 1993), pp. 48-54.

DiMotta, Susan, et al. "Long-Term Care Design: Blazing New Territory—Code Reform and Beyond," *Journal of Healthcare Design* 5 (1993), pp. 197-203.

Donovan, Michelle Regan. "The Changing Face of Emergency and Trauma Centers: Promoting Efficacy with Design," AHA Healthcare Facilities Management Series 055350. October 1992.

———. "An Endangered Resource: Hospital Emergency Departments Are Threatened by Closures and a Reduction in Services," *Health Progress* (May 1991), pp. 50-53.

Dorn, Suzanne. "The Beat Goes On: Heart Center of Sarasota Florida," *Hospitality Design* 15, no. 1 (January/February 1993), pp. 46-49.

———. "Fresh Start: Imaginative Interiors Lift the Spirits of Young Patients at This Children's Burn Hospital," *Hospitality Design* 15, no. 5 (June 1993), pp. 40-44

———. "Separate But Equal: A New Women's Hospital in San Diego Offers State-of-the-Art Care with a Warm and Cheery Look," *Hospitality Design* 15, no. 8 (October 1993), pp. 54-59.

Downes, John J. "The Historical Evolution, Current Status, and Prospective Development of Pediatric Critical Care," *Critical Care Clinics* 8, no. 1 (January 1992), pp. 1-23.

Downing, Jack W. "Hospital Doubles Size of Emergency Center—Without Disrupting Care," *Health Facilities Management* 5, no. 12 (December 1992), pp. 12-13.

Dubin, Fred S. "Intelligent Buildings: HVAC, Lighting and Other Design Trends," *The Construction Specifier* 43, no. 8 (February 1990), pp. 51-57.

Dubnicki, Carol, and James B. Williams. "The People Side of TQM," *Healthcare Forum Journal* 35, no. 5 (September/October 1992), pp.54-61.

Duffy, Tama M., and Barbara J. Huelat. "Psychiatric Care Units," *Journal of Health Care Interior Design* 2 (1990), pp. 89-101.

Duffy, Tama M., and J. Michael Florell. "Intensive Care Units," *Journal of Health Care Interior Design* 2 (1991), pp. 167-79.

"DuPont/HFM Forum on Carpet in Health Care Facilities," *Health Facilities Management* 7, no. 2 (February 1994), pp. 38-46.

Dyer, Dorothy. "Rehab Center Offers Hotel-Like Comforts for Injured 'Guests,'" *Health Facilities Management* 2, no. 5 (May 1989), pp.14-15.

Dyer, Ian D. "Meeting the Needs of Visitors—A Practical Approach," *Intensive Care Nursing* 7 (1991), pp. 135-47.

Earl Swensson Associates. "Healthcare Systems of the Future: 2000 and Beyond," leaflet, n.p.: n.d.

Eastman, A. Brent. "Blood in Our Streets: The Status and Evolution of Trauma Care Systems," *Archives of Surgery* 127 (June 1992), pp. 677-81.

Eaton, Kate, "Industrial Rehabilitation—A Win/Win Outpatient Program," *Trustee* 44, no. 2 (February 1991), p. 22.

Eckert, Marvina Kay, and Lorene Newberry. "A Look at Our New Emergency Department: Kennestone Hospital Emergency Center, Marietta, Georgia," *Journal of Emergency Nursing* 18, no. 3 (June 1993), pp. 29A-33A.

Eckholm, Eric. "Study Links Paperwork to 25% of Hospital Costs," *New York Times* (August 5, 1993), sec. A, p. 14.

Ehlinger, Edward P. "Access to Health Care and the Year 2000 Objectives," *Minnesota Medicine* 74 (January 1991), pp. 15-17.

Elmer-Dewitt, Philip. "The Genetic Revolution: New Technology Enables Us to Improve on Nature. How Far Should We Go?" *Time* 43, no. 3 (January 17, 1994), pp. 46-53.

Eubanks, Paula. "Chronic Care: A Future Delivery Model," *Hospitals* 64, no. 6 (March 20, 1990), pp. 42-46.

———. "Wayfinding: More Than Just Putting Up Signs," *Health Facilities Management* 2, no. 6 (June 1989), pp. 20, 22-23, 25.

———. "Wellness Programs Pay Off for Hospitals and Their Employees," *Trustee* 45, no. 1 (January 1992), p. 15.

"Expanding Up and Out: Eastern Maine Medical Center," *Architectural Record* 162, no. 6 (May 1984), pp. 130-35.

Exter, Thomas G. "The Baby Boomers Turn 40: Implications for Healthcare Marketing," *Healthcare Forum Journal* 32, no. 1 (January/February 1989), pp. 19-22.

Fairchild, Susan. *Perioperative Nursing Principles and Practice.* Boston: Jones and Bartlett, 1993.

Farris, Bain J. "Converting a Unit to Patient-Focused Care," *Health Progress* 74, no. 4 (April 1993), pp. 22-25.

Fegelman, Andrew. "New Cook Hospital Gets Lift from Study," *Chicago Tribune* (December 10, 1993), sec. 2, pp. 1, 7.

Ferguson, Tom. "Patient, Heal Thyself: Health in the Information Age," *The Futurist* 26, no. 1 (January-February 1992), pp. 9-13.

Field, Roger. "Surgeons Perform From a Remote Location," *Medical World News* 34, no. 2 (February 1993), p. 35.

Findlay, Steven. "Help! This Is an Emergency!: Despite Heroic Rescues, Ambulance Service and Trauma Centers Are Hurting," *U.S. News and World Report* 107, no. 19 (November 13, 1989), pp. 28, 33, 34.

———. "Portrait of a Hospital: Boston's Massachusetts General," *U.S. News and World Report* 108, no. 17 (April 1990), pp. 63-67.

Findlay, Steven, et al. "No More Knives," *U.S. News and World Report* 110, no. 19 (May 20, 1992), pp. 76-78.

Fitzgerald, Joan. "Architects and Builders Optimistic, Even in the Face of Healthcare Reform," *Modern Healthcare* 24, no. 12 (March 21, 1994), pp. 41-54.

Fletcher, Jim. "Interactive Video in Health Care," *International Hospital Federation 1988 Official Yearbook,* pp. 157-58.

"Florida Hospital Medical Center: D.W. Welch Dining Center," *Food Management* 27, no. 4 (April 1992), p. 120.

"For 'Minor' Emergencies," *Architectural Record* (October 1985), pp. 128-31.

Fox, Renée C. *The Sociology of Medicine: A Participant Observer's View.* Englewood Cliffs, N.J.: Prentice Hall, 1989.

Franta, Gregory. *Environmentally Sustainable Architecture in a Health Care Facility.* Washington, D.C.: American Institute of Architects, 1992.

Franz, Julie. "Triangle Design Saves Time, Money," *Modern Healthcare* 14, no. 3 (March 1984), pp. 127-28.

Frayer, William W. "Neonatal Intensive Care Unit Renovation: The New York Hospital-Cornell Medical Center, 1975-76," *Clinics in Perinatology* 10, no. 1 (February 1983), pp. 153-65.

Frick, Mathis P. et al. "Consideration in Setting Up a Positron Emission Tomography Center," *Seminars in Nuclear Medicine* 22, no. 3 (July 1992), pp. 182-88.

Friedman, Eliot, ed. *The Hospital in Modern Society.* Glencoe, Ill.: The Free Press, 1963.

Friedman, Emily. "The Sagging Safety Net: Emergency Departments on the Brink of Crisis," *Hospitals* 66, no. 4 (February 20, 1992), pp. 26-35.

Gappell, Millicent. "Design Technology: Psychoneuroimmunology," *Journal of Healthcare Design* 4 (1992), pp. 127-30.

―――. "Hospice Facilities," *Journal of Health Care Interior Design* 2 (1990), pp. 77-80.

Gardner, Elizabeth. "A Direct Line Between Buyer and Supplier," *Modern Healthcare* 19, no. 11 (March 17, 1989), pp. 26-28.

―――. "Hospitals Not in a Hurry to Plug in Computers by the Bedside," *Modern Healthcare* 20, no. 28 (July 16, 1990), pp. 31-55.

―――. "Hospitals on Road to Data 'Highways,'" *Modern Healthcare* 23, no. 23 (June 7 1993), p. 32.

―――. "Hospitals Put Wireless Terminals to the Test," *Modern Healthcare* 23, no. 14 (April 5, 1993), p. 38.

―――. "Revamping *Hospitals*' Approach to Renovation," *Modern Healthcare* 19, no. 15 (April 14, 1989), pp. 34-46.

―――. "Telemedicine Goes the Distance: Advancing Technology Allows Transmission of Data to Practitioners in Remote Locations," *Modern Healthcare* 20, no. 32 (August 13, 1990), pp. 25, 28-32.

Gaskie, Margaret. "Kindly Light: Lighting for a New Hospital Contributes to Both the Image of Hospitality and the Real Thing," *Architectural Record Lighting* 6, no. 55 (May 1992), pp. 56-61.

Giffien, Mary. "Hospital-Based SNFs: A Good Bet for Institutions?" *Health Care Strategic Management* 8, no. 6 (June 1990), pp. 1, 20-22.

Gilbert, Fred I., Jr. "Health Care in the United States: The Need for a New Paradigm," *Hawaii Medical Journal* 52, no. 1 (January 1993), pp. 8, 10, 12-13.

Gill, Kenneth E. "Hospital Retrofit: Dual-Duct HVAC Systems," *Heating/Piping/Air Conditioning* 65, no. 11 (November 1993), pp. 31-40.

———. "HVAC Design for Isolation Rooms," *Heating/Piping/Air Conditioning* 66, no. 2 (February 1994), pp. 45-52.

Gill, Kenneth E., and Alan L. Wozniak. "Hospital Gets IAQ Checkup," *Heating/Piping/Air Conditioning* 65, no. 8 (August 1993), pp. 43-51.

Godfrey-June, Jean. "Cross-Dressing: How Are Residential Looks Finding Their Way into Offices, Hospitals, Department Stores, and More—at the Same Time Contract Design Is Going Home?" *Contract Design* 34, no. 7 (July 1992), pp. 70-71.

———. "Powerful Medicine: Design Speeds Up the Medical Learning Curve in Dramatic Ways in Schaetzel Center for Health Education at Scripps Memorial Hospital, La Jolla, Calif.," *Contract Design* 35, no. 10 (October 1993), pp. 59-62.

———. "What Do the Aging Want?" *Contract Design* 34, no. 3 (March 1992), pp. 55-57.

Goldsmith, Jeff C.. "Keynote Address: The New Generation of Healthcare and Design," *Journal of Healthcare Design* 5 (1993), pp. 3-9.

———. "A Radical Precription for Hospitals," *Harvard Business Review* 89, no. 3 (May-June 1989), pp. 104-11.

———. "The Reshaping of Healthcare: Part 1," *Healthcare Forum Journal* 35, no. 3 (May/June 1992), pp. 19-27.

———. "The Reshaping of Healthcare: Part 2," *Healthcare Forum Journal* 35, no. 4 (July/August 1992), pp. 34-41.

Goldsmith, Jeff C., and Richard Miller. "Restoring the Human Scale: Healthcare Facilities WIll Be Designed as Living Spaces for Families, Not Warehouses for Sick People," *Healthcare Forum Journal* 33, no. 6 (November/December 1990), pp. 22-27.

Goldsmith, Marsha F. "Long-Term Care for Older Americans: The Institutionalization of Senescence," *JAMA* 269, no. 18 (May 12, 1993), p. 2331.

Gorman, Jean. "Critical Condition: What Is the Role of Design in the Transformation of a Health Care System Undergoing Financial Crisis and Flux?" *Interiors* 151, no. 12 (December 1992), pp. 28, 32, 36,96.

Gorner, Peter, and Ronald Kotulak. "Gene Therapy Poised to Reinvent Medicine," *Chicago Tribune* (April 13, 1990), sec. 1, p. 1.

Gottschalk, Mark A. "Sensors Add Smarts to Medical Products," *Design News* 15, no. 15 (August 2, 1993), pp. 58-63.

Graven, Stanley N., et al. "The High-Risk Infant Environment: Part 1. The Role of the Neonatal Intensive Care Unit in the Outcome of High-Risk Infants," *Journal of Perinatology* 12, no. 2 (1992), pp. 164-72.

———. "The High-Risk Infant Environment: Part 2. The Role of Caregiving and the Social Environment," *Journal of Perinatology* 12, no. 3 (1992), pp. 267-75.

Green, Robert. "Well Equipped: Architect Who Specialize in Equipment Increasingly Must Specialize to Keep Abreast of Changing Technology," *The Construction Specifier* 45, no. 6 (June 1992), pp. 78-88.

Greene, Jay. *Health-Care Policy Reform: Issues and Implications. A Report of the AIA Academy of Architecture for Health Conference.* Washington, D.C.: American Institute of Architects, 1993.

————. "If You Can't Stem the Tide, Try Diverting a Trickle: More Hospitals Are Taking to Strategies Like Fast-Tracking to Direct Non-Emergency Cases to more Appropriate Settings for Care," *Modern Healthcare* 22, no. 15 (April 13, 1992), pp. 49, 52-61.

————. "Paying Attention to Emergency Care: Hospitals Look Internally to Raise Revenues Through Better Billing, Pricing Practices," *Modern Healthcare* 21, no. 13 (April 1, 1991), pp. 27-33.

Gregory, Mary M. "Concepts in Headwall Selection and Design," *Critical Care Nursing Quarterly* 16, no. 3 (November 1993) pp. 51-55.

————. "On Humanizing the Critical Care Environment," *Critical Care Nursing Quarterly* 16, no. 3 (November 1993), pp. 1-6.

Grumet, Gerald W. "Sounding Board: Pandemonium in the Modern Hospital," *New England Journal of Medicine* 32, no. 6 (Febraury 11, 1993), pp. 433-37.

Guerin, Thomas B. "Materials Management Considerations in Critical Care Areas," *Critical Care Nursing Quarterly* 15, no. 3 (1992), pp. 56-62.

"Guidelines for Establishment of Gastrointestinal Endoscopy Areas," *Gastrointestinal Endoscopy* 37, no. 6 (1991), pp. 661-62.

Guinn, Robert M. "Good Design Is Good Medicine," *Hospital Management International 1991*, pp. 210-11.

Gulak, Morton B. "Architectural Guidelines for State Psychiatric Hospitals," *Hospital and Community Psychiatry* 42, no. 7 (July 1991), pp. 705-707.

Gunby, Phil. "Adult Day Care Centers Vital, Many More Needed," *JAMA* 269, no. 18 (May 12, 1993), pp. 2341-42.

Gunten, Cahrles F. von, et al. "AIDS and Hospice," *The American Journal of Hospice and Palliative Care* 8, no. 4 (July/August 1991), pp. 17-19.

Guynes, David A. "Physical Rehabilitation Centers," *Journal of Health Care Interior Design* 2 (1993), pp. 37-46.

Hadfield, Robert W. "Custom Ceilings: Accoustical Ceilings Offer a Number of Innovations for Unique Installations," *The Construction Specifier* 45, no. 3 (March 1992), pp. 134-41.

Hager, Douglas E., and Christopher C. McClave. "LDR *v* LDRP: A Comparison," *Frontline Planning* 8, no. 9 (1990); reprinted in Ross Planning Associates. *LDRs and LDRPs: What's Working and What's Not.* N.p: Ross Planning Associates, 1990.

Hajworonsky, Michael, and Joanne M. Conway. "Trends in Radiology: Part I," *Radiology Management* 14, no. 1 (Winter 1992), pp. 46-57.

Hall, Brenda, et al. "Designing a Critical Care Unit: Description of a Multidisciplinary Process," *Nursing Clinics of North America* 27, no. 1 (March 1992), pp. 129-39.

Hall, Jill H. "Child Health Care Facilities," *Journal of Health Care Interior Design* 2 (1990), pp. 65-69.

Halm, Margo A., and Michele A. Alpen. "The Impact of Technology on Patients and Families," *Nursing Clinics of North America* 28, no. 2 (June 1993), pp. 443-57.

Hamilton, Kirk, ed. *Unit 2000: Patient Beds for the Future.* Houston: Watkins, Carter Hamilton Architects, 1993.

Hansell, Heidi Nerwin. "The Behavioral Effects of Noise on Man: The Patient with 'Intensive Care Unit Psychosis,'" *Heart & Lung* 13, no. 1 (January 1984), pp. 59-65.

Hanson, Margaret, and Richard L. Kobus. "Medical Office Design: Brugham and Women's Hospital Ambulatory Services Building II," *Journal of Healthcare Design* 4 (1992), pp. 93-98.

Hard, Rob. "More Hospitals Move Toward Bedside Systems," *Hospitals* 66, no. 19 (October 5, 1992), pp. 72-73.

———. "Robots: Can They Help Solve the Technologist Shortage?" *Hospitals* 65, no. 12 (June 20, 1991), pp. 56-57.

Hardy, Owen B., and Lawrence P. Lamers. *Hospitals: The Planning and Design Process*. 2d edition. Rockville, Md.: Aspen, 1986.

Harrell, James W. "User Driven Design Process," *Critical Care Nursing Quarterly* 14, no. 1 (1991), pp. 21-29.

Harrell, Michelle F. "Designing Critical Care Units: An Overview," *Critical Care Nursing Quarterly* 14, no. 1 (1991), pp. 1-8.

———. "Headwall Considerations for Critical Care Unit Designs," *Critical Care Nursing Quarterly* 14, no. 1 (January 1991), pp. 50-53.

Harriman, Marc S. "Clean Rooms: Contaminant-Free Workspaces Require a Design and Mechanical Synthesis," *Architecture* 80, no. 7 (July 1991), p. 83.

Hawkins, H. Ralph. "Health Care Malls," *Journal of Health Care Interior Design* 2 (1990), pp. 137-40.

———. "The Health Care Mall Design," AHA Technical Document Series 055908. July 1988.

"Health Forecasts for the Year 2000," *The Futurist* 22, no. 3 (March-April 1988), p. 50.

Hemmes, Michael, comp. *Managing Health Care Construction Projects: A Practical Guide*. Chicago: American Hospital Publishing, 1993.

Hemperly, Stephen W. "Hazardous Materials and Waste Program: Chemical Exposure, Evaluation, and Control," AHA Technical Document Series 055941, February 1991.

Henderson, John. "Hospitals Seek Bigger Cut of Outpatient Surgeries," *Modern Healthcare* 23, no. 26 (June 28, 1993), pp. 82-85.

Henderson, John A. "Surgery Centers' Success Challenges Hospitals," *Modern Healthcare* 19, no. 22 (June 2, 1989), pp. 78-80.

Henderson, Justin. "Quiet Compassion: A Comforting Refuge for Terminally Ill AIDS Patients," *Interiors* 151, no. 12 (December 1992), pp. 62-63.

———. "Tendering Care: The Northlake Cancer Treatment Center Places High-Tech Medicine in a Soothing Environment," *Interiors* 150, no. 5 (December 1991), pp. 60-63.

Herbig, Paul, and William Koehler. "Implications of the Baby Bust Generation upon the Health Care Market," *Health Marketing Quarterly* 10, nos. 3/4 (1993), pp. 23-37.

"Hexagonal Sinatra Patient Tower Maximizes Space, Improves Operations," *Contract* 23, no. 2 (February 1984), pp. 68-72.

Hiatt, Lorraine. "Breakthroughs in Long Term Care Design," *Journal of Healthcare Design* 4 (1992), pp. 205-215.

———. "Long-Term Care Facilities," *Journal of Healthcare Design* 5 (1993), pp. 195-205.

———. "Long-Term Care: Future Possibilities," *Journal of Healthcare Design* 4 (1992), pp. 55-63.

———. *Nursing Home Renovation Designed for Reform.* Boston, London, etc.: Butterworth Architecture, 1991.

Highton, Marybeth. "Putting the Focus on Health: Wellness Centers Energize Hospital and Community," *Trustee* 46, no. 10 (October 1993), pp. 4-6.

Hinz, Christine A. "Aging Population Gives Hospitals Potential Focus," *Health Care Strategic Management* 9, no. 4 (April 1991), pp. 1, 19-22.

———. "PET Offers High-Tech Tool—But with High Price Tag," *Health Care Strategic Management* 9, no. 12 (December 1991), pp. 1, 18-22.

———. "Recovery Centers Rx for Excess Beds in Hospitals," *Health Care Strategic Management* 9, no. 1 (January 1991), pp. 1, 19-22.

———. "Sports Medicine Centers Offer Marginal Profits," *Health Care Strategic Management* 8, no. 11 (November 1990), pp 1, 23-26.

Hoffman, Thomas. "Hospital Robots Have the Rx for Efficiency," *Computer World* 27, no. 114 (January 11, 1993), pp. 69, 72.

Holness, Gordon. "Breathing Easy: Approaches to Hospital HVAC Design Are Numerous and Conflicting," *The Construction Specifier* 45, no. 6 (June 1992), pp. 63-77.

Honaker, Charles. "Home Health Care Renaissance: A $16 Billion a Year Industry by 1995," *Group Practice Journal* 40, no. 3 (March/April 1991), pp. 8-12.

Horn, Miriam. "Hospitals Fit For Healing: Designers Are Proving That Medical Institutions Need Not Be Sickeningly Dreary," *U.S. News & World Report* (July 22, 1991), pp. 48-50.

Hospital Research and Educational Trust. "Hospitals and Physicians in the Year 2000," pamphlet. Chicago: Hospital Research and Educational Trust, 1990.

Hoss, Jeff. "A Look at Our New Emergency Department: St. Luke's *Hospitals*-Meritcare, Fargo, North Dakota," *Journal of Emergency Nursing* 18, no. 4 (August 1992), pp. 36A-40A.

Hoyt, Jeffrey. "Immediate Care Facilities: Designing Convenient Medicine," *The Construction Specifier* 40, no. 10 (October 1987), pp. 78-79.

Huebner, J., et al. "Influence of Architectural Design on Nosocomial Infections in Intensive Care Units—A Prospective 2-Year Analysis," *Intensive Care Medicine* 15 (1989), pp. 179-83.

Huelat, Barbara J. "Current Trends in Cancer Center Design," *Journal of Health Care Interior Deisgn* 3 (1991), pp. 9-16.

Humphreys, H. "Infection Control and the Design of a New Operating Theatre Suite," *Journal of Hospital Infection* 23 (1993), pp. 61-70.

IES Health Care Facilities Committee. *Lighting for Health Care Facilities.* New York: Illuminating Engineering Society of North America, 1985.

Ilg, Deann. "Senior Communities," *The Construction Specifier* 45, no. 2 (June 1992), pp. 120-23.

Jacobson, John S. "Patient Relations Program Eases Construction's Inconvenience," *Health Progress* 76, no. 10 (December 1986), p. 101.

James, W. Paul, and William Tatton-Brown. *Hospitals: Design and Development.* London: Architectural Press; New York: Van Nostrand Reinhold, 1986.

Janower, Murray L. "Patient-Focused Care: Radiology Department Beware," *Radiology* 187 (1993), pp. 313-15.

Jaspen, Bruce. "Mayo, Deere Join Forces to Spread Plan to Des Moines," *Modern Healthcare* 23, no. 49 (December 6, 1993), p. 18.

Jenna, Judith K. "Toward the Patient-Driven Hosptial," parts 1 and 2. *Healthcare Forum Journal* 9, no. 4 (May/June 1986), pp. 8-18; (July/August 1986), pp. 52-59.

Johnson, Donald E. L. "Integrated Subacute Care: 20% of Your Patient Days," *Health Care Strategic Management* 11, no. 8 (August 1993), pp. 2-3.

———. "Window of Opportunity for Subacute Services Is Small," *Health Care Strategic Management* 11, no. 7 (July 1993), pp. 2-3.

Jones, Wanda J. "Acute Care Design: The New Genration," *Journal of Healthcare Design* 5 (September 1993), pp. 33-38.

Jones, Wanda J., and Milton Bullard. *New Century Hospital: Patient-Focused Planning and Design.* San Francisco: New Century Healthcare Press, 1992.

———. "Translating Operational Change into Facility Design: Measuring the Feasibility, Cost-Effectiveness, and Space Requirements of Patient-Focused Facilities," *Healthcare Forum Journal* 36, no. 1 (January/February 1993), pp. 67-69.

Jurow, Alice, and Marc Schweitzer. "Planetree Patients Come First in Health Care Design," *California Hospitals* 6, no. 3 (May/June 1993), pp. 14-16.

Kaiser, Leland. "The Hospital as a Healing Place," *Healthcare Forum Journal* 35, no. 5 (September/October 1992), pp. 39-40.

Kalb, Paul E., and David H. Miller. "Utilization Strategies for Intensive Care Units," *JAMA* 261, no. 16 (April 28, 1989), pp. 2389-95.

Kalymun, Mary. "Relationships Between Sensory Decline Among the Elderly and the Physical Environment: Implications for Health Care," *Rhode Island Medical Journal* 72 (May 1989), pp. 161-67.

Kanaly, George W., Jr. "Systamodule: Hospital Environments for Today, Tomorrow, and Beyond," *Mississippi Pharmacist* (May 1975).

Kane, Robert E., and Rosalie A. Kane. "A Nursing Home in Your Future?" *New England Journal of Medicine* 324, no. 9 (February 28, 1991), pp. 627-29.

Kania, Alan J. "Hospital-Based Home Care Integral to Seamless Service," *Health Care Strategic Management* 11, no. 8 (august 1993), pp. 1, 19-23.

———. "Hospital-Health and Fitness Centers Promote Wellness," *Health Care Strategic Management* 11, no. 6 (June 1993), pp. 1, 18-23.

———. "Trauma Centers Form a Health-Care System," *Health Care Strategic Management* 11, no. 3 (March 1993), pp. 1, 20-23.

Kantrowitz, Min, and Associates. *Design Evaluation of Six Primary Care Facilities for the Purpose of Informing Future Design Decisions.* Martinez, Calif.: Center for Health Design, 1993.

Kay, Bruce G., et al. "Designing a Modern Hospital Pharmacy," *American Journal of Hospital Pharmacy* 43 (February 1986), pp. 339-43.

Keenan, Linda A., and Ellen F, Goldman. "Positive Imaging: Design as Marketing Tool in Diagnostic Centers," *Administrative Radiology* 8, no. 2 (February 1989), pp. 36-41.

Keep, P. J. "Stimulus Deprivation in Windowless Rooms," *Anaesthesia* 32 (1977), pp. 598-600.

Keep, Philip, et al. "Windows in the Intensive Therapy Unit," *Anaesthesia* 35 (1980), pp. 257-62.

Kellman, Neil. "History of Health Care Environments," *Journal of Health Care Interior Design* 1 (1989), pp. 19-27.

Kelly, Lucie S. "High Tech/High Touch—Now More Than Ever," *Nursing Outlook* 32, no. 1 (January/February 1984), p. 15.

Kenkel, Paul J. "Companies Sweeten Wellness Plans," *Modern Healthcare* 22, no. 47 (November 23, 1992), p. 49.

Kenkel, Paul J. "Financial Incentives in Wellness Plans Aimed at Reducing Insurance Costs by Helping Workers Shed Unhealthy Habits," *Modern Healthcare* 22, no. 3 (January 20, 1992), p. 38.

Kight, Douglas. "Hospital Women's Centers That Work," *Health Care Strategic Management* 6, no. 10 (October 1988), pp. 12-13.

Kile, Denise. "Tom Landry Sports Center Takes Wellness, Physical Performance to High-Tech Levels," *Dallas Business Journal* (August 30-September 5, 1991), pp. 28-29.

Kim, Howard. "Trauma Networks Look for Rescue: Hospitals Dropping Out as Uncompensated Costs Mount," *Modern Healthcare* 20, no. 5 (February 5, 1990), pp. 33-35.

Klaus, Marshall H., ed. *Care of the High-Risk Neonate*. 4th ed. Philadelphia: Saunders, 1993.

Klein, Susan. "Respite Program Gives Care Givers a Break," *Health Progress* 70, no. 12 (November 1989), pp. 64-68.

Kleman, Marie, et al. "Physiologic Responses of Coronary Care Patients to Visiting," *Journal of Cardiovascular Nursing* 7, no. 3 (April 1993), pp. 52-62.

Knowles, E. W. (Bucky). "In a Time of Change, Construction Planning Takes on Complex New Dimensions," *Hospitals* 66, no. 4 (February 20, 1992), pp. 42-51.

Knowles, Fred T. "ADA's Signage Rules: Significant, Strict, Specific," *Health Facilities Management* 5, no. 11 (November 1992), PP. 44-53.

Koch, Richard M. "Design Considerations for Electrical Power, Lighting, and Auxiliary Systems in Critical Care Areas of Hospitals," *Critical Care Nursing Quarterly* 14, no. 1 (1991), pp. 54-59.

Kolanowski, Ann M. "The Clinical Importance of Environmental Lighting to the Elderly," *Journal of Gerontological Nursing* 18, no. 1 (1992), pp. 10-13.

Koska, Mary T. "Patient-Centered Care: Can Your Hospital Afford Not to Have It?" *Hospitals* 64, no. 21 (November 5, 1990), pp. 48-54.

———. "Total Quality Improvement: A Hospital Case Study," *Trustee* 43, no. 8 (August 1990), pp. 16-17.

———. "Urgent Care/Primary Care Concept Proves Profitable," *Hospitals* 63, no. 17 (September 5, 1989), pp. 74-76.

Kovner, Anthony R., et al. *Healthcare Delivery in the United States* 4th ed. New York: Springer, 1990.

Kowalski, Karen. "LDRs and LDRPs: What's Working and What's Not," in Ross Planning Associates. *LDRs and LDRPs: What's Working and What's Not.* N.p: Ross Planning Associates, 1990.

Kreiss, Kathleen. "The Sick Building Syndrome in Office Buildings—A Breath of Fresh Air," *The New England Journal of Medicine* 328, no. 12 (March 25, 1993), pp. 877-78.

Kurmel, Thomas David. *Projecting Building Technology for Hospitals: A Study of Growth and Change in Diagnostic Imaging.* Harvard University Graduate School of Design Dr. Des. diss., 1991.

Lamprecht, Loren J., and Ann B. Kulik. "Through a Child's Eyes," *The Construction Specifier* 46, no. 8 (August 1993), pp. 38-47.

Land, Karen Brumley. "Activity Room Design, Equipment Impact Programming Success," *Provider* 19, no. 9 (September 1993), p. 95.

Larson, Tom. "Research Laboratory Attuned to Needs of Scientists: Wexner Institute for Pediatric Research," *Health Facilities Management* 2, no. 3 (March 1989), pp. 8-9.

"Laser, Laparoscopic Surgery Center Called First in Nation," *Same-Day Surgery* 15, no. 4 (April 1991), pp. 42-43.

Laskowski-Jones, Linda. "Will Trauma Centers Become Extinct? A Review of Factors Affecting Trauma Center Financial Viability," *Emergency Nursing* 19 (1993), pp. 121-26.

Lathrop, J. Philip. "The Patient-Focused Hospital," *Healthcare Forum Journal* 34, no. 4 (July/August 1991), pp. 17-20.

Lave, Judith R., and Lester B. Lave. *The Hospital Construction Act: An Evaluation of the Hill-Burton Program, 1948-1973.* Washington, D.C.: American Enterprise Institute for Public Policy Research, 1974.

Lebovich, William L. *Design for Dignity: Accessible Environments for People with Disabilities.* New York: Wiley, 1993.

Leib, Roger K. "Bed vs. Chair-Based Care," *Aesclepius* 2, no. 2 (Spring 1993), p. 3.

Leibrock, Cynthia. *Beautiful Barrier-Free: A Visual Guide to Accessibility.* New York: Van Nostrand Reinhold, 1993.

Lewin, Tamara. "Alzheimer's and Architecture: A Search for Order," *New York Times* (May 2, 1990), p. A9.

Liberman, Jacob. *Light: Medicine of the Future.* Santa Fe, New Mexico: Bear, 1991.

"Light, Bright, and Beautiful: Ellerbe Becket Remodels Hospital Youth Wing with Bright Colors 30 Years Later," *Contract* 31, no. 2 (February 1989), pp. 104-105.

Lindner, Ulrich M. "Formulas for Flexibility: Adaptability Is the Essential Ingredient in Laboratory Design—and Modular Planning Can Provide It," *The Construction Specifier* 46, no. 4 (April 1993), pp. 53-62.

Lindsey, Mark S. "'Landlocked' Hospital Finds Room for Its MRI Unit Under the Ground," *Health Facilities Management* 5, no. 9 (September 1992), pp. 14-15.

Linn, Charles. "Labor and Delivery Rooms Use Warm Incandescent and Fluorescent Lighting to Create a Soothing Atmosphere," *Architectural Lighting* 4, no. 6 (June 1990), pp. 36-39.

Linton, Patrick E. "Healing Environments: Creating a Total Healing Environment," *Journal of Healthcare Design* 5 (September 1993), pp. 167-73.

Llewellyn, Jane G. "Short Stay Surgery: Present Practices, Future Trends," *AORN Journal* 53, no. 5 (May 1991), pp. 1179-91.

Longinow, Lillian T., and Louise B. Rzeszewski. "The Holding Room: A Preoperative Advantage," *AORN Journal* 57, no. 4 (April 1993), pp. 914-23.

Loper, Dawn M. "Lighting and Health—An Annotated Bibilography," AHA Technical Document Series 055906. May 1988.

Loukin, Andrea. "Tuttleman Center: Stained Glass Murals Help Ease Patient Concerns in the Hospital by KPA Design Group," *Interior Design* 63, no. 6 (April 1992), pp. 110-11.

Lower, Mary S., and Lois B. Nauert. "Charting: The Impact of Bedside Computers," *Nursing Management* 23, no. 7 (July 1992), pp. 40-44.

Lubic, Ruth Watson, and Eunice M. Ernst. "The Childbearing Center: An Alternative to Conventional Care," *Nursing Outlook* 26, no. 11 (December 1978), pp. 754-60.

Ludman, Dianne. "Emergency/Ambulatory Department—A New 'Front Door' to Hospital," *Health Facilities Management* 1, no. 3 (November 1988), pp. 15-16.

Lumsdon, Kevin. "The Clinical Connection: Hospitals Work to Design Information Systems That Physicians Will Use," *Hospitals* (May 5, 1993), p. 16.

———. "Moving Target: Hospitals Take Careful Steps in Acquiring PET," *Hospitals* 66, no. 7 (April 5, 1992), pp. 58-62.

Lutz, Sandy. "Ambulatory Care of the 1990s Stretches the Imagination," *Modern Healthcare* 20, no. 49 (December 10, 1990), pp. 24-34.

———. "Home-care Franchises Soar in Popularity," *Modern Healthcare* 23, no. 23 (June 7, 1993), pp. 34-35.

———. "Hospitals Continue Move into Home Care," *Modern Healthcare* 23, no. 4 (January 25, 1993), pp. 28-32.

———. "Hospitals Gird to Fight "Disease of the Future," *Modern Healthcare* 22, no. 49 (December 7, 1992), pp. 22-28.

———. "Hospitals Reassess Home-Care Ventures," *Modern Healthcare* 20, no. 37 (September 17, 1990), pp. 23-30.

———. "Pumping Up Profits: Hospitals Lean Toward Fitness Centers to Fatten Bottom Line," *Modern Healthcare* 21, no. 29 (July 22, 1991), pp. 26-28.

Lyons, Rosemary F. "Cross-Training: A Richer Staff for Leaner Budgets," *Nursing Management* 23, no 1 (January 1992), pp. 44-46.

Mack, Alan W. "Medical/Surgical Nursing Units," *Journal of Healthcare Design* 5 (1993), pp. 29-36

Madden, Christine S. "Environmental Considerations in Critical Care Interiors," *Critical Care Nursing Quarterly* 14, no. 1 (1991), pp. 43-49.

Mahnke, Frank H., and Rudolf H. Mahnke. *Color and Light in Man-Made Environments.* New York: Van Nostrand Reinhold, 1993.

"Making Special Care Special: Lake Pavilion/Family Birth Center, Baptist Hospital of Miami," *Architectural Record* 178, no. 7 (June 1993), pp. 98-101.

Malkin, Jain. "Beyond Interior Design," *Health Facilities Management* 6, no. 11 (November 1993), pp. 18-25

———. "Clinic Design: The Mystery Ingredient for Profit and Productivity," *Group Practice Journal* 40, no. 4 (July/August 1991), pp. 20-30.

———. "Gentle Delivery: Jain Malkin Documents the Criteria for a Successful Birthing Center," *Interiors* 151, no. 12 (December 1992), pp. 64-67.

———. *Hospital Interior Architecture: Creating Healing Environments for Special Patient Populations.* New York: Van Nostrand Reinhold, 1992.

———. *Medical and Dental Space Planning for the 1990s.* New York: Van Nostrand Reinhold, 1990.

———. "Medical Office Design: New Possibilities," *Journal of Healthcare Design* 4 (1992), pp. 99-108

———. "Medical Office Design: Theory and Types," *Journal of Healthcare Design* 4 (1992), pp. 77-85.

———. "Medical Offices," *Journal of Healthcare Interior Design* 2 (1990), pp. 23-28.

———. "Wayfinding: Are Your Staff and Visitors Lost in Space?" *Health Facilities Management* 5, no. 8 (August 1992), pp. 36, 38-41.

Mannix, Margaret. "The Case for Home Care: A New Guide by Anne Werner and James Firman Explains How Older People Can Find —and Pay For—Reliable Care at Home," *U.S. News and World Report* 114, no. 16 (April 26, 1993), pp. 71-72.

Marshall Erdman and Associates. *Planning, Designing, and Constructing Group Practice Facilities: A Practical Guidebook.* Madison, Wis.: Marshall Erdman and Associates, 1993.

Martin, M. Caroline. "Working Out for the Best," *Healthcare Forum Journal* 36, no. 6 (November/December 1993), pp. 57-63.

Martin, Charlotte. *Interior Design for Hospitals: Preferences of Patients and Staff for Colors in the Patient Room.* Oklahoma State University Ph.D. diss., 1992.

Martinsons, Jane. "The Planetree Model: Personalized Patient Care," *Trustee* 43, no. 9 (September 1990), pp. 8-9, 17.

Maserjian, Karen. "H O K: Tradiitonal Georgian Styling Defines an In-Patient Nursing Unit at the University of Alabama Hospital," *Cahner's Publishing,* Health Care Supplement to *Building Design and Construction.* (February 1993), pp. S58-S61.

Mason, James O. "Healthy People 2000: The Challenge of Academic Medicine," *Academic Medicine* 66, no. 10 (October 1991), pp. 598-99.

Matson, Theodore A. *Restructuring for Ambulatory Care: A Guide to Reorganization.* Chicago: American Hospital Publishing, 1990.

Mayer, Dean. "Florida Hospital," *Healthcare Forum Journal* 35, no. 5 (September/October 1992), pp. 75-80.

McConnell, Edwina A. "The Impact of Machines on the Work of Critical Care Nurses," *Critical Care Nursing Quarterly* 12, no. 4 (March 1990), pp. 45-52.

McGowan, Maryrose. "Restoring Choice," *The Construction Specifier* 46, no. 8 (August 1993), pp. 62-73.

———. "Visual Field: Wall Surfaces Are Justifiably a Major Focus of Both Specifier and Client," *The Construction Specifier* 46, no. 8 (August 1993), pp. 96-104.

McKahan, Donald C. "The Healing Environemnt of the Future," *Healthcare Forum Journal* 33, no. 4 (May/June 1990), pp. 37-39.

———. "Healing Environments: Healing by Design—Thereapeutic Environments for Healthcare," *Journal of Healthcare Design* 5 (September 1993), pp. 159-66.

McKee, Bradford. "Reforming Healthcare Design," *Architecture* (March 1994), pp. 109-13.

McKnight, John L. "Hospitals and the Health of Their Communities," *Hospitals and Health Networks* 68, no. 1 (January 5, 1994), pp. 40-41.

McLarney, V. James. "Health Care Reform: What to Expect, What AHA Proposes and What It Will Mean to You," *Health Facilities Management* 6, no. 3 (March 1993), pp. 18-25.

McNamara, Peggy, et al. "Patchwork Access: Primary Care in EDs on the Rise," *Hospitals* (May 20, 1993), pp. 44, 46.

McQuarrie, Donald G., et al. "Laminar Airflow Systems: Issues Surrounding Their Effectiveness," *AORN Journal* 51, no. 4 (April 1990), pp. 1035-49.

"Medical Mission: Children's Hospital and Health Center Patient Care Pavilion," *Architecture* 82, no. 4 (April 1993), pp. 76-81.

"Meditation Room Opens in San Diego," *Aesclepius* 2, no. 4 (Fall 1993), pp. 1-2.

Meeker, Margaret Huth, and Jane C. Rothrock. *Alexander's Care of the Patient.* 9th ed. St. Louis: Mosby, 1991.

Meis, Rev. J. Anthony. "A Haven for the Spirit: A Well-Designed Chapel Can Improve Nursing Home Residents' Spiritual and Psychological Health," *Health Progress* 72, no. 5 (June 1991), pp. 56-59.

Melin, Anna-Lisa, et al. "The Cost-Effectiveness of Rehabilitation in the Home: A Study of Swedish Elderly," *American Journal of Public Health* 83, no. 3 (March 1993), pp. 356-62.

Mellenger-Blouch, Judd. "New Diagnostic Center Brings Radiology, Lab Services into the '90s," *Health Facilities Management* 5, no. 7 (July 1992), pp. 16-17.

Meub, Eric. "The Room and the Cure: Some Preliminary Guidelines for Architecture That Heals," *Erikture* 3 (July 1993), pp. 24-25

Middleton, William G. "Homelike Setting Aids in Creation of Restraint-Free Environment," *Provider* 19, no. 5 (May 1993), pp. 45-46.

Militello, Philip R., and Ameen I. Ramzy. "Safety by Design: Shock Trauma Center's Helipad Received Special Consideration During its Planning and Construction." *Journal of Air Medical Transport* 9, no. 8 (August 1990). pp. 15-17.

Millenson, Michael L. "1-Day Medical Wonders on Rise—Study: Most Surgery Patients Now Skip Hospital Stay," *Chicago Tribune* (April 22, 1992), sec. 1, p. 11.

Miller, Richard L., "Basic Information: Triangular Floor Design," leaflet, n.p.: n.d.

Mills, George. "Space Allocation Committee: Backbone to Facility Management," AHA Technical Document Series 055929. March 1990.

Milshtein, Amy. "Coming Home," *Contract Design* 36, no. 2 (February 1994), pp. 66-70.

———. "Going for the Gold: Azalea Trace, Pensacola," *Contract Design* 34, no. 3 (March 1992), pp. 63-68.

———. "One-Stop Healing: University of Nebraska Medical Center Outpatient Care Center," *Contract Design* 35, no 10 (October 1993), pp. 66-69.

———. "Queens for a Day," *Contract Design* 36, no. 2 (February 1994), pp. 72-74.

———. "Tree of Life: St. Luke's Medical Center Outpatient Wing," *Contract Design* 35, no 10 (October 1993), pp. 54-57.

Modeland, Vern. "ICU: Hospital within a Hospital," *FDA Consumer* 23, no. 1 (February 1989), pp. 31-35.

"Modern Vision: Shiley Eye Center, University of California, San Diego," *Architecture* 80, no. 7 (July 1991), pp. 58-63.

Moderow, Richard R. "The Quest for the Perfect Patient Unit Design," AHA Technical Document Series 055301. September 1991.

Moeser, Shannon Dawn. "Cognitive Mapping in a Complex Building," *Environment and Behavior* 20, no. 1 (January 1988), pp. 21-49.

Monteleoni, Philip. "Imaging Adjacencies: Three Recent Projects Illustrate Central vs. Dedicated Specialty Planning Considerations," *European Journal of Radiology* 16 (1992), pp. 26-29.

Moore, Kim. "Critical Care Unit Design: A Collaborative Approach," *Critical Care Nursing Quarterly* 16, no. 3 (1993), pp. 15-26.

More, Vincent, et al., eds. *The Hospice Experiment.* Baltimore: Johns Hopkins University Press, 1988.

Morrow, Lisa A. "Sick Building Syndrome and Related Workplace Disorders," *Otolaryngology—Head and Neck Surgery* 106, no. 6 (June 1992), pp. 649-54.

Mosher, Cynthia M. "The Child Care Business: Should Hospitals Invest?" *Nursing Management* 23, no. 8 (August 1992), pp. 50-51.

Moulas, Guy. "Bar Codes in Hospitals and Pharmacies," *Hospital Management International 1991,* pp. 149-50.

"MRI: What Are Its Applications; What Will It Replace?" *Health Technology* 2, no. 1 (January/February 1988), pp. 3-11.

Mullan, Fitzhugh. "The Future of Primary Care in America," *American Family Physician* 44, no. 4 (October 1991), pp. 1481-84.

Murayama, Koji. "Housing and the Elderly," *Erikture* 3 (July 1993), pp. 4-9.

Murphy, Emmett C., and Patricia Ruflin. "How to Design a Horizontal Patient-Focused Hospital," *Health Care Strategic Management* 11, no. 5 (May 1993), pp. 17-19.

Naisbitt, John, and John Elkins. "The Hospital and Megatrends," *Hospital Forum* 26, nos. 3 and 4 (May/June and July/August 1983), pp. 9, 11-12, 17 and pp. 52-56.

Nasatir, Judith. "OWP&P: The Prairie Style Interior of Oak Park Hospital's ICU, CCU and Telemetry Units Treats Patients, Family and Staff in a Comfortably Familiar Home-Like Environment," *Cahner's Publishing,* Healthcare Supplement to *Building Design and Construction.* (February 1993), pp. S62-S65.

Naylor, Arthur F. "Radiology Department Design to Accommodate the Future Introduction of Global PACS," *European Journal of Radiology* 16 (1992), pp. 51-53.

Neill, Harry M. "Isolation-Room Ventilation Critical to Control Disease," *Health Facilities Management* 5, no. 9 (September 1992), pp. 30-31, 34, 36, 38.

Nesmith, Lynn. "Designing for 'Special Populations,'" *Architecture* 76, no. 1 (January 1987), pp. 62-64.

"New Directions in Long Term Care," *Provider* 19, no. 8 (August 1993), pp. 22-28.

"The New Hospital," *The Futurist* 21, no. 1 (January-February 1987), p. 11.

Nielson, Gail A. "Trends in Radiology: Part I—Exam Charges, Workload and Procedure Volume," *Radiology Management* 12, no. 1 (Winter 1990), pp. 39-46.

———. "Trends in Radiology: Part II," *Radiology Management* 12, no. 2 (Spring 1990), pp. 53-65.

Noble, Ann. "New Use for Old Hospital," *International Hospital Federation 1988 Official Yearbook,* p. 84.

"North Kansas Hospital: Employee/Visitor Cafeteria," *Food Management* 27, no. 4 (April 1992), p. 124.

Northrup, Scott. "Patient Monitoring," *Hospital Management International 1990,* pp. 311-12.

"Northwestern Memorial Hospital: Cafeteria and Central Production Kitchen," *Food Management* 27, no. 4 (April 1992), p. 126.

Nuelsen, Peter H. "AIDS Care and Architecture," *Journal of Ambulatory Care Management* 11, no. 2 (1988), pp. 47-54.

O'Hare, Patrick K., and William T. Schmidt, Jr., "Required Reading: Federal Disabilities Act Increases Litigations Risks for Providers," *Health Progress* 72, no. 4 (April 1991), pp. 43-46.

O'Neill, Michael J. "Effects of Signage and Floor Plan Configuration on Wayfinding Accuracy," *Environment and Behavior* 23, no. 5 (September 1991), pp. 553-74.

O'Reilly, Joseph Matthew. *Legal Privacy and Psychological Privacy: An Evaluation of Court Ordered Design Standards.* University of Arizona PhD. diss., 1985.

Olds, Anita Rui. "With Children in Mind: Novel Approaches to Waiting Area and Playroom Design," *Journal of Health Care Interior Design* 3 (1991), pp. 111-22.

Oliver, Joan Duncan. "Resorting to Water: The Curative Powers May Be Questionable, but Mineral Springs Will Certainly Soothe Your Nerves," *Health* 22, no. 4 (April 1990), pp. 58-63.

Olsen, Richard V. "Redesigning Facilities for People with AIDS," *Health Facilities Management* 2, no. 2 (February 1990), pp. 28, 30-33.

Olson, Christopher. "A Place for Kids: Replacement Hospital Benefits from Experience with the SPecial Needs of Pediatric Burn Patients," *Building Design and Construction* (September 1993), pp. 60-62.

Orem, Helen G. "Art for Health: Emerging Trends," *Journal of Healthcare Design* 5 (September 1993), pp. 73-81.

Ornstein, Suzyn. "First Impressions of the Symbolic Meanings Connoted by Reception Area Design," *Environment and Behavior* 24, no. 1 (January 1992), pp. 85-110.

Orr, Robin. "Executive Forum: The Planetree Philosophy," *Journal of Healthcare Design* 4 (1992), pp. 29-34.

———. "Health Care Environemnts for Healing," *Journal of Health Care Interior Design* 1 (1989) pp. 71-76.

———. "Planetree Update," *Journal of Health Care Interior Design* 2 (1990), pp. 181-86.

Osborn, June E. "AIDS: The Challenge to Ambulatory Care," *Journal of Ambulatory Care Management* 11, no. 2 (1988), pp. 19-26.

Ottolino, Rick. "Mammography Center Easily Accessible in Large, Urban Mall," *Health Facilities Management* 1, no. 2 (November 1988), pp. 12-13.

Palmer, Janice B., and Florence Nash. "Taking Shape: Environmental Art in Health Care," *NCMJ* 54, no. 2 (February 1993), pp. 101-104.

Park, Katharine, and John Henderson. "'The First Hospital Among Christians': The Ospedale di Santa Maria Nuova in Early Sixteenth-Century Florence," *Medical History* 35 (1991), pp. 164-88.

"Parking Deck Security," *The Easton Hospital Beeper: Easton Hospital Employee Newsletter* (February 1993).

Perry, Linda. "Single-Room Maternity Care Begets More Utilization," *Modern Healthcare* 20, no. 5 (February 5, 1990), p. 46.

——. "Staff Cross-Training Caught in Cross Fire," *Modern Healthcare* 21, no. 18 (May 6, 1991), pp. 26-29.

Perry, Philip A. "Baylor Opens $20 Million Landry Sports Medicine Research Center in Dallas," *Health Care Strategic Management* 9, no. 2 (February 1991), p. 4.

Persily, Nancy Alfred, ed. *Eldercare: Positioning Your Hospital for the Future.* Chicago: American Hospital Publishing, 1991.

Peterson, Kristine. "Guest Relations: Substance or Fluff?" *Healthcare Forum Journal* 31, no. 2 (March/April 1988), pp. 23-25.

Phelps, Stephen E., Jr., and Richard B. Birrer. "Do You Know Where You Are? A Look Into One Hospital's Emergency Department," *Health Progress* 73, no. 4 (May 1992), pp. 43-47.

——. "Traumatic Trends: Emergency Departments Abound as the Number of Trauma Centers Spirals Downward," *Health Progress* 72, no. 4 (May 1991), pp. 48-49.

Pica-Furey, Wendy. "Ambulatory Surgery—Hospital-Based vs Freestanding," *AORN Journal* 57, no. 5 (May 1993), pp. 1119-26.

Piergeorge, A. R., et al. "Designing the Critical Care Unit: A Multidisciplinary Approach," *Critical Care Medicine* 11, no. 7 (July 1993), pp. 541-45.

Popovich, John, Jr. "Intermediate Care Units: Graded Care Options," *Chest* 99, no. 1 (January 1991), pp. 4-5.

Recommended Practices Coordinating Committee. "Proposed Recommended Practices: Traffic Patterns in the Surgical Suite," *AORN Journal* 56, no. 2 (August 1992), pp. 312-15.

Regnier, Victor A. *Assisted Living Housing for the Elderly: Design Innovations from the United States and Europe.* New York: Van Nostrand Reinhold, 1994.

Reid, Robert N. "Power Panels: Headwall Units Must Meet Anticipated Medical Needs at the Bedside," *The Construction Specifier* 45, no. 6 (June 1992), pp. 108-113.

Ratcliff Architects and the H.O.M. Group, Inc. *Patients First: Research into Patient Focusing.* N.p.: The Ratcliff Architects and the H.O.M. Group, 1992.

Riedel, Philip. "How Safe and Efficient Are LDRs/LDRPs?" *Frontline Planning* 8, no. 12 (1990); reprinted in Ross Planning Associates. *LDRs and LDRPs: What's Working and What's Not.* N.p: Ross Planning Associates, 1990.

Rifkin, Glenn. "New Momentum for Electronic Patient Records," *New York Times* (May 2, 1993), sec. 3, p. 8.

Riggs, Leonard M., ed. *Emergency Department Design.* Dallas: American College of Emergency Physicians, 1993.

Riley, Joanne. "Cross-Training Maximizing Staffing Flexibility," *Nursing Management* 21, no. 6 (June 1990), pp. 481-82.

Roberts, Percy E., III. "Renovation and Addition Turn Hospital Cafeteria into Bigger Profit Center," *Health Facilities Management* 4, no. 2 (February 1991), pp. 12-13.

Robey, Peter E. and Carrie Valiant. "The Americans with Disabilities Act: Public Accommodations Will Never Be the Same," *Group Practice Journal* 40, no. 4 (July/August 1991), pp. 90-91.

Rochon, Donald. "Hospital Security," *The Construction Specifier* 45, no. 6 (June 1992), pp. 90, 94-97.

Rockey, Alexandra. "The Exceptional Environment: Preparing for Dementia Care," *Provider* 19, no. 7 (July 1993), 22-36.

Rodriguez, Glenn S., and Bruce Goldberg. "Rehabilitation in the Outpatient Setting," *Clinics in Geriatric Medicine* 9, no. 4 (November 1993), pp. 873-81.

Roebuck, E. J., et al. "Building or Extending a Hospital Department: Radiology— A Path Through the Planning Minefield (1)," *Journal of the Royal Society of Medicine* 80 (January 1987), pp. 40-46.

———. "Building or Extending a Hospital Department: Radiology—A Path Through the Planning Minefield (2)," *Journal of the Royal Society of Medicine* 80 (February 1987), pp. 107-13.

———. "Building or Extending a Hospital Department: Radiology—A Path Through the Planning Minefield (3)," *Journal of the Royal Society of Medicine* 80 (March 1987), pp. 173-79.

———. "Building or Extending a Hospital Department: Radiology—A Path Through the Planning Minefield (4)," *Journal of the Royal Society of Medicine* 80 (April 1987), pp. 239-45.

———. "Building or Extending a Hospital Department: Radiology—A Path Through the Planning Minefield (5)," *Journal of the Royal Society of Medicine* 80 (May 1987), pp. 308-13.

———. "Building or Extending a Hospital Department: Radiology—A Path Through the Planning Minefield (6)," *Journal of the Royal Society of Medicine* 80 (June 1987), pp. 376-82.

———. "Building or Extending a Hospital Department: Radiology—A Path Through the Planning Minefield (7)," *Journal of the Royal Society of Medicine* 80 (July 1987), pp. 449-55.

———. "Building or Extending a Hospital Department: Radiology—A Path Through the Planning Minefield (8)," *Journal of the Royal Society of Medicine* 80 (August 1987), pp. 515-22.

———. "Building or Extending a Hospital Department: Radiology—A Path Through the Planning Minefield (9)," *Journal of the Royal Society of Medicine* 80 (September 1987), pp. 577-83.

———. "Building or Extending a Hospital Department: Radiology—A Path Through the Planning Minefield (10)," *Journal of the Royal Society of Medicine* 80 (October 1987), pp. 640-4

Roesch, Anthony, and Julia Thomas. "Is This an Emergency?" *Contract Design* 36, no. 2 (February 1994), pp. 63-65.

Rogers, Pamela J. "Bedside Revolution in Robotics," *Hospital Management International 1991*, pp. 318-21.

Ropper, Allan H. "Neurological Intensive Care," *Annals of Neurology* 32, no. 4 (October 1992), pp. 564-69.

Rosenfeld, Erika. "Taking the Pulse of the Market," *Cahner's Publishing,* Healthcare Supplement to *Building Design and Construction.* (February 1993), pp. S46-S53.

Rosenthal, Samuel. "Ensuring Plant Flexibility for Telecommunications," *Health Facilities Management* 5, no. 11 (November 1992), pp. 26, 28-31.

Ross Planning Associates. *Recommended Standards for Newborn ICU Design.* Report of the Consensus Conference on Newborn ICU Design, January 17-18, 1992.

Ruffin, Marshall. "Medical Informatics: The Computer-Based Patient Record Will Be the Integrated Regional Healthcare System's Most Valuable Asset," *Healthcare Forum Journal* 36, no. 2 (March/April 1993), pp. 47-50.

Ruga, Wayne. "Selecting Interior Design Finishes and Furnishings to Create a Successful Health Care Environment," AHA Technical Document Series 055914. January 1989.

Rus, Mayer. "Hermanovski Lauck: More than a Spoonful of Inspiration Helps the Medicine Go Down at Children's Medical Center of Dallas," *Cahner's Publishing,* Healthcare Supplement to *Building Design and Construction.* (February 1993), pp. S54-57.

Sabatino, Frank. "Mind and Body Medicine: A New Paradigm?" *Hospitals* 67 (February 20, 1993), pp. 66-71.

———. "New Concepts of Health and Healing May Affect Hospitals' Approach to Care," *Trustee* 46, no. 3 (March 1993), pp. 8-10.

———. "New Products as Well as New Space Improve Gift Shop's Old Image," *Health Facilities Management* 6, no. 2 (February 1993), pp. 14-15.

Sachner, Paul M. "A Place of Passage: Coming Home Hospice," *Architectural Record* 176, no. 13 (November 1988), pp. 104-107.

"St. Joseph's Hospital Emergency Dept. Addition," *Design and Cost Data* (January-March 1994), pp. 35-36.

Sand, Barbara, et al. "Alzheimer's Disease: Special Care Units in Long-Term Care Facilities," *Journal of Gerontological Nursing* 18, no. 3 (March 1992), pp. 28-34.

Sanders, Margaret. "Hospitals: The Prognosis," *The Construction Specifier* 44, no. 8 (Ausgust 1991), pp. 46-54.

Sandrick, Karen. "Hospitals and MDs Vie for Imaging Business," *Hospitals* 67, no. 21 (November 5, 1990), pp. 31-33.

Schaal, Dennis. "Total Computerized Care in Hospitals," *Medical World News* 34, no. 2 (February 1993), p. 54.

Schicht, Hans H. "Cleanroom Technology in Surgery," *Hospital Management International 1991,* pp. 301-302.

Schneider, Edward L, and Jack M. Guralnik. "The Aging of America: Impact on Health Care Costs," *JAMA* 263, no. 17 (May 2, 1990), pp. 2335-40.

Schomer, Victoria. *Interior Concerns Resource Guide: A Guide to Sustainable and Healthy Products and Educational Information for Designing and Building.* Mill Valley, Calif.: Interior Concerns Publications, 1993.

Scott, Lisa. "Construction Key: Keep Options Open," *Modern Healthcare* 23, no. 10 (March 15, 1993), pp. 35-44.

————. "New and Improved: Eight Annual Competition Honors Architectural Projects That Build on Changes in Healthcare Delivery," *Modern Healthcare* 22, no. 44 (November 1, 1993), pp. 39-47.

Seligmann, Jean, and Laura Buckley. "A Sickroom with a View: A New Artificial Window Brightens Patients' Days," *Newsweek* 115, no. 13 (March 26, 1990), p. 61.

"Sentara Norfolk General Hospital's River Pavilion: Cutting Down Patient Travel Time," *Facilities Planning News* 12, no. 7 (July 1993), industry insert.

Sherer, Jill L. "Retooling Leaders," *Hospitals and Health Networks* 68, no. 1 (January 5, 1994), pp. 42-44.

Shirani, Khan Z., et al. "Effects of Environment on Infection in Burn Patints," *Archives of Surgery* 121 (January 1986), pp. 31-35.

Shrive, Charles A. "Balancing Act: Achieving the Isolation That Is Manadtory in Laboratories Involves Balancing the Scope, Quality, and Cost of the Engineered Systems That Serve the Lab," *Health Facilities Management* 46, no. 4 (April 1993), pp. 63-71.

Simpson, Roy L. "Automating the ICU: Facing the Realities," *Nursing Management* 23, no. 3 (March 1992), pp. 24, 26.

"Six Types of Health Care Consumers Identified by Gallup," *Health Care Strategic Management* 8, no. 8 (August 1990), p. 3.

Slater, James M., et al. "The Proton Treatment Center at Loma Linda University Medical Center: Rationale for and Description of Its Development," *Journal of Radiation Oncology, Biology, Physics* 22, no. 2 (1992), pp. 383-89.

Sloan, Susan Lynn. "The Hospice Movement: A Study in the Diffusion of Innovative Palliative Care," *The Journal of Hospice and Palliative Care* 9, no. 3 (May/June 1993), pp. 24-31.

Smith, Lee. "The Coming Health Care Shakeout," *Fortune* 127, no. 11 (May 17, 1993), pp. 70-75.

Smith, Mary S. "ADA's Parking Requirements Pose Big Challenge," *Health Facilities Management* 4, no. 12 (December 1991), pp. 38-40.

Smyth, Angela. "See the Light!" *Hospital Development* (March 1990), pp. 17-29.

Smyth, Maureen E. "Hospital Sees Its Child Care Facility as 'Fringe Benefit for the 1990s,'" *Health Facilities Management* 4, no. 7 (July 1991), pp. 18-19.

Snook, I. Donald, Jr. *Hospitals: What They Are and How They Work.* 2d. ed. Gaithersburg, Md.: Aspen, 1992.

Solovy, Alden. "Health Care in the 1990s: Forecasts by Top Analysts," *Hospitals* (July 20, 1989), pp. 34-46.

Souhrada, Laura. "Imaging Devices' Shifting Uses Affect Market," *Hospitals* (November 5, 1990), pp. 28-31.

————. "New Rules of Success for Outpatient Facilities," *Hospitals* 65, no. 19 (October 5, 1991), pp. 42-43.

Soule, Dan. "Information Systems in Critical Care," *Hospital Management International 1990,* pp. 223-24.

Spector, Deborah, and Carole Runyan Price. "Fast-Tracking in Hospitals," *Healthcare Forum Journal* 31, no. 1 (January/February 1988), pp. 26-31.

Sraeel, Holly. "The 'Kids' Set Pace for Shriners Burns Institute," *Facilities Design and Management* (March 1993), pp. 48-53.

Stalder, Felix. "Designing and Building with the Handicapped," *Hospital Management International 1991*, pp. 232-34.

Starr, Paul. *The Social Transformation of American Medicine: The Rise of a Sovereign Profession and the Making of a Vast Industry*. New York: Basic Books, 1982.

Stennert, E., et al. "Incubator Noise and Hearing Loss," *Early Human Development* 1, no. 1 (June 1977), pp. 113-15.

Stichler, Jaynette, and Ronald Stichler. "Innovative Women's Center Design Features," *Facilities Planning News* 10, no. 11 (November 1991), pp. 3, 11-12.

Stinson, William. "On-Site Facilities," *Journal of Air Medical Transport* 9, no. 8 (August 1990), pp. 18-19.

Stoddard, Sandol. "Hospice: Approaching the 21st Century," *The American Journal of Hospice and Palliative Care* 7, no. 2 (March/April 1990), pp. 27-30.

Stoline, Anne M., and Jonathan P. Weiner. *The New Medical Marketplace: A Physician's Guide to the Health Care System in the 1990's*. Revised and updated. Baltimore: Johns Hopkins University Press, 1993.

Stoops, Michael D. "In-House Group Builds Muir's Unique Outdoor Rehab-Therapy Garden," *Health Facilities Management* 4, no. 4 (April 1991), pp. 12-13.

Strange, Gary R., et al. "Use of Emergency Departments by Elderly Patients: Projections from a Multicenter Data Base," *Annals of Emergency Medicine* 21, no. 7 (July 1992), pp. 819-24.

Strasen, Leann. "Redesigning Hospitals Around Patients and Technology," *Nursing Economics* 9, no. 4 (July-August 1991), pp. 233-38.

Strauss, Michael J., et al. "Rationing of Intensive Care Unit Services: An Everyday Occurrence," *JAMA* 255, no. 9 (March 7, 1986), pp. 1143-46.

Strawn, Ben F. *Planning and Design Considerations for a Hospital Magnetic Resonance Imaging Facility*. Technical Document Series 055902. Chicago: American Society for Hospital Engineering of the American Hospital Association, 1988.

Strawser, Robert A, and Mary M. Gregory. "Design Considerations for Heating, Air Conditioning, and Exhaust Systems in Critical Care Units," *Critical Care Nursing Quarterly* 16, no. 3 (1993), pp. 27-30.

Struble, Becky, et al. "Recovery Care Centers," *Journal of Health Care Interior Design* 2 (1990), pp. 141-48.

Studnicki, James. "The Medical Waste Audit," *Health Progress* 73, no. 3 (March 1992), pp. 68-77.

Suh, Young S. "A System for the Future," *Health Progress* 74, no. 10 (December 1993), pp. 51-60.

Swensson, Earl S. "Shifting Paradigms: A New Vision for the Future," address to the American College of Greece Career Forum, Athens, Greece, March 21, 1991.

————. "The Synergenial Suburban Village in the Year 2000," address to the 28th Annual Meeting and Exposition of the American Association of Homes for the Aging, Baltimore, Md., November 8, 1989.

Swensson, Earl S., et al. "Synergenial Design of Health Care Facilities for the Future." Report of research, March 15, 1986.

Taravella, Steve. "Hospitals Dispose of Destructive Waste Habits," *Modern Healthcare* 20, no. 1 (December 24, 1990), pp. 26-28, 30, 42.

———. "Recovery Centers Gaining Interest," *Modern Healthcare* (July 2, 1990), p. 27.

Task Force on Guidelines, Society of Critical Care Medicine. "Guidelines for Categorization of Service for the Critically Ill Patient," *Critical Care Medicine* 19, no. 2 (1991), pp. 279-85.

Task Force on Guidelines, Society of Critical Care Medicine. "Recommendations for Critical Care Unit Design," *Critical Care Medicine* 16, no. 8 (August 1988), pp. 796-806.

Task Force on Guidelines, Society of Critical Care Medicine. "Recommendations for Services and Personnel for Delivery of Care in a Critical Care Setting," *Critical Care Medicine* 16, no. 8 (August 1988), pp. 809-11.

Taylor, Kathryn S. "Biotech on the Brink," *Hospitals and Health Networks* 67, no. 21 (November 5, 1993), pp. 36-37.

———. "Robodoc: Study Tests Robot's Use in Hip Surgery," *Hospitals* 67, no. 9 (May 5, 1993), p. 46.

Technique et Lumiere Vernier, France. "The Bed Head Unit," *International Hospital Federation 1988 Official Yearbook,* pp. 275-76.

Tetlow, Karin. "Children's Scale: The Ratcliff Architects Create a Warm and Carefully Scaled Child Development Center for the Children's Hospital in Oakland," *Interiors* 150, no. 6 (January 1991), pp. 126-27.

———. "Design Heals: Orlando Diaz-Azcuy Brings a Fresh Perspective to Issues of Privacy and Autonomy in an Intensive Care Unit Designed for Change," *Interiors* 145, no. 5 (December 1990), pp. 87-92.

———. "Healing Spirit: The Newest Interiors Intitiative is a Meditation Room," *Interiors* 151, no. 12 (December 1992), pp. 52-59.

———. "ICU Roundtable: Beyond State-of-the-Art—Health Care Professionals Discuss the 1990 Interiors Initiative," *Interiors* 150, no. 17 (December 1991), pp. 58-59.

———. "Neo-Natal Environments," *Interiors* (June 1992), p. 94.

———. "New Home Heals: In a Stunning Transformation of a Sober House in Gloucester, Payette Associates Write a New Page for Healthcare History," *Interiors* (December 1991), pp. 50-54.

———. "Prototype Home: A New Respite Home and Day Care Center for Children with AIDS," *Interiors* 151, no. 12 (December 1992), pp. 70-71.

Thames, Debby. "Valet Parking Because: 'It's the Little Things That Matter,'" *Texas Hospital* 43, no. 1 (June 1987), p. 27.

Thiele, Jennifer. "No Bones About It: Resurgens Orthopedics," *Contract Design* 34, no. 10 (October 1992), pp. 46-49.

Thomas, Karen A. "Design Issues in the NICU: Thermal Effects of Windows," *Neonatal Network* 9, no. 4 (December 1990), pp. 23-26.

Thomas, Richard K. "What Hospitals Must Do," *American Demographics* 15, no. 1 (January 1993), pp. 36-41.

Thompson, John D., and Grace Goldin. *The Hospital: A Social and Architectural History.* New Haven and London: Yale University Press, 1975.

Thweatt, Albert A. "4 Basic Approaches Key to Health-Facility Design," *Health Facilities Management* 6, no. 7 (July 1991), pp. 28-34.

Toland, Drexel, and Susan Strong. *Hospital-Based Medical Office Buildings.* Chicago: American Hospital Publishing Company, 1986.

"Tom Landry Sports Medicine and Research Center Baylor Medical Center Campus, Dallas, TX," *Athletic Business* 15, no. 6 (June 1991), pp. 40-41.

Topf, Margaret. "Effects of Personal Control over Hospital Noise on Sleep," *Research in Nursing and Health* 15 (1992), pp. 19-28.

Topf, Margaret. "Sensitivity to Noise, Personality Hardness, and Noise-Induced Stress in Critical Care Nurses," *Environment and Behavior* 21, no. 6 (November 1989), pp. 717-33.

Topf, Margaret, and Jean E. Davis. "Critical Care Unit Noise and Rapid Eye Movement (REM) Sleep," *Heart & Lung* 22 (May/June 1993), pp. 252-58.

Townsend, Mary B. "Patient-Focused Care: Is It for Your Hospital?" *Nursing Management* 24, no. 9 (September 1993), pp. 74-80.

Trafford, Abigail, et al. "Top 10 Health Stories to Watch," *U.S. News and World Report* 114, no. 18 (May 10, 1993), pp. 81-90.

Treiber, Steve. "CA Hospital 'Recycles' a 10-Year-Old Buidling as Urgent Care Center," *Health Facilities Management* 4, no. 10 (October 1991), pp. 14-15.

"Trends in Health Care," *Academy of Architecture for Health Newsletter* (April 1993), pp. 2-3.

Trofino, Joan. "Voice-Activated Nursing Documentation: On the Cutting Edge," *Nursing Management* 24, no. 7 (July 1993), pp. 40-42.

Tusler, Wilbur H. "Tib," and Jenifer Altenhoff. "Architecture and Technology," *Design Management Journal* 4, no. 2 (Spring 1993), pp. 62-68.

U.S. General Accounting Office. *Long-Term Care: Projected Needs of the Aging Baby Boom Generation.* Washington, D.C.: U.S. General Accounting Office, 1991.

U.S. Senate Special Committee on Aging, et al. *Aging America: Trends and Projections.* 1991 Edition. Washington, D.C.: Department of Health and Human Services, n.d.

Ullman, Dana. "The Mainstreaming of Alternative Medicine," *Healthcare Forum Journal* 36, no. 6 (November/December 1993), pp. 24-30.

Ulrich, Roger S. "How Design Impacts Wellness," *Healthcare Forum Journal* 35, no. 2 (September/October 1992), pp. 20-25.

———. "Wellness By Design: 'Psychologically Supportive' Patient Surroundings," *Group Practice Journal* 40, no. 4 (July/August 1991), pp. 10-19.

Unruh, Karen. "A Link to Life: High Technology in Long Term Care," *Provider* 19, no. 3 (March 1993), pp. 26-43.

Urbanowicz, Gary R. "How to Store Medical Waste When Space Is Tight," *Health Facilities Management* 6, no. 12 (December 1993), pp. 56-59.

Valins, Martin S. *Primary Health Care Centres.* Harlow, Eng.: Longman, 1993.

Van Der Ryn, Sim. "Healing Environemnts: Environmental Awareness and Healing," *Journal of Healthcare Design* 5 (September 1993), pp. 175-86.

Verderber, Stephen. *Windowness and Human Behavior in the Hospital Rehabilitation Environment.* University of Michigan Arch. D. diss., 1983.

"Veterans Administration Outpatient Clinic," *Architectural Record* 181, no. 2 (February 1993), pp. 100-103.

Viladas, Pilar. "The Road to Recovery: Cedars-Sinai Comprehensive Cancer Center," *Progressive Architecture* 64, no. 7 (July 1988), pp. 67-75

Vogel, Morris J. *The Invention of the Modern Hospital: Boston, 1870-1930.* Chicago: University of Chicago Press, 1980.

Voggler, Joyce H. "Birthing Centers," *Journal of Healthcare Design* 5 (1993), pp. 121-26.

Vogl, Angeline. "Patient-Oriented Design: The Johns Hopkins Outpatient Center," *Designer's World* 40, no. 1 (November 1992), pp. 56-59.

Voros, Sharon V. "New Women's Center Links Traditional Care with Health Promotion," *Health Facilities Management* 2, no. 12 (December 1989), pp. 18-19.

————. "Psychiatric Facility—One with Nature," *Health Facilites Management* 2, no. 4 (April 1989), pp. 14-15.

Wagner, Lynn. "Hospitals Feeling Trauma of Violence, *Modern Healthcare* 20, no. 5 (February 5, 1990), pp. 23-24, 26, 28, 32.

Wagner, Mary. "PET Projects: Providers Like What They See," *Modern Healthcare* 22, no. 47 (November 30, 1992), pp. 34-40.

————. "Report Views Imaging Equipment Trends," *Modern Healthcare* 21, no. 48 (December 2, 1991), p. 44.

————. "Study Finds Stockless Inventory Saves Money, but Many Barriers Keep It From Gaining Favor," *Modern Healthcare* 20, no. 40 (October 8, 1990), p. 44.

————. "Vanderbilt's Stockless System Relies on Distributors as its Materials Managers," *Modern Healthcare* 20, no. 5 (February 5, 1990), p. 44.

Wagner, Michael. "Healing Revolution: A New Medical/Surgical Unit Designed to Encourage Patients to Participate in Their Own Treatment," *Interiors* 150, no. 5 (December 1990), pp. 76-77.

Wallace, William E. "Hospice and AIDS: Clinical Issues Which Affect Care," *The American Journal of Hospice and Palliative Care* 8, no. 3 (May/June 1990), pp. 13-16.

Ward, Michael P. "NH Hospital Relocates Main Entrance, ED to Reflect Shift in Care," *Health Facilities Management* 3, no. 2 (February 1990), pp. 10-11.

"Washington University School of Medicine/Mallinckrodt Institute of Radiology," *Ekriture* 3 (July 1993), pp. 26-29.

Weathersby, William, Jr. "Easy Access: A 'Medical Mall' Plan Links a Diagnostic and Treatment Center with a Professional Building and Inpatient Bed Tower," *Hospitality Design* 14, no. 4 (May 1992), pp. 46-50.

Webb, William A. "Rights of Passage: Efforts to Establish Uniform Accessibility Requirement in the Model Codes Are Now Taking Shape," *The Construction Specifier* 43, no. 8 (August 1991), pp. 91-95.

Weber, Chari. "Long-Term Care Design: Emerging Trends," *Journal of Healthcare Design* 5 (September 1993), pp. 187-95.

————. "Long-Term Care Design: The New Generation," *Journal of Healthcare Design* 5 (September 1993), pp. 213-17.

Weber, David O. "Planetree Transplanted," *Healthcare Forum Journal* 35, no. 5 (September/October 1992), pp. 30-37.

————. "Rewriting the Human Prospect," *Healthcare Forum Journal* 35, no. 5 (September/October 1992), pp. 24-33.

————. "Six Models of Patient-Focused Care," *Healthcare Forum Journal* 34, no. 4 (July/August 1991), pp. 23-31.

Weinhold, Virginia B. "Flooring Options: Carpet Now a Major Contender," *Health Facilities Management* 5, no. 5 (May 1992), pp. 96-100.

Weinstein, Robert A., and Gina Pugliese. "How (and Why) to Set Up a Facilitywide TB Program," *Health Facilities Management* 7, no. 3 (March 1994), pp. 42-46.

Weisman, Ellen. "Engineering Controls and TB: What Works? How Well?" *Health Facilities Management* (February 1994), pp. 18-24.

———. "Renovation Work Makes up 72% of 1991 Projects," *Health Facilities Management* 5, no. 7 (July 1992), pp. 79-81.

———. "Sports Medicine Attracts a Young, Healthy Market," *Hospitals* (November 20, 1990), p. 49.

Weiss, Rhoda. "Southern Hospitality," *Health Progress* 74, no. 10 (December 1993), pp. 62-75.

Wilkinson-West, Ann. "Facility Design: An Architectural Perspective," *The Hospital Emergency Department: A Guide to Operational Excellence.* Chicago: American Hospital Publishing, Inc., 1992.

Wilson, Larkin M. "Intensive Care Delirium: The Effect of Outside Deprivation in a Windowless Unit," *Archives of Internal Medicine* 130 (August 1972), pp. 225-26.

Winchester, Johanna P., and Hazel N. Brown. "Patient Is Discharged—But Still in the Bed! Providing a Discharge Lounge Can Be a Cost-Effective Strategy," *Nursing Management* 23, no. 10 (October 1992), pp. 57-61.

Wolfson, Jay, et al. "Freestanding Ambulatory Surgery: Cost-Containment Winner?" *Healthcare Financial Management* 47, no. 7 (July 1993), pp. 27-32.

Wuchter, Thomas B. "Four-Story Mall Helps Consolidate Obstetrics and Outpatient Services," *Health Facilities Management* 7, no. 2 (February 1994), pp. 16-17.

Wyke, Alexandra. "The Future of Medicine," *The Economist* 330, no. 7855 (March 19, 1994), pp. 3-18.

Yamamoto, Loren G. "Scanned Emergency Department to Emergency Department Image Transfer (SEE-IT): Implementation and Standardizing Protocols to Optimize Tertiary Referrals," *American Journal of Emergency Medicine* 11, no. 1 (January 1993), pp. 70-75.

Yee, Roger. "What's Healthy About Health Care Design" *Contract Design* 34, no. 10 (October 1992), pp. 41-43.

Young, Diony. "Family-Centered Maternity Care: Is the Central Nursery Obsolete?" *Birth* 19, no. 4 (December 1992), pp. 183-84.

Zablocki, Elaine. "Quality Management Targets Health Care," *Nation's Business* 81, no. 2 (February 1993), pp. 40-41.

Zeidler, Eberhard H. *Healing the Hospital: McMaster Health Science Center—Its Concenption and Evolution.* Toronto: Zeidler Partnership, 1974.

Zilm, Frank. "Four Key Decisions in the Evolution of a Critical Care Unit," *Critical Care Nursing Quarterly* 14, no. 1 (1991), pp. 9-20.

Zubatkin, Allen D. "Psychological Impact of Medical Equipment on Patients," *Journal of Clinical Engineering* 5, no. 3 (July-September 1980), pp. 250-55.

Zun, Leslie. "Observation Units: Boom or Bust for Emergency Medicine," *Journal of Emergency Medicine* 8 (1990), pp. 485-90.

INDEX